OLD COTSWOLD

OLD COTSWOLD

by

EDITH BRILL

DAVID AND CHARLES
NEWTON ABBOT

7153 4223 I

© Edith Brill
1968

Printed in Great Britain by
Latimer Trend & Company Limited Plymouth
for David & Charles (Holdings) Limited
South Devon House Railway Station
Newton Abbot Devon

Contents

Illustrations

PLATES

Illustrations

LINE DRAWINGS IN TEXT

SKETCH MAP OF THE COTSWOLDS

VALE O

Tewkesbury

Winchcom

Cleev
Comm

R. SEVERN

GLOUCESTER

CHELTENH

GLOUCESTER

Leckhampton

GLOUCEST

VALE OF

Prinknash
Park

Cranham

Birdlip

Coles

Ermine Street

Sheepscombe

Painswick

Lypiatt
Park

STROUD

Sapperton

CIRENCESTE

Frocester

Minchinhampton

Nympsfield

Nailsworth

Stinchcombe

Uley

Owlpen

Dursley

Wotton under
Edge.

Tetbury

CHAPTER ONE

Cheltenham Spa

Although Cheltenham is not a Cotswold town in the sense
that it owed its being to wool, raw or manufactured, and
although it shows nothing of the Cotswold vernacular in
its architecture, yet its position under the high escarpment, the
part it plays as a cultural, social and shopping centre for the wolds
has given it a strong claim to be included. Before the railway and
the motor-car brought London within easy reach, Cheltenham
was a metropolitan world on the doorstep, keeping the Cotsaller
in touch with fashion and new ideas generally. In some instances
it probably made him feel that his own fastnesses and rural occupations were superior to those designed for the elegancies of
leisure, but on the whole the benefits were mutual.

For the local historian the growth of the town offers a less
complicated problem than most; its years of change and progress
from the days of Henry VIII and Leland's 'Longe Towne' to the
middle of the nineteenth century can be peeled off in neat layers,
the work of the architects concerned with each new phase easily
recognizable.

Perhaps the most significant fact about Cheltenham's early history, and one which helped to make its later flowering easier, was
that there was no 'big house' with a resident family owning all the
land and dominating its affairs. All that has come down from
medieval times and before is the ground plan of the original long
High Street and St Mary's Church with its additions and alterations
throughout the centuries.

Only the base of the tower remains from the early Norman
church, for it was rebuilt in the twelfth century and enlarged again
in the fourteenth. The size and decoration of its fabric show that
Cheltenham was no small village at that time and must have had a
population equal to a small town. Later fourteenth-century additions included a simple broached spire, some 167 feet high, which

during the opening stages of Cheltenham's transformation into a spa was recognized as a picturesque addition to the town's vistas, and until the accretions of the late nineteenth and twentieth centuries swamped it, was a landmark making a point of emphasis in a Grecian Revival setting.

St Mary's also possesses an unusual feature for a parish church, a rose or wheel window in the north transept with the perfect symmetry of curvilinear tracery spreading out from a small centre circle and ending in a greater circle, the overall diameter being forty-five feet.

Little remains of Cheltenham's Tudor heritage, for this was a layer swept away when the need for improving the streets became imperative. Pate's Tudor almshouses were rebuilt in a late Georgian style not long after the old pillared Market House standing in the middle of the High Street was demolished.

By the beginning of the eighteenth century Sir Robert Atkyns in his *History of Gloucestershire* was recording that Cheltenham was a market town with 'a considerable trade in making malt'. The picture at that time, some four years before its emergence as a spa, is of a small town or large village with a population of about 1,500, its thatched houses strung out along both sides of one long High Street, with stepping-stones across the little river Chelt which had its course down the street itself.

The first saline spring was discovered in 1716 in a field owned by a Mr Mason, who, discovering that the local inhabitants used the spring, enclosed it with a fence and built a well-house of rustic pattern over it. By 1721 the waters had become known to a wider public, for this was the age when the healing properties of water were becoming a fashionable form of medicine, and with the prosperity of Bath in mind there soon followed the discovery of other springs containing sulphates of sodium and magnesium. The waters were taken for digestive complaints and rheumatism; hot and cold bathing followed later. The importance of these discoveries to Cheltenham was that they were not all concentrated in one area; there were several spas, each needing its Pump and Assembly Rooms and the necessary housing for visitors in the vicinity.

In the beginning the Old Well, as Mason's spring was called, was the one most frequented, though for a score of years he did not spend very much on making it an architectural asset to the town. It was the famous Captain Skillicorne, a retired Bristol merchant sea captain who married Mason's daughter Elizabeth and came to end his days in the town who could be said to be the real founder of Cheltenham Spa. He built a small Pump Room and a roofed canopy on brick arches over the well, and in 1743, to the design of a friend and patron Norbone Berkeley, laid out a long avenue of elms, Old Well Walk, which ran for 900 yards to finish on the lower slopes of Bayshill. To close the vista, after a manner dearly loved by the landscape improvers of the time, there were the tower and spire of St Mary's Church, a charming prospect for those taking a promenade after their morning dose of the waters. To reach the Old Well there was an upper and lower walk under an avenue of lime-trees and across orchards and gardens, culminating in the elm-walk leading to the Pump Room, while on either side of the entrance were the library, offices and a breakfast-room. The purging waters have been described as 'limpid, brackish and nauseously bitter, the dose from one pint to three or four, nor is it ever attended with gripes, but creates a keen appetite'.

Brick was still the main building material. Fauconberg House, erected on the slopes of Bayshill for Lord Fauconberg, the most palatial building in the town, was built of brick, not stone. Here, before the end of the century, the King was to spend a few weeks when he came to take the waters and give Cheltenham the social boost it needed to expand.

A serious obstacle to Cheltenham's development was poor communications. Only a narrow road, unsuitable for coaches, connected it with the London road at Frog Mill Inn near Andoversford; from there passengers had to transfer into smaller post-chaises until 1776 when a new road was made to Andoversford.

The unpaved streets of the town were unsatisfactory for the notable visitors the owners of the spa wished to attract, and in 1786 the Corn Market and Butter Cross in the High Street on their ageing stone pillars with the prison below were demolished and foot-pavements laid down with lamps to light the streets in dark months on nights when there was no moon.

A supply of building stone became necessary as the town grew, and—what was equally necessary—transport to carry it. There was stone in plenty on the nearby escarpment, and Leckington quarries were opened to provide it. All that remains now of the

Leckington quarries above the town is an isolated pinnacle of hard limestone blocks known as the Devil's Chimney behind the ramparts of an Iron Age encampment. It had a shorter life than most Cotswold quarries, falling into disuse when the new town, with its fine villas and terraced houses, its Pump Rooms and Assembly Halls and the pavements to keep the feet of its distinguished patrons from the mire and dust were built. From this stone arose a small Regency town in architectural units of good proportion and design, spacious in its layout of tree-shaded walks and avenues. Though most of the terraces were finished in painted stucco, many of the larger buildings were faced with natural stone, and it is these which are the most comely today, for stucco through the years cracks and peels and generally presents a depressing and dowdy appearance unless it is well-preserved by frequent attention.

During the short life of the quarries, both they and the quarrymen were worked hard. The prosperity of Bath, Cheltenham's rival and already well established, acted as a constant urge, and the fashionable people and invalids attracted even to such small spas as the Hotwell Springs near Bristol showed that mineral springs and elegant entertainment could be a profitable business. Everything was ripe for the experiment. There were capital and patronage in plenty, cheap labour and stone in abundance, and, most important of all, there was a splendid site waiting to be developed with unlimited space to plan a worthy layout.

Visitors had to be entertained. The first theatre was not built until 1782, but by that time there were many improvements to attract the fashionable world. Cheltenham's first 'Long Room' was built by Skillicorne and a Mr Miller, who leased Old Well from Skillicorne's son William who had inherited the well after the Captain's death in 1763. The Long Room was some sixty-six feet long and in keeping with the original Cheltenham whose buildings were mostly of brick.

In 1780 Simon Moreau was appointed as Master of Ceremonies, a forward-looking man of many parts and valuable social contacts. He worked not only as Master of Ceremonies but in other ways behind the scenes and it was partly due to his efforts that the Paving and Improvement Acts of 1786 were passed. He also produced the first guide book to Cheltenham. It was not long after his appointment that new Assembly Rooms were built in the

High Street where could be held the balls and other formal enter-
tainments the new visitors would expect.

This rival to Miller's Long Room was erected on land belonging
to Thomas Hughes, the first to ask the advice of a famous architect
on such a project. Henry Holland is believed to have surveyed the
site and planned the new buildings. A contemporary print shows
the Grand Ballroom with a concave wall ornamented with pilas-
ters and windows and a frieze of garlands. A dado of the pattern
used by Henry Holland many times in other buildings surrounds
the room and it was lit by glittering chandeliers of hanging
lustres. The effect is of a graceful delicacy without the heaviness
the style developed in later years; perhaps its modest size, sixty
feet by thirty, helped to create this impression of elegance and
refinement. As the years went by it became too small for the
number of visitors who flocked to Cheltenham and was superseded.

The summer of 1788 saw George III in Cheltenham. He was
lodged in Fauconberg House, some seventeen rooms being added
to accommodate his household, which included the Princess
Royal, the Princesses Sophia and Amelia, Lady Weymouth, two
ladies-in-waiting and Fanny Burney, the authoress, whose detailed
account of the visit gives an intimate picture of the royal establishment.

In spite of the added rooms and a portable wooden annexe for
the Duke of York when he joined the party, quarters were cramped
and Miss Burney gives an amusing account of the ladies-in-
waiting fixing up their tea-table by a passage window and having
to make the tea themselves because there was no room for personal
maids, though perhaps the beautiful view of the Malverns they
could see while drinking tea was some compensation.

King George's visit seems to have followed the usual pattern
taken by Cheltenham's visitors. He drank the waters regularly, he
used the walks for promenades and chatting with his friends and
subjects, he took excursions into the surrounding countryside to
see places of interest and to be entertained by the local nobility.
He went to visit Lord Bathurst and inspect the entrance to the
Sapperton tunnel of the Thames and Severn canal in course of
construction, and to see the Bishop at Worcester. His visit gave
Cheltenham the publicity it wanted, and when the royal party departed on 16 August 1788 the foundation had been laid for Chel-

tenham's new building programme and its final architectural flowering. London now knew about Cheltenham's delights; after the King's visit Cheltenham bonnets, buckles, buttons and other such novelities were soon being sold in the London shops.

Despite the war period the opening years of the new century saw the sinking of several new mineral wells, and as a Pump Room was necessary at each well, with lodgings for the water-drinkers, Cheltenham's expansion into a town of many spas began. Land to the south of the Old Well was bought by Henry Thompson in 1801, and this eventually materialized into the famous Montpellier Spa when his son Pearson Thompson took over. Hygeia House, the Thompsons' own dwelling, was used as the centre at first. This was a Regency house faced with stone and set about by a Roman-Doric colonnade in a pastoral setting of fields and lanes. By 1813 the spa was moved to its present site, first as a simple rustic building with timber pillars and verandah, then some years later the Long Pump Room was erected, designed by a local architect, John Forbes. Its colonnade can still be seen unaltered today.

By this time a chalybeate spa at Cambray had opened. Its Pump Room, built in 1830, was an octagonal building and one can visualize it because it corresponded to Oriel House on the opposite side of the road which still survives, while the area around the spa was developed in Regency style. One of the villas housed the Duke of Wellington in 1816. He stayed there with a Colonel Riddell who had acquired the spa and who, despite his military title, does not seem to have taken any part in the Napoleonic Wars. It is said that he invited his friends to drink his chalybeate waters for nothing, offering them at the same time glasses of his special Madeira; whether this was to dispel the taste of the chalybeate we are not told. Many of the stories about him suggest he was one of those free-drinking, free-loving and free-handed Regency bucks who lived mainly for the pursuit of pleasure, the kind of man, in fact, who caused Cobbett to denounce Cheltenham as 'a resort of the lame and lazy, the gourmandising and the guzzling, the bilious and the nervous'.

The Sherborne Spa, named after the lord of the manor, opened its Pump Room in 1818 south of the High Street. This building has now been obliterated by the Queen's Hotel, but old engravings show a design based on rows of Ionic columns inside and outside, its decorations Grecian urns and a central figure of

Hygeia, a goddess spa owners felt was particularly their own. Sherborne Spa was designed by G. A. Underwood, a local architect of taste and talent, and it also had a setting of leafy walks and shady avenues, thus adding a typically English pleasance to buildings of a classical style.

Cheltenham had a population of over 13,000 by 1831, and was now approaching Bath in status with a list of important visitors including the Prince Regent, the Dukes of Gloucester and Sussex and many others. The Royal Crescent, its name reminiscent of Bath and perhaps so named as a tribute to that city, was finished around 1813, the most ambitious building project so far and providing lodgings of taste and elegance for many visitors. It had the perfect proportions of early Regency design, its plain front relieved by a canopied balcony of ironwork following the curve and emphasising it. The delicately patterned fanlights, the doorframes with corner rosettes, and ceilings with ornamental plaster centre-pieces reveal an austere elegance and precision that in later Regency buildings could develop into a handsome but empty pompousness, but here the design is never overstated but is restrained throughout. The Royal Crescent is mostly used as offices today, for like most dwellings of the period the comfort of its inhabitants depended upon the employment of armies of servants, the designers concentrating all their efforts on the principal rooms with little regard for the domestics who served it.

The town at this time was still a summer resort, James King, the then Master of Ceremonies being also employed in the same capacity at Bath during the winter months. It seems likely that, being a man of parts like his predecessor Simon Moreau, and helped by his Bath experience, he had much to say in the imposing and important changes that were yet to come. The Paving and Improvement Act of 1821 foreshadowed a new expansion as two preceding Acts had done. One of the Commissioners, Mr J. R. Scott, a man of wealth, taste and an intimate knowledge of Greek architecture, began to build himself a mansion on the Bath road, a mansion on a scale more imposing than any the town had ever possessed. This was Thirlestane House, now incorporated into the College, and named after the Selkirkshire seat of the Scott family. In its first stages it consisted of a large central block adorned on the Bath Road side by a large portico with four columns and a plain pediment. The Greek detail of the mahogany doors, pilaster and plasterwork could only be the work of one deeply steeped in the Greek idiom. The entrance hall has a coved ceiling with a central panel of decorated plaster work and twelve fluted Ionic columns. The stables were built in keeping with the rest of the building, being unusually spacious and crowned with two copies of the Athenian monument of Lysicrates. When it was put up for sale in 1831 it was suggested that it would be a suitable residence for William IV should he visit the town. It was finally bought by Lord Northwick, who added side galleries to house his art collection, and in keeping with the Grecian idea adorned the outside with copies of the Parthenon frieze. He allowed visitors to use the galleries freely, and for many years they added much to the amenities of the town.

A more systematic development from 1825 onwards was mainly undertaken by two landowners, Pearson Thompson, son of Henry Thompson, and Joseph Pitt, Pearson Thompson employing John Buonarotti Papworth as architect and Joseph Pitt a local man, John Forbes. Papworth was an architect of renown, whose interests went beyond the siting and designing of buildings and their strictly architectural ornament to details of interior furnishings. His designs covered chandeliers, chronometer cases, furniture, even decanters, and he was the author of several books much used at the time by gentlemen to form their own taste. Two of them, *Rural Residences* and *Hints on Ornamental Gardening*, had a tremendous vogue and were responsible for many improvements in country houses carried on throughout the country. He had a wide practice and worked from an office in London, and among his clients and patrons were the Shah of Persia and the King of Wurttemburg, thus entitling him to be called 'Architect to the King', a name gratifying to one of his flamboyant personality.

Pearson Thompson's land became the Montpellier and Lansdown estates, with the existing Montpellier Pump Room planned by Papworth to be turned into an Assembly Hall leading into a new Rotunda Pump Room. His further supplementary designs, however, never came into being, for the original plans had to be modified when a banking crisis of 1825 gave the finances of Pearson Thompson a serious setback. By the time the building could be started again Papworth was no longer available, but there is no doubt that his ideas on town planning influenced all further transformation of the town. His were the basic schemes inspiring

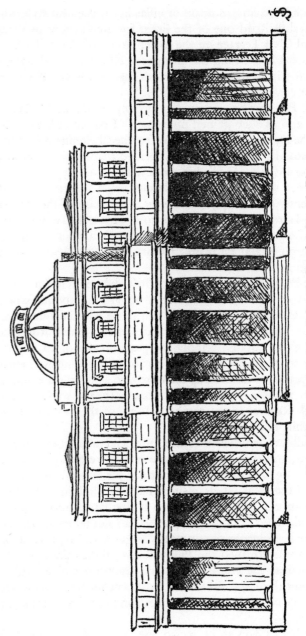

Pump Room designed by John Forbes for Joseph Pitt

the splendid, spacious domain of villas in the classical style which make Bayshill Road one of the finest for architecture in Britain, and Royal Well Terrace on the lower slopes of Bayshill was certainly his work. He rang the changes in all the classical styles yet kept them within the convention, so that one is amazed that so much variety is contained within it.

Joseph Pitt was one of the 'lay impropriators' of Cheltenham Rectory, and as such gained possession of common land handed over to the lay rector of the parish after the Cheltenham Enclosure Act of 1801. In 1820 Joseph Pitt decided that another spa would be a good investment for his money. His land lay north of the town, never the most fashionable quarter, a hundred acres that sloped gently down to the little river, a tributary of the Swilgate, which had already been enlarged into an artificial lake by a former owner. The lake and the lie of the land generally lent themselves to landscaping, and he planned more lakes, walks and pleasant promenades.

Unlike Papworth, John Forbes, Pitt's chosen architect, had the advantage of starting from scratch on virgin ground, whereas Montpellier's dome and rotunda had to be additions and alterations to an earlier building. Forbes designed a Pump Room containing a great hall of assembly, lofty within and of an imposing grandeur without, the dome resting above the windows, cornice and parapet of a pilastered upper storey, so achieving a height and subtlety of planning which makes it one of the few masterpieces of the Greek Revival in the town, and one of the best of Cheltenham's public buildings.

The builders had their troubles. Financial difficulties made progress slow, and then the building was discovered to be not only on the wrong side of the town but too far away from the High Street and the areas where visitors had their lodgings. It did not have the success it deserved when it first came into being as a social rendezvous because Joseph Pitt had not taken into account the fact that, however picturesque the gardens, however impressive and well-furnished the Pump Room, these things could not prevail against the conservatism and tradition which made the area around the High Street the most acceptable in the town; it had been the centre in medieval times and has remained the centre ever since.

Cheltenham's days as a Grecian Spa town lasted until well into the middle of the last century, and then we see the insidious beginnings of a return to Gothic, with the Anglican churches dominant in its revival. For some years the two styles went on side by side, even together in some buildings such as Christ Church in the very heart of Classical Cheltenham, the Lansdown estate. Its passionate advocate was Francis Close, once curate-in-charge of Holy Trinity Church and later Dean of Carlisle, who regarded the architecture of Greek and Rome as expressing a pagan ideal. For him only Gothic could express the Christian faith. His influence and the changing spirit of the times was soon to turn Cheltenham into a residential town, with new schools and colleges springing up to serve not only the town but the outside world, with the spas becoming part instead of the main concern of its inhabitants.

CHAPTER TWO

Painswick

It is difficult today to picture the comely little town of Painswick as the centre of thriving industry; one feels it must always have held people engaged in the arts and cultivating their gardens, in fact the 'Proud Painswick' of the jingle. Here are some of the most picturesque streets of stone-roofed and stone-walled cottages on the Cotswolds, and spacious elegant houses whose names can be found in books on English architecture as the best examples of their kind. Yet it was industry, the clothing trade, which was mainly responsible for the eighteenth-century development which gives so much delight today to the lover of the Cotswold scene, with the added factor that many of the important clothing families of Painswick lived in the town for more than two hundred years. They did not use it as a place to make money and then depart to fairer places; they belonged to it and it belonged to them. Painswick can show the finest collection of clothiers' tombs. Bigland's *Collections* record eighty-one headstones and tombs between 1684 and 1829 whose inscriptions bear the word CLOTHIER. Some have lost their inscriptions, others have disappeared altogether; a sufficient number remain to show that for about 200 years clothiers dominated the town. There are also memorials erected to clothiers though not inscribed as such, including those engaged in the trade during the boom years and who abandoned it before they died, as well as those unfortunates ruined in the recurrent depressions. With a little imagination one can follow in its churchyard the rise, the peak and then the fall of Painswick's prosperity as a clothing town. On the southern fringe 194 acres were formed into the civil parish of Uplands. The parish the clothiers knew contained some 6,100 acres and measured about five miles from its most northerly point to its southern extremity. Francis A. Hyett, in his *Glimpses of the History of Painswick*, says there were looms in many cottages in Vicarage Lane and Tibbiwell

Lane and in cottages behind the Stockhouses, at Clattergrove and Paradise, as well as four looms at the Back-Edge. Window and room space larger than is usual in cottages gives a clue to their occupation by weavers.

What kind of men were these clothiers, the Webbs and Tock-nells, Pallings, Pooles and Packers, the Lovedays and Baylisses and Coxes, and all the others? They lived in substantial, gracious houses and some were buried in substantial, gracious tombs made by a local stonemason, John Bryan, who served them well, his excellent craftsmanship keeping their memory alive long after their mills and cloth had disappeared. A number of clothiers bought estates and became country gentlemen, using their business acumen in acquiring and working them. The making of profit was not the main objective; social prestige and the pleasures that went with it were the chief reasons. As Adam Smith says in *The Wealth of Nations*, 'Merchants are commonly ambitious of becoming country gentlemen and when they do are generally the best of all improvers'.

The earliest of them, the sixteenth-century clothiers, were mainly in a small way of business, for this was the age of undyed broadcloth. Painswick became important between 1620 and 1800 mainly because of coloured cloths, when it was realized that the pure water of her springs and streams produced the clearest and best dyes in the West Country.

These were the prosperous years, but the clothiers had their discontents and voiced them loudly. They knew the value of their trade to the country's economy. They regarded the home trade as their preserve and wanted to exclude all foreign woollen cloth and other textiles. In this contention, though in few others, their workers were with them, for when in 1696 a Bill was introduced into the House of Commons, a great crowd of weavers and their wives thronged the precincts in support of its enactment 'that the weaving of Indian and Persian silks and printed calicoes were very destructive to the woollen manufacturers'.

Another serious complaint was the sale of raw wool and fleeces overseas, and in the late seventeenth century the transport of English wool abroad was forbidden. The smuggling which followed was another grievance; 'notwithstanding this kingdom is at great charge in maintaining vessels and men to prevent exportation of wool, yet within these two years many thousand packs have been exported into France and other foreign parts,' they complained.

Arthur Young, the eighteenth-century writer and traveller, was against the clothiers in this matter, declaring that the sweets of a monopoly of their raw material had made the clothiers 'indolent and devoid of the ardour of enterprise or the spirit of invention', while Lord Cecil, Earl of Salisbury, in his *Export in Cloth and Wool*, thought the 'diminution of the clothing trade would be useful, first because the tillage of the realm decayed because of it, and secondly the people who depended on the clothing trade for a living were more difficult to govern than husbandmen'.

What the clothiers did not realize, though their wives in many cases could have enlightened them, was that the exotic quality of goods from distant markets made an irresistible appeal that was part romantic, part snobbish, and that people who had become rich enough to pay for these luxuries were resolved to have them.

Painswick is watered by four streams, and it is on these streams that the older mills were situated. The most important running down Painswick valley served at least twelve cloth mills, one of the earliest, Tocknell's Mill, taking its name from James Tocknell, buried in the church in 1602, 'son of Walter Tocknell, Clothier'. On the waterpipes at Tocknell's the initials G.N. and date 1716 refer to George Newland, a Bristol merchant who married Elizabeth, the daughter of Edward Tocknell. Newland made many alterations to the old house, shortening the gables, roughcasting the walls, inserting windows and a sundial, before he died in 1756.

Tocknell's Mill was also worked by one of the Poole family who married into the Tocknells; Richard Poole is named 'of Tocknell's' in his will of 1707. As was only natural in such a community, the clothiers married among themselves and this often explains why the mills were worked first under one name then another, particularly in the first half of the eighteenth century. The mills seem to have changed their names as often as the inns. Change of ownership in the next century, however, seems to have been caused more by the clothiers being unable or unwilling to install new machinery to keep up with the times and then giving up as it became increasingly difficult to make a profit. Tocknell's Mill in 1885 became known as Eddell's Mill. It was used as a grist mill for many years and finally fell into disuse.

King's Mill took its name from John King who worked

'Kynesgesmill' in 1495 as a flour mill. It was worked by the Palling family as a cloth mill until about the middle of the nineteenth century. Tradition says that Edward, who died in 1684, worked this mill, but we do not know if this was the beginning of its life as a clothing mill. King's Mill has been pulled down except for a small part incorporated into King's Mill House, but before it ceased to function it was used as a pin-factory by Messrs Watkins and Okey in 1870 and afterwards by Messrs Savory & Co, who bought the business from them.

The Pallings are one of the clothing families said to have been enriched by the increase in the trade after the Civil War. The family lived at Painswick for about 300 years. In the records of Painswick the name occurs repeatedly, showing that they played an important part in the town, one of the earliest being a William who gave £20 in 1707 towards a Charity School, while another, John Palling of Cirencester, also gave £20, suggesting that although he no longer lived there he kept an interest in his birthplace.

An Edward Palling lived at Court House, one of Painswick's most handsome houses, which passed to William Carruthers in 1789; he owned it until 1840. Another fine house, Sheephouse, was restored by a John Palling, who shortened it by removing the third gable to form a yard. Beyond the pump the stone floor of this last portion can still be seen. It has two circular stone stairways, part of the original seventeenth-century house. The family lived at Sheephouse for at least sixty years; Edward, who succeeded John, was living there in 1784. *Our Family History*, by E. Carruthers Little, published in 1892, gives the history of the Palling family, who intermarried with the various important clothiers of the district, including the Carruthers, Littles, Walthens and others.

One of the handsomest tombs to be seen in the churchyard was made by John Bryan for Edward Palling, who died in 1758. It is a massive table tomb, its intricate ornament of delicate shell pattern and cherubs' heads restrained and dignified. Bold coils of acanthus hold up the corners and the ornament is kept within bounds by the fine proportions of the mouldings of plinth and top, so that one does not feel the craftsman has let the classical influence run to seed, as so often happens in this type of monument. If further evidence were needed the tomb shows that Edward Palling was a clothier of considerable substance and importance in the prosperous Painswick of his time.

Rock Mill, also on the Painswick stream, belonged to the Gardner family, who, like the Pallings, lived in Painswick for over 250 years. We find a John Gardner, clothier, in a Court Roll of 1567–8, while in 1695 a Stephen left £10 for bread to be distributed to the poor every year on Christmas Day. Thomas Gardner, a rich mercer, built Court House, afterwards inhabited by the Pallings, and W. St Clair Baddeley tells us in his *A Cotteswold Manor*, 1929, that the Gardners rented all the Upper Court Orchard several generations before Court House was built at the end of the sixteenth century and that in 1590 Thomas held 119 acres in all.

Thomas Gardner did not enjoy his new mansion very long, for he parted with it after a critical dispute between the lord of the manor and his tenants. The value of land rose steeply at that time and the lord of the manor believed he should benefit from the new valuation. A Commission was appointed to examine an Indenture of 1592 and all Court Rolls, and a costly suit followed.

Court House is built of the local silvery-grey stone, a stone having less yellow in it than the oolite of the north Cotswolds, and it is this pale stone, allied to Painswick's position high on the wolds, which gives the impression of a town bathed in air and sunlight. Dr Seaman, Chancellor of the diocese of Gloucester, was living here in 1606 and he added a wing in 1620. With his wife Elizabeth he is buried in the church. Their effigies of Derbyshire alabaster were originally in the chancel, but were placed in their present position at one of the restorations at the beginning of the nineteenth century, when they were combined with a late Tudor canopy once forming part of the tomb of Sir William Kingston, who died in 1540, and a table tomb believed to be part of a monument to one of the Talbots, a former lord of the manor. Ida Roper, in her *Effigies of Gloucestershire*, suggests that the effigies were probably the work of Samuel Baldwin, a sculptor of Stroud. Dr Seaman had indirect connection with the clothing trade, for he came of a family of woollen drapers of Chelmsford, Essex.

In 1707 Luke Gardner gave £10 towards the Charity School, and, if one wanted evidence that at this time the town lived by the clothing trade, the fact that all the contributors to this fund were clothiers would confirm it.

There are eight Gardners buried in Painswick, all of them described as clothiers, two as clothiers of Rock Mill. The earliest memorial is to Daniel, who died in 1712, the latest to Thomas, who died in 1768. The name, however, continues to be found in the Painswick records as late as the last quarter of the nineteenth century, though not in connection with the clothing trade.

Rock Mill passed through the usual vicissitudes after the Gardners left it towards the end of the eighteenth century. About 1858 it was used for a dye-wood business by Mr John Thomas, a member of a family of dye-wood manufacturers who settled in Chewton Keynsham in Somerset after the Napoleonic Wars. After two ventures, first at Wotton-under-Edge and then in the Slad Valley, Mr Thomas took Rock Mill where his business flourished until 1870, when Albert Mill, on the river Chew, the original site of his family's business, came up for sale; he bought it and returned to Somerset. A fascinating sidelight on the Thomas family is given in an article in *The Journal of Industrial Archaeology*, Volume 3, No 2, which tells how the founder of the business, during a period of naval service in Jamaica, took the opportunity of studying the production of dyes from native dyewoods, particularly from the logwood trees, and when he returned home found employment in a logwood mill in Chewton where he could test his new knowledge, finally starting up on his own.

The brook which rises on the Ebworth estate and goes through Sheepscombe village served three mills. One of these, Wight's Mill at Brookland, almost in the village of Sheepscombe, was one of the largest in Painswick parish, and was still being worked by John and Edward Wight in 1820. Situated at the bottom of the valley and shaded by a curtain of trees making it almost invisible from the hill-top, its position at first sight could not have seemed more idyllic. Here was a remote hamlet with the advantage of a local industry to keep its inhabitants employed. Actually its position aggravated the lawlessness which by 1817 had given Sheepscombe a bad reputation, so that its more self-righteous neighbours at Painswick, some two miles away, disliked being associated with it.

The majority of Sheepscombe's 500 inhabitants worked at the mill and it was said that the conduct of the men was so riotous, even at work, that the owner was sometimes obliged to close down and turn them all out for part of the day to quell the tumult;

and one must remember that no work in those days meant no pay. Unfortunately the reasons for the rioting are not given, the contemporary records being written from the clothiers' point of view. We do know, however, that there were eight unlicensed alehouses and no school or church.

About 1780 a Sunday School had been started by two brothers, John and William Twining, in John's cottage. The Twinings were weavers and came from a family who had once held two mills just below the Knap and who must have been interested in education, for Thomas Twining, Clerk, gave £5 towards the founding of a Charity School in 1707. By 1817 their Sunday School had dwindled to one old man who occasionally gathered together a few rough lads but was unable to control them.

A little booklet, *A Gloucestershire Parson's Wife, 1814–1826*, tells how the young wife of the Painswick curate, Mrs Agnes Neville, her sympathy aroused by the neglected state of the Sheepscombe mill-workers, opened a Sunday School for them, walking the two miles each way in all weathers. She was warned that no woman could control the wild young ruffians and that she might meet with insult if not violence, but the young weavers, by no means as bad as they were painted, soon became devoted to this pretty young woman. Her husband, the Rev Charles Neville, felt the good work should be established and that a resident clergyman was essential, and he began to collect money for a church at Sheepscombe. By this time the enthusiasm of the mill-workers was aroused and a delegation came to Mr Neville and asked to be allowed to help. They could give no money but offered their labour. Mrs Neville suggested that they should prepare the ground, as before the actual building could begin the top of a knoll had to be removed and the site levelled. The weavers put in many hours after their long days at the mill, often working on moonlight nights until well into the small hours, which shows that the 'wild, lawless weavers' wanted a church of their own and were not so unprincipled as the clothiers made out. Anyone who has done any digging on high Cotswold, where stone brash lies just below the surface and solid rock beneath the brash, will know what heavy work it can be. The church was quickly built, the local clothiers being generous in their donations, and the Rev Charles Neville became the resident clergyman, living with his wife and child in a cottage until a parsonage was built for them.

By 1825 Sheepscombe was transformed into a docile church-going community and had become the 'Peaceful Valley' of a tract of that name written by the Rev Hugh Stowell. As in all such tracts, the mill-workers themselves are given little credit for this miraculous change of heart. One factor in the reformation must have been the shop Mrs Neville opened in her house where she sold clothing at cost price. We get a glimpse here of the dress of the weavers, for among the items sold were leather breeches, blue 'jerkins', scarlet duffle cloaks and linsey-woollen petticoats. The gay scarlet cloaks and blue jerkins must have made a fine splash of colour when the weavers trooped to church on Sundays, and the leather breeches and linsey-woollen petticoats were sensible garments for keeping out the piercing Cotswold winds.

If one has the suspicion that the Rev Hugh Stowell was using the fact that the Sunday School was one of the first established in the country as an example to the rest of England, one must remember that propaganda was not invented in our times. We are told that all the unlicensed ale-houses were closed, the church filled with an orderly and reverent congregation, the very porch filled with worshippers who could not find room inside, while the mill-owners gave thankful testimony to the reformed character of the weavers. It did not occur to them that much of this gentler spirit may have come about because at last a little interest in their welfare was being shown at a time when they were working for the meanest pittance, and, not understanding the hazards of the trade, had been aware only that the clothiers lived in affluence while they were always on the borderline of want.

The Cap Mill is one of the few which kept their original names, perhaps because it recalled the Act of 1571 when Parliament, to help the trade, ordered everyone above six years of age 'except ladies and gentlemen' to wear a cap of wool on Sundays and holidays, the wearing of caps being 'very decent and comely for all estates and degrees'. This Act was repealed in 1598. Towards the end of the nineteenth century Nathaniel Wood ceased to work Cap Mill. For a short time it was a saw-mill and then it became outbuildings for Cap Mill House.

It was one of the oldest mills, for we know it was owned by John Beard in 1662 and was then rebuilt to pass into the ownership of Henry Webb and his widow until 1697. Jasper Selwin of the Matson-King's Stanley family held it for some years but by the time he relinquished it the demand for caps of different shapes, colours and materials, laid down officially to distinguish trades and professions, had completely disappeared.

By 1729 the Cap Mill had been taken over by the Packers, another of Painswick's important clothing families. Nine members are buried in the churchyard, the earliest Richard, who died, aged 80, in 1719. The Christian names favoured were Richard, John and Daniel, and there were four Johns, three Daniels and two Richards between 1719 and 1774, all recorded as clothiers except Richard 'of the lower mill'. He was a wool-stapler, a useful member of the family who probably supplied the others with their raw material. Obtaining wool was an important part of the clothing trade and had its difficulties. Dr E. Lipson in his *History of the Woollen and Worsted Industries*, 1921, gives three ways this was done, the 'richer' clothier purchasing his wool direct in the fleece from the wool-grower, the 'meaner' clothier, having neither the leisure to travel to the wool country nor the means to make large purchases, buying the wool from the wool-stapler, while the 'poor' clothier bought yarn in the markets. 'This yarn is weekly brought into the markets by a great number of poor people that will not spin to the clothier for small wages, but have stock enough to set themselves on work.'

We know something of one Daniel Packer because his letter-books are now in the Gloucester Records Office. He was probably the Daniel who died in 1769. Many of the letters were written to his factor, Thomas Misenor, and deal mostly with the selling of his cloth. They show how much a clothier depended on his factor, or agent, and how during the last half of the eighteenth century the struggle for markets had increased, with the hazards of the trade including not only the continual alteration of fashion in the home market but the risk of war abroad.

They also show that around 1768 the boom was nearly over for the smaller Painswick clothiers, and ruin just round the corner if they did not watch the fluctuations of the markets and use imagination to get in first with, as Rudder put it, 'all the variety to be found in a well-stored draper's shop'. This variety consisted of 'superfines, seconds, forests, drabs, naps, duffles', and the ribbed stuff that could only be made by using new machinery involving a greater expenditure many clothiers could not afford. Some who might have afforded it believed that the new fashions would pass and people would return to broadcloth with its hard-wearing and other excellent qualities.

Through his agent, Thomas Misenor, Daniel Packer dealt with two London firms, Messrs Marsh & Hudson and Sir T. Fludyer & Co. He realized that Misenor, being 'on ye spott', must understand the market better than he did and the letters show that he trusted him in every way.

'I have left the price of all my cloths to you . . . who must know best ye price of Cloth this year,' he wrote in January 1769. 'When you have my cash in Hand I must beg the favour of you to lay it out at a time you think the most adventageous. Some of us here think we shall soon have a War, if this should be the case I suppose Government Securities would fall.'

Daniel relied on Misenor to tell him which kind of cloths were most likely to sell, and sent samples of different varieties. We read about the weather and labour troubles. Because of the fluctuating state of the trade it was seldom possible to know how many weavers and other workers would be needed. In some seasons orders might not justify keeping on all the hands, while in other seasons as many again would be required. The economics of the time meant that however unwilling a clothier might be to dismiss his workers he would be forced to do so if he had no work for them.

Daniel Packer fully understood his workers' predicament as well as his own, for if he let them go a sudden increase of orders might make it impossible for him to find spinners and weavers in time to execute the orders. In one letter to Sir T. Fludyer in December 1760 he even hints that periods of good trade were as troublesome as bad, because then the workers were more difficult to find 'so long as the superfine-makers can give such good wages they take a great many of our best hands from us'. A remark which has a modern sound.

Another letter shows there were occasions when he tried to keep on his workers although trade was poor. 'Indeed I wish I am not the great loser by keeping on my workpeople,' but a week later he writes 'I shall lessen my trade . . . I should be glad to keep on my neighbours if it could be done to pay but common interest.' The use of the word 'neighbours' makes it plain that he identified himself with his workpeople as being close to them. Indeed, in those days when the clothier lived next door to his

mill he had more sympathy with their conditions than in the nineteenth century when many of the clothiers built themselves residences well away from their mills and factories.

On this occasion Daniel was obliged to dismiss his spinners a
month later. 'I must part with all my spinners, what they will do
I cannot tell, I fear they will not find employment elsewhere.'

Tantalizing glimpses of the life of the times are revealed in these
letterbooks. On 28 August 1768 Daniel reports the tragic end of a
local clothier and the sad tale of another imprisoned for debt, and
one can well imagine both incidents made a great stir amongst the
clothiers, and aroused misgivings about their own positions if
trade did not improve.

> We shall have fewer clothiers another Year. I hear there was one
> sent to Gloster Jail Thursday last. And Last Tuesday John Haines,
> brother to Mr Daniel Haines shot himself thro' the Head; he was
> deeply in debt for Wool, and Messrs E and I refused to accept his
> bills for payment thereof. And so he took it into his Head to make
> short work of it by the above rash action.

Bad weather is not a risk we associate with the factories of
today, but in the eighteenth century it was one that the clothiers
had to reckon with and which could bring ruin to them and their
workers. Water being essential, work could be held up by severe
frost; in the summer the hazard was drought. Again and again we
learn from the letterbooks that there was either too much or not
enough water in the streams. As the cloth was dried out of doors,
heavy rains for too long a period meant it could be spoilt, particularly dyed fabric.

Two of Daniel's letters in 1768 mention that in one instance he
could not send any cloth because of shortage of water, while in
December of the same year 'owing to this uncommon wet season
the Blues are Dy'd and the Whites are whitened, but when I shall
get them dry I cannot tell'.

On the whole Daniel's letters reveal him as a kindly man,
anxious to do his best for the people he employed even when
wrestling with his own problems. If he was the Daniel Packer who
was buried in 1769 he was the last of the family to carry on business in the town, for no other Packer was known as a clothier in
Painswick after that date. In a list of Painswick wills the last
Packer mentioned is Mary, whose will was proved in 1793. One

1. Painswick (Chapter 2)

2. Remains of Mill pond, Ozleworth Bottom (Chapter 4)

3. Ruined Mill, Ozleworth Bottom (Chapter 4)

can only infer that the family either left the town or died out at the end of the century.

The Webbs carried on a flourishing business for about 150 years. Thomas Webb, one of the earliest of them, was known as Webb of the Hill, from a house he built or rebuilt from an old one. This house is still known as The Hill but is now in the parish of Uplands. It stands on Wickerage Hill on a tongue of land east of the Painswick valley, and Thomas's initials and the date 1634 are carved on the lintel of the porch.

The name of Webb of the Hill has passed into national history as one who defied the bureaucracy of his day by infringing a Statute requiring a clothier to weave his name or mark in a certain position on his cloth.

'This clothier has sewn his mark, in two Stroudwater Reds, between the forrels and not inside the piece,' complained Anthony Withers of His Majesty's Commission for Clothing, and he ordered the cloths to be forfeited. According to an affidavit sworn by Henry Ackenback,

> when Anthony Withers caused Laomedon Bliss to seize the same cloths as forfeited to his Majesty's use, Bliss having one of the said Cloths in his arms to carry away to the King's storehouse, the said Thomas Webb violently took the same away, saying to Withers, in a railing manner, that he hoped the curses of the poor would root him out, that the marks on the said cloths stood where they ought to stand, where they should stand, and where he would have them stand, neither would he make it otherwise while he live.

Thomas won his case or it was allowed to lapse, and doubtless he was congratulated by the other clothiers of Painswick on triumphing over tyrants in high places. There was a lot of the John Bull in Thomas Webb of the Hill.

With some of the other clothiers he put in a petition to the Lords of the Treasury fully stating the origin and progress of the manufacture of red cloth, for which the Stroudwater district was famed, and declaring that their forefathers beyond the memory of man used the trade for making red cloth, but had only made coarse cloths of a blood colour. Webb's people, however, about 1605, began to make finer cloth and dress it much better, at the same time dying it with grained and bastard stammels. 'These stammell cloths with bastard scarlet are found very good and

C   33

marketable; and we make of the same near 3,000 every year; and we hope, if allowed to go on in our lawful calling to revive the trade of making white cloth.' The petition finished by expressing the hope that they had satisfied the Commissioners that their using 'mosing-mills' and dying stammells was for the general benefit.

Webb must have been the richest clothier in Painswick at this time, for he was assessed seven shillings more than any customary tenant in the manor. In later subsidies he was assessed at even more, so it would seem that the petition was successful.

Five Webbs described as clothiers are buried in the churchyard, the latest being John who died in 1736. There is no visible memorial to Thomas of the Hill. His son or grandson Edmund gave a bell to the church in 1686. Sir Robert Atkyns mentions a Mr Webb of the Hill who had a good estate and house in Sroud-End tithing, evidence that by 1712 the family belonged to the land-owning 'gentlemen' clothiers. They afterwards changed their name to de Hill as they went up the social scale, but I wonder if the first Thomas would have approved!

One of the earliest Sunday Schools in the country was started in Painswick in 1784 by Mr Samuel Webb of Ebworth, son of John de Webb, a wealthy cloth manufacturer, according to the biography of Robert Raikes by Josiah Harris. Raikes visited this school some two years after it had been started and with Mr Webb decided that a sermon should be preached in Painswick church in support of the Sunday School movement, Dr Samuel Glasse FRS to be the preacher. The date was chosen deliberately. It was to be 24 September, the day of Painswick Feast. Raikes puts forth his reasons in a letter to the *Gentleman's Magazine* of January 1787.

> An annual festival has from time immemorial been held on that day, a festival that would have disgraced the most heathen nations. Drunkenness and every species of clamour, riot and disorder formerly filled the town on this occasion.

It was 'to divert the vulgar from their brutal prostitution of the Lord's Day' that this date was fixed. In this same letter Raikes says that the crowds who came into the town for the Feast

> instead of repairing to the ale-houses as heretofore, they hastened to the church which was filled in such a manner as I never remember to

have seen in any church before. . . . In the meantime the town was remarkably free from those pastimes which used to disgrace it; wrestling, quarrelling, fighting were totally banished and all was peace and tranquillity.

I am always willing to believe in miracles, but sermons, by their very nature—and in those days they went on for hours—have been known to have soporific effects, and I wonder if this may have assisted in bringing about 'the peace and tranquillity' Raikes noted. The occasion brings out not only the contrast between Thomas of the Hill, defying his Majesty's Commissioners in 1634, and Mr Samuel Webb of 1784, but the puritanical fervour which had overtaken Painswick in the days of the latter.

Painswick Feast combined a festival commemorating the dedication of the church with the annual fair, dating from 1321 when Almer de Valence, lord of the manor, obtained this right for the town. Its inhabitants had continued to spend the Holy Day in games and feasting and had seen no wrong in it. Raikes and the other Mrs Proudies of the period, however, saw evil where none existed, regarding the wrestling and other rough sports, as well as the drinking which went with them, as things to be stamped out. The fact that the townspeople assembled in such numbers to hear a sermon by a famous preacher and were delighted to see the 'cleanliness and good behaviour' of the children paraded on the occasion, shows that the town could not have been as far gone in wickedness as these good men believed. We are also told that the people contributed so generously to a collection that the organisers were astonished.

The Lovedays, another important Painswick clothing family, were Quakers. Two of them suffered for their faith. John Loveday was imprisoned for eight months for refusing to attend service in the parish church in 1663, and John Loveday junior in 1685 had goods valued at £60 taken from him as a fine for the same offence. Another John, of the Farmhouse at Holcombe, had a small mill where the Washwell spring runs into the Painswick stream, but this has been pulled down.

The Lovedays are believed to have given the Meeting House ground and the Dell cemetery where no less than sixteen members of the family were buried between 1685 and 1771. They built Yew Tree House about 1700 and the monogram above the porch appears to include D.R.—for Deborah Roberts—within E. Love-day. An Edward Loveday was one of the overseers of Painswick from 1778 to 1800. His heir, Daniel Roberts, lived and died in Yew Tree House. The only Loveday described as clothier on his tombstone is Charles, who died in 1801. The family belonged to the town for at least 250 years, as the first will recorded in Glouces-ter is of Thomas who died in 1588, and in 1844 a John Loveday was a churchwarden. Some seventeen wills are recorded, from Thomas, 1858, to Mary, 1779.

Another family who lived in Painswick for more than two centuries were the Pooles. They intermarried with the Lovedays, Gardners and Tocknells. Two of the most handsome tombs in the churchyard by John Bryan are to the brothers Richard and John.

The Pooles came originally from Poole in the Wirrall in Cheshire. The first recorded as living in Painswick is William, third son of John Poole of Poole in the Wirrall. William was reeve of the manor under one of the Lord Lisles, and it is just possible that he came to the town with Lord Shrewsbury in the fifteenth century, during one of the pauses in the wars with France when Henry V and Henry VI were endeavouring to establish their right to the French throne.

The next Poole we hear about is in 1548, in connection with the church. A David Poole owned the advowson at that date, it hav-ing been granted to him by the late Prior of Llanthony, the advowson having been the property of the Priory from the time whence it was granted to them in 1100 by Hugh de Lacy, lord of the manor of Painswick. The Pooles probably became clothiers when one of the younger sons was put to the trade, as was the fashion in those days.

For roughly 200 years the making of cloth was Painswick's chief concern, the trade rising to its peak in the middle of the eighteenth century and then falling slowly to its extinction in the early 1900s as the geographical basis of the industry changed. The streams and watercourses which had supplied the motive power were the chief reason the industry had flourished there, and these could now be replaced by machinery driven by steam and later electricity, with the necessary water pumped from underground sources.

In 1838 there were 154 persons working as weavers in Pains-wick, of whom 41 were heads of families and the rest women and children, while the indoor and outdoor paupers in the parish amounted to 1,366 out of a population of 3,700; grim evidence that the trade had fallen away. One of the reputed sayings of Painswick: 'we are in a quandary; we are so poor we cannot live, and the place is so healthy we cannot die' may have originated with the weavers when trade was bad.

The last mills to be used for the cloth trade in the Slad valley were the New Mills, worked by John Libby & Co, until 1897, and Woodland Mills by Messrs Humphries until 1924, though in 1870 the latter was used by Frederick James, twine-spinner, the motive power being supplied by oxen. None of the old families had survived until the end.

CHAPTER THREE

The Cotswold hand-loom weavers

B y the first half of the sixteenth century the south Cotswolds, particularly the Stroudwater valleys and those in the Wotton-under-Edge area, were steadily developing into a busy weaving centre, chiefly because of the abundance of pure soft water available from the Frome and the many streams of the valleys. Lack of water for power, cleansing, fulling and dyeing was one of the reasons why the expanding industry had to spread beyond the big towns such as Salisbury and Bristol, so that when the Act of 1555 tried to confine the manufacture of cloth to the towns an exception had to be made in favour of

> any of the towns and villages near adjoining to the Water of Stroud in the county of Gloucester where Clothes have been usually made by the space of twenty years past, and having been Prentice to the Occupation of Cloth making, or exercised the Feat or Mystery of making, weaving or rowing of Cloth.

The number of people engaged in the clothing industry and its distribution in the area can be found in a list of able-bodied men for 'his Majesty's Services in the wars within the County of Gloucester' compiled by John Smith in August 1608. Those engaged in the clothing trade represented about forty-two per cent of the able-bodied population. The concentration of the woollen manufacture was along the western escarpment from Painswick in the north to Hawkesbury in the south. Only in one town, Cirencester, a Guild of Weavers or Weavers' Company, survived as a working body into the seventeenth century, but eventually it had to give way to the competition of the Stroudwater valleys. The 'Register Book for the whole company of Weavers inhabiting within the town of Cirencester' sets out the company's constitution, with its regulations about apprenticeship and setting up of looms.

38

The Cotswold hand-loom weavers

It was a determined effort, in the manner of the ancient guilds, to keep out unqualified craftsmen, possibly agricultural workers and others made workless by the enclosures or the increase in sheep farming. The two 'discretest and wisest men in the mystery of weaving' were chosen to control the others each year on the eve of St Katherine, and it is the use of the word mystery, or 'mistery' which occurs again and again in documents relating to the weavers which shows the respect in which the craftsmen expected to be held. The Weavers' Company was determined to keep that mystery within its protection, but by the 1700s only a few weavers remained in the town and these probably did not work for the clothiers but for private customers.

By 1608 Gloucester had lost her earlier importance in the trade; one report gives only six or seven looms working, though 'within living memory there had been a hundred', showing how the restrictions of the guilds here as elsewhere had influenced the flow of industry to the western slopes of the Cotswolds.

Bristol, though it lost its weavers in the same fashion, still had a big part to play, for much of the West of England cloth at that time was exported from there, the Bristol merchants providing some of the capital for the increasing trade. The Merchant Adventurers of Bristol soon became strong enough to manipulate it to their advantage; again and again the Cotswold clothiers complained that the practice of limiting the number of cloths bought by its members was ruining the industry. A petition to Parliament in 1571 received a reply from the Merchant Adventurers that they had exported 400 more cloths than in the two years before the trade was opened to them, but in 1621 the clothiers again complained bitterly that the Merchant Adventurers were the cause of a depression which had fallen upon the industry.

In their turn, to make the profit they felt was due to them the clothiers further depressed their workers. The weavers, however, cared little for the clothiers' troubles. They saw them living in comfortable circumstances, buying land and building fine new houses and mills, taking over old manor houses and insinuating themselves into the ranks of the landed gentry while weavers worked for long hours for wages that barely kept them alive. They knew that without their work there would be no rich clothiers, no increase in the country's wealth, and their frustration and bitterness was to grow with each succeeding decade.

The Cotswold hand-loom weavers

Complaints of inadequate wages began at the same time as the capitalist system. Dr Lipson, in his *History of the Woollen & Worsted Industries*, quotes a fifteenth-century pamphlet *England's Commercial Policy*, which sums up in a phrase the weavers' position. 'The poor have the labour, the rich the winning.' In 1621 a member of Parliament complained in the House of Commons that clothiers 'give not the poor competent wages—threepence a day and no more to divers'. It was a countrywide grievance, not confined to the Cotswolds, as can be seen by a ballad sung in the streets at the time, entitled *The Clothiers Delight, or the Rich Man's Joy, and the Poor Men's Sorrow*, 'Where is expresst the craftiness and subtility of many Clothiers by beating down their workmen's wages.'

> Of all sorts of callings that in England be,
> There is none that liveth so gallant as we;
> Our trading maintains us as brave as a Knight,
> We live at our pleasure and take our delight;
> We heapeth up riches and treasures great store,
> Which we get by griping and grinding the poor,
>   And this is the way to fill up our purse,
>   Although we do get it with many a curse.
>
> Throughout the whole kingdom, in country and town,
> There is no danger of our trade going down,
> So long as the Comber can work with his comb,
> And also the Weaver can work with his loom;
> The Tucker and Spinner that spins all the year,
> We'll make them to earn their wages full dear.
>   And this is the way . . .
>
> In former ages we us'd to give
> So that our work folks like farmers did live;
> But now times are altered and we'll make them know
> All we can for to bring them under our bow;
> We will make to work hard for sixpence a day,
> Though a shilling they deserve if they had their just pay.
>   And this is the way . . .

That such a ballad should be sung in the streets shows that the poverty of the weavers was common knowledge and not confined to those interested in the industry.

The Cotswold hand-loom weavers

When the government took over the regulation of wages after the decay of the guilds they were aware of their responsibilities to the workers. The Statute of Apprentices of 1563 came about, as its preamble states, 'to yield unto the hired person both in times of scarcity and in the time of plenty a convenient proportion of wages'. The Justices of the Peace at the annual Easter Sessions were ordered to 'rate and appoint' wages. And as there seems to have been some doubt as to whether the workers in the cloth trade were included in the order it was definitely stated in 1597 that the Justices were 'to rate wages of any labourers, weavers, spinsters and workmen or workwomen what ever'. This Act was confirmed in 1604 with two additions, obviously rendered necessary because the rulings had been evaded. The first addition was that a Justice who was also a clothier was not to be allowed to be 'a rater of wages for any artisan that depended upon the making of cloth', a necessary precaution in Gloucestershire where many clothiers were Justices, and secondly, penalties were to be imposed upon any employer who paid less than the authorized wages, so that the Act of 1604 was actually a minimum wage Act.

In some parts of the country, however, the Justices continued to fix maximum rates which the clothiers were forbidden to exceed, and often the wages paid fell much below the maximum authorised by the Justices, though a clause providing that

> if any clothier or other shall refuse to obey the said order, rate or assessment of wages as aforesaid, and shall not pay so much or so great wages to other weavers, spinsters, workmen or workwomen . . . the person offending shall for every offence pay 10s to the aggrieved party.

The weavers pressed hard for the enforcement of the Act; in spite of their reputation for lawlessness their behaviour throughout shows a pathetic trust in the good faith of the government. Rioting broke out when the clothiers flouted the Act; knowing its administrative difficulties better than the weavers they felt fairly safe in taking the risk. Time and time again the weavers protested about the illegal practices of the clothiers and time and time again legislation was passed against them. One wonders why the weavers continued to believe in the government, as they did throughout the sixteenth and most of the seventeenth century, enduring the inevitable delays and the government's ineffectual efforts to keep control, until one realises there was nowhere else they could turn for help.

The payment of truck wages was one of the methods used by the clothiers to reduce their wages bill, the workers being obliged to take the greater part of their wages in provisions or goods at a price in excess of their value and including 'pins, girdles and other unprofitable wares' they did not want. This lack of control over the money they earned further increased the burning sense of grievance and injustice. Another device was to defer the payment of wages until they amounted to a considerable sum and then compel the weavers to take promissory notes payable at a future date. This meant part of the money owing to them went in getting the notes discounted.

The weavers kept up their complaints, and we know of one instance where they were successful. In 1637 some weavers complained that their employers had not only reduced their wages but also made them accept truck. The offender was put in prison and only released when he had paid his workmen double the amount they had lost and the cost of the proceedings. But the times when the weavers won a case were few. To bring a case at all was often far beyond their means, for when the magistrates imposed penalties on the clothiers the trials were removed to Westminster, thus involving the weavers in expenses they could not afford.

There were occasions when the clothiers could use their workers' conditions to bring their own distresses to the notice of the government. During the depression around 1620, when the export of cloth was reduced to nearly two-thirds and trade generally was in a precarious state, they protested

... these times do more than threaten to throw us and everyone of us, yea, many thousands of poor and others who depend on us, into the bottomless pit of remidiless destruction. ...

The Justices of Gloucestershire wrote to the Privy Council for advice.

We very much fear that the peace hereof will be shortly endangered, notwithstanding all the vigilance we use or can use to the contrary, since workmen do wander, beg, steal, and are in case to starve as their faces (to our great griefs) do manifest.

The picture this letter calls up of faces gaunt with malnutrition shows how acute the general distress must have been, and the Privy Council thereupon summoned representatives of the clothiers to London to discuss the matter, as well as sending a letter to all Justices in the clothing districts to see that the clothiers kept their workfolk in employment, 'for those who have gained in profitable times must now be content to lose for the public good till the decay of trade be remedied'.

The Justices reported that the clothiers, ordered to keep on their workpeople, would only agree to do so for a fortnight, saying that trade had been dead for the past year and their stock and credit exhausted. As an example of the clothiers' goodwill towards their workpeople they cite 'One William Bennett, a very ancient and good clothier, doth offer to live by brown bread and water rather than his great number of poor people should want work, if he had the means to keep them on work'. The only clue to this 'very ancient and good clothier' is that a William Bennet, of Oxlynch, is to be found in John Smith's *Names and Surnames*. This same reply also gives 1,500 looms in Gloucestershire and 24,000 people employed in the trade.

In July 1622, when the Justices again reported the distress of the weavers, they gave an account of the examination of one of them, Richard Webb, whom they had recently committed to prison for rioting. Webb had told them that the starving weavers of Stroudwater were planning to attack the Severn trows as they carried malt down from Gloucester. The scarcity of corn had already provoked riots in Wiltshire and Devonshire and the Privy Council had ordered the Justices to put some restriction upon the malting of grain so there should be more for bread. Anxious to minimise the accounts of the rioting they announced that the trouble had been largely caused by 'the turbulent and seditious spirits of some idle and clamourous persons', even when it was pointed out that for many years the prices of foodstuffs had been rising while wages had remained stationary and thousands of weavers were on the verge of starvation.

In one instance we find Cotswold weavers on the side of the clothiers. As often happens in bad times, new methods to cut costs were introduced and clothiers in other districts had begun to use gig- or mosing-mills instead of hand labour to raise the nap of the cloth. The workers complained that 'one man and a boy' could 'row' as many cloths as eight or ten by hand and petitioned that an old prohibition against the use of gig-mills should be enforced. Now gig-mills had been used in the Cotswolds for many years, and this prohibition had the disastrous effect of reducing the number of cloths the clothiers could finish, whereupon all interested in the industry in the Stroudwater area appealed against the restriction, pointing out that as producers of the famous red cloth the reasons for the prohibition did not apply. There was little chance of damage by stretching because the cloth was thoroughly shrunk in the dyeing process, and their gig-mills held small teazels instead of the large king-teazels used in hand rowing. The broadweavers, in their turn, pointed out that rowing by hand meant a great reduction in output and alleged that many hundreds of weavers would be unemployed if the use of gig-mills were prohibited.

The Privy Council's action on this occasion could be taken as an example of their thoroughness in investigating complaints from clothiers and weavers alike. They decided that two Stroudwater red cloths, one dressed by the gig-mill and the other by hand should be compared, and until then the prohibition stayed. The comparison was unfavourable to the gig-mill and the Council could not reverse their decision, and when the Gloucestershire clothiers ignored the order their cloths were seized. But, as had happened before, the enforcement was not always followed up, though for some years at least it contributed to the depression which brought much poverty to the weavers in the 1630s.

Throughout the early seventeenth century the failure of the Cockayne experiment and the wars ravaging central Europe interfered with the export trade and the weavers suffered greatly, their status decreasing still further. Those who had a sizeable plot for vegetables or kept a cow or a few sheep, managed to live without the aid of the parish, but the Enclosure Acts were taking in much of the common land, thus depriving them of free pasture for their animals. When, early in the nineteenth century, Timothy Exell, the Gloucestershire weaver, described the idyllic life of the weaver in days gone by: 'Their little cottages seemed happy and contented . . . it was seldom a weaver appealed to the parish for relief . . .' and 'Peace and content sat on the weaver's brow', nostalgia for a golden age had cast a rosy glow over the past. However, although his picture has its extravagance, the fact re-

mains that the weavers before the Civil Wars were not left entirely
to the mercy of the clothiers and had not been driven by hopeless-
ness to organised violence against their masters and drink and
degradation amongst themselves. The Civil War and then the
Revolution of 1688 brought serious changes in the old system of
state control of the clothing industry. Before the war the Privy
Council had been actively concerned with the way the industry
was organised, its hold on local authorities enabling it to inter-
vene on the weavers' behalf. Its administrative capacity had not
been strong enough to enforce all its pronouncements, yet the
weavers had felt that their rights were recognized by the government. But now they had to watch the industrial legislation of past
centuries falling into disuse, with the power in the hands of a
parliament under the direct influence of the capitalists.

As the century came to an end the clothiers no longer feared a
summons to appear before the Privy Council. The country was
fast recovering from the ravages of war and, helped by Parliament's policy of forbidding the import of foreign cloth, the export
of raw wool and the killing of the Irish wool trade, English
clothiers were flourishing. Trade with the American colonies and
India was already on the way to its great expansion of the eighteenth century, and during the last quarter of the seventeenth
many clothiers built up substantial fortunes and became landed
gentry.

The weavers did not share in this prosperity and poured out a
series of complaints and petitions, both to the King and to the
Justices. They led a precarious existence, being engaged by the
piece, and when they took in their work they could never be
certain what rate they would receive for it or if more work would
be forthcoming. By various tricks, such as improperly counting
the number of hundreds of threads in a chain, they were often
defrauded of part of the meagre wage they earned.

Fluctuations in demand inseparable from dependence upon
foreign markets bore more heavily upon them than on the
clothiers, who were cushioned by capital, and their lot deteriorated
rather than improved despite larger demand and new markets
opening up. By the time the new century was under way all traces
of their medieval status as craftsmen had disappeared. Men who
had to beg for Poor Law relief when there was no work or
when the work did not bring in sufficient to keep them alive found

it difficult to hold on to their self-respect or the respect of the rest of the community.

The future was rosy for the clothiers; they had a marketing organisation capable of dealing with foreign trade evolved out of the experiences of the past two centuries, they had a large labour force at their command and they were gradually freeing themselves from the domination of the state over the industry.

The weavers' complaints increased as their conditions worsened. In 1719, the broad and narrow weavers of Stroud and the surrounding districts petitioned Parliament to put down the 'tyrannical capitalist clothier by enforcing the Act of 1555'. In 1728 they appealed to the King for help against what they described as fraud and oppression. A committee of the Privy Council drew up articles between the parties of the dispute and the weavers were admonished for the future not to try and help themselves by unlawful combinations but always 'to lay the grievances in a regular manner before his Majesty who would always be ready to grant them relief suitable to the justice of their cause'. We get the first hint here that the weavers were banding together and the authorities were aware of it, and feared it. The Justices were persuaded, despite protests from the clothiers, to fix a more liberal scale of wages.

Each clothier, in his own fashion, contrived ways to defeat the new assessment. Some of them drew up contracts for their weavers to sign acknowledging they were satisfied with their present wages and agreeing to continue work on the same terms. There were weavers who signed the contracts in fear of unemployment or being black-listed by other clothiers. The clothiers, however much they disagreed amongst themselves, were united in their efforts to defeat the weavers. In the case of one clothier, Joseph Ellis, the angry weavers took action themselves, first going to a magistrate, John Stephens, for advice on the matter. He told them that 'unless these contracts were put a stop to, their Act of Parliament was of no value', whereupon the weavers brought Ellis's mill to a standstill, telling him the Justices were on their side. Ellis, afraid of the consequences, destroyed the contracts which had been signed in the presence of his workers.

Thirty years later, as conditions again deteriorated, the weavers secured an Act providing for the fixing of piece work rates by the Justices in order that the practice of cutting down wages could be

stopped. A *Table for the Scheme of Rates of Wages* was accordingly
arrived at in November 1756. The weavers followed up their
legislative success by sending a petition to the Justices in which
they pointed out that the clothiers had ignored the rates fixed by
the Justices in 1728, and that their misery had increased
because of the great reduction in their earnings 'inasmuch that
the weavers cannot get above 4d for sixteen hours' labour upon
many kinds of work'. The petition went on to express the
weavers' content with

> the said rates and readily acquiesced with the said order hoping that
> the clothiers would also on their part have conformed thereto and
> paid due obedience to the said order and to the Authority of this
> Court. . . . But so far from any such compliance the clothiers treated
> the said order with the Greatest Contempt . . . knowing that the
> Weavers could not bear the Expense of Applying to this Court
> every Breach thereof the good intent of the said order could not be
> answered nor the Unhappy Weavers be any ways relieved thereby.

The evil of truck, or payment in kind, also comes into the
petition, which asks that the clothiers should be made to comply
with an order that the payment of the workman's wages should
not be made in any other manner than in money.

The last paragraph in the petition is a cry from the heart begging
that an Act already passed in their favour should be enforced.

> The great hardships which the Weavers thus groan under and the
> Extreme poverty to which many of them are reduced thereby calling
> for immediate Relief they are induced to lay their case before your
> Worships and humbly entreat you will please to take the same in
> consideration by making of rates for the payment of wages to Weavers
> and others Employ'd in the Woollen Manufactures in Pursuance and
> According to the directions of the said Act of Parliament and to
> make such order therein as your Worships shall deem meet.

It is apparent from this petition that the weavers still had faith
in the legislature and, knowing their claims were legal, could not
see how they could possibly lose their case.

The clothiers immediately drew up a counter-petition signed by
seventy-three of the most important of their number in the
Stroudwater and surrounding districts, a list helpful to historians
of the industry because it supplies not only the names but the

number of clothiers in the district in the last half of the eighteenth century, though several names, including the Sheppards of Minchinhampton, one of the largest employers, are not included. Those who signed the petition evidently did not regard the threat of the government about 'unlawful combinations' as applying to them.

It was a more complex and longer document than the one presented by the weavers. It sets forth their case under ten headings, skilful in their appeal to the ruling class instincts to control and preserve their property, wealth and position. After a preamble in which they remonstrate against the passing of the new Act the first paragraph begins

AND FIRST Because we apprehend that every Law which tends towards raising the Price of Labour will be greatly prejudicial to the Trade of the nation . . . as we have to encounter many potent rivals in forreign Markets, which have grown upon us (particularly our greatest Enemies the ffrench) who happily for them have already this great advantage over us that Labour is much cheaper in ffrance than here . . . that instead of raising our Manufacturies, to which this Law directly tends, every Scheme should be adopted that would cheapen them . . . and to remove all temptation to Idleness, Luxury and Intemperance out of their way; Hereby only shall we be enabled to vye with our Rivals in foreign Markets.

SECONDLY Because the execution of this Law tends to invert the Laws of Society, and to destroy that due subordination which ought to be religiously observed in all communities. The Weavers by this Act will be rendered more our masters than we are theirs. A Levelling and Turbulent Spirit ought never to be countenanced among the common people and labouring Manufactures.

FOURTHLY Because we are assured that the Honest and Industrious weaver, who is a good workman, and has employment at the Rates generally paid may get a comfortable subsistence . . . and an increase in Wages would only make them who are now wanting in Diligence to become more idle . . . for Trade is a tender plant that can only be nursed up by Liberty; if you cramp it 'twill die away like untimely fruit. . . .

The last paragraph, however, is significant in that the clothiers signing the petition are against the payment of truck wages:

4. Water outlet showing arch, Ozleworth stream (Chapter 4)

5. Ruined Millhouse, Ozleworth stream (Chapter 4)

But as to that part of the Act which relates to the payment of
Workmen in any other Manner than in Money It is our sincere desire
that it may be put in Execution in the strictest Manner.

Today the clothiers' petition reads like a hypocritical and arro-
gant assessment of the weavers' rights not only as workers but as
human beings. They knew well the conditions under which the
weavers suffered, for the majority lived near their mills. Many
even expected their workers to perform menial jobs as unpaid
domestics, as the weavers themselves complained in one of their
many petitions, though this custom may have been left over from
the early days of the industry when the master-weaver's household and workshop were one, and his apprentices, if not the
journeymen, were expected to help with the household duties.
By this document the social conscience of the eighteenth
century is seen to be superficial. It was unaware of or tolerant
of much injustice and it relieved only the outermost fringe of
misery.

Under the sixth heading of the clothiers' petition cloth for the
Turkey trade is mentioned: 'whereby the distinguishing excellence
of the Cloth consists in the smallness of the spinning and the
height of the Hundred', and this was one reason for the complaint
of fraud put forward by the weavers against their masters. In the
Stroud district, although they specialised mainly in broadcloth,
they had begun to manufacture a finer material containing some
3,000 to 3,800 threads in the warp, and the weaver was paid according to the hundred threads. A hundred, according to Austin, the
Assistant Commissioner for Wiltshire and Somerset, 'technically
consists of five biers—and each bier contains thirty-eight threads'.
The weavers' so-called hundred therefore consisted of 190 threads.
The twilled cassimers or twilled woollens were also paid by the
hundred, and although these cloths were of a narrower width,
being necessarily spun very fine for this kind of cloth, there were
more breakages in weaving, and a weaver could earn more on
broadcloth despite its width. The weavers of twilled woollens
found that, although their cloths were getting finer, they were expected to weave them in the same time. The fact that the home
trade now demanded more fancy weaves and finer materials, and
that the clothiers found it difficult to sell their cloth unless it
followed or jumped ahead of fashion, meant nothing to the

D   49

weavers, who only knew they were being asked to work harder and longer for the same wage.

The clergy of the day certainly encouraged the clothiers in their determination to insist upon the subordination 'which ought to be religiously observed in all communities'. Josiah Tucker, Dean of Gloucester, was the voice of the clothier. 'Each man walking Godlywise in his state of poverty or wealth' as William Law put it, often degenerated into a determination that the poor should know their stations and that rank and wealth were divinely decreed. The literature of the period shows this was a genuine belief, the inevitability of poverty was accepted as one of God's mysteries, a faith comforting to the rich and philosophically endured by the less fortunate. The weavers were not rebelling against this philosophy; they had been driven so far that they were only concerned with the struggle to exist.

Rudder, writing of Uley village, the centre of the Sheppard family, one of the largest employers in the district, said in 1779 that the trade furnished

> Employment for the lowest sort of people but idleness and debauchery are so rooted in them by means of these seminaries of vice, the alehouses, that the poor are very burdensome. These houses are scattered all over the country and are daily increasing which we owe either to the magistrates' inattention or indulgence or perhaps to a mistaken notion of serving the community by increasing public revenue from licenses, but they may be assured that nothing can compensate for depravity and loss of industry.

The weavers, with an Act of Parliament in their favour, and with a pathetic faith in the power and goodwill of the Justices to enforce it, were jubilant, but their rejoicings soon came to an end, for the clothiers had petitioned so successfully that in the following year, 1757, the Weavers Act of 1756 was repealed.

The shock of this betrayal, the realisation that they could only depend upon their own efforts to win the battle, left them with only one weapon, to withhold their labour. For six weeks they refused to work, and these must have been six long weeks in terms of suffering for few had anything put by, while the rest of the community, apprehensive of rioting and arson, regarded them as creatures who had lost all sense of decency.

Finally, the men's leaders arranged a meeting in Stroud with the clothiers. The weavers put forward their proposals, a ratification of the piece-rates drawn up in 1728, but the clothiers refused. They were determined to keep the affairs of the industry in their own hands and suggested their own scheme, but the men's leaders rejected this proposal, still unable to believe that rates confirmed by the Justices were not more legal and therefore more binding. As soon as their decision was known to the congregation of weavers waiting outside, the mob broke into the room where the negotiations were taking place. Their attitude was so menacing that the clothiers attempted to escape by the windows, but the weavers dragged them back by the coat-tails and forced them to yield to their demands. The men returned to work and at the next session the Justices confirmed the 1728 rates, probably because they wanted to avoid making the county notorious as a place of rioting and disorder. They also tightened up the penalties, and a different climate became apparent in the increased severity of sentences passed upon the workers.

The weavers' victory was a short one. Few clothiers kept to the assessments, and soon began to petition for a repeal of the Act, and won their appeal. It signified, as Dr Lipson in his *History of the Woollen and Worsted Industries* puts it 'that the principles of *laissez-faire* received legislative sanction in the woollen manufacture half a century before they were adopted as the authoritative basis of state action'.

From now on the clothiers claimed the right to make their own contracts with the weavers. Parliament also abandoned the legal enforcement of the apprenticeship system, thus leaving the way open for the employment of child labour and destroying the last shreds of the weavers' self-respect as craftsmen who had served seven years' apprenticeship. It encouraged the weavers to establish a kind of trade union or association between themselves. These associations began in most cases as benefit clubs where the members paid a few coppers a week and received six shillings weekly in times of sickness. It is easy to see how out of these meetings grew a sense of unity, an awareness of the fact that by uniting they were not entirely bereft of power.

The Act of 1756 which the clothiers had soon nullified had also contained a clause

> That great numbers of weavers and others concerned in the woollen manufacture ... have lately formed themselves into unlawful clubs and societies ... and the said persons so unlawfully assembling and associating themselves have committed great violences and outrages upon many of his Majesty's good subjects. . . .

It goes on to forbid under penalty of imprisonment all combinations of weavers and wool-combers formed with the object of regulating industry and improving the conditions of labour. The clothiers, however, had the right of combining and did so openly, though their actual meetings were 'always conducted with the utmost silence and secrecy' according to Adam Smith.

It is from the clothiers we get what little we know about the weavers' associations, and their reports are naturally biased, for they saw in the most innocent association a threat to their own interests. The weavers had to conduct their meetings with the utmost caution, fearful of spies within their own ranks as well as those without. Because of this, only the barest records were kept, thus surrounding the whole business with an aura of mystery which encouraged fantastic tales of devilish plotting. Penalties for infringing the clause had been tightened, the severity of the sentences increasing after each incident, which multiplied the fears of the timid and inflamed the reckless spirits of the bold.

Though it seems that labour problems went from one crisis to another, the incidents did not keep the trade from flourishing, and a great deal of the discontent rumbled beneath the surface, a nuisance to the progress of manufacture rather than a hindrance. Defoe's picture of England suits the Cotswolds at that time—

> ... the villages stand thick, the Market towns not only more in number but larger and fuller of Inhabitants; and in short, the whole country full of little End-shops or hamlets and scattered houses, that it looks all like a planted Colony, everywhere full of people, and the People everywhere full of busyness.

The 'busyness' of the eighteenth-century clothing trade is something we find hard to realise in the little clothing towns of Cotswold today.

The Stroud district, always in advance of the rest of the West of England cloth trade in technical development—the early use of the gig-mill is one instance—introduced the flying shuttle or spring loom towards the end of the eighteenth century. This device was not a mechanisation but a better way of propelling the shuttle by hand, making it possible for the weaver to work his loom alone, instead of having to employ an assistant. It resulted in faster working. At first it looked as if it would spark off more riots, but this time clothiers and weavers came to an amicable settlement, the employers showing understanding of the weavers' fears it would reduce their wages. One clothier, Nathanial Watts, was arranging to have his weaving done in his own mills by the new method but as a result of a meeting in Stroud he agreed to sell the spring looms to the weavers and so averted another crisis. The weavers explained they were not afraid of new methods as long as they did not suffer loss by them, which shows they were as alive as their masters to the necessity of progress in the industry.

The average earnings of a weaver towards the end of the eighteenth century were around 10s a week, a normal working day being fourteen hours. Gloucestershire rates were a little higher than the other clothing counties of the west, but the actual amount is difficult to estimate as the weavers were paid by the piece. A piece took from a fortnight to three weeks to weave for which they received the gross sum of 40s to 44s and deductions had to be made for glue, candles, wear and tear of looms. There was often a walk of six miles or more to fetch the wool from the wool-loft and to take home the woven cloth; this usually occupied one day without pay. It was the custom of the weavers on this day to dress in their one good suit of broadcloth, presenting themselves as respectably as possible.

Their employment was not continuous. Periods of trade depression occurred regularly when they received no work or wages. Winter, drought or excessively rainy weather held up the finishing of cloth and this, of course, affected the weavers, who would not be given more work until the cloth already woven was out of the way. The clothiers shared these hazards with their workpeople. In the west country it was not unknown for a weaver to be out of work for seventeen weeks together. The people who argued that when not at his loom the weaver could be employed on the land were trying to come to terms with their own social consciences. Few weavers owned or rented land of their own, the enclosures put an end to that, and hay-time and harvest, when casual labour was wanted, were miserably paid.

When put to work on the roads and forced to break stones the weaver fared badly. His long days of sedentary work and poor feeding made him physically unfit for hard labour, while the rough work ruined his hands for weaving, particularly for handling the finer thread used in the twills and new kinds of cloth then coming into fashion. Enforced idleness inevitably led to more time being spent in alehouses.

Another serious cause of complaint between master and workpeople was the employment of unapprenticed weavers, such as agricultural labourers out of work who had taken to the craft. It was not difficult to learn and this facility made it, as one writer of the period observed, 'a receptacle for the destitute from all other classes'. As these unapprenticed workers were generally willing to work for less wages they became a menace to those who had served their seven years' apprenticeship, for it not only reduced their chances of a decent rate for the job but lowered their status; they felt that serving an apprenticeship raised them above the level of the agricultural labourer. It also kept the number within bounds and lessened their fears of unemployment.

At the August Assize in Gloucester in 1803 the weavers began a prosecution against the clothiers for employing unapprenticed labour against the Elizabethan Statute of Apprentices which had not been repealed. The weavers asked that the clothiers be made to keep to the Limitation of Looms of the Weavers Act of 1555, which prohibited clothiers from having more than one loom or hiring out looms, though the Stroudwater area had been excluded from this Act almost from the beginning. They raised funds and employed an attorney to bring an action on their behalf against workmen who had not been legally trained. The clothiers in return petitioned Parliament for a repeal of all the old statutes which had become obsolete, and a Bill to this effect was introduced. As usual, a committee was set up to investigate the claims of both sides, and it is from the reports of evidence given to this committee that we learn much about the clothing trade of the period.

There were the usual attempts by the clothiers to present the weavers and their attorney in a poor light. Mr Jessup, of Stroud, representing the weavers, was a forthright man, a good fighter but hardly a match for the clothiers with their more sophisticated attack. He was asked if he had been promised an annuity if he won his case. He replied he did not know of such a promise.

54

'You would not accept pay?'

'Indeed I would,' Mr Jessup replied, and oddly enough did not point out that the attorney for the clothiers was also being paid for the job.

It was evident the clothiers had been breaking the law, that they had been breaking it for centuries, but the discussion dragged on, the clothiers using delaying tactics to wear out the weavers' patience and use up their funds.

Wilberforce supported the workers and helped to prepare a Bill which, if passed, would have given them the victory. It repealed some of the old statutes, its chief intention being to strengthen the restrictions relating to apprenticeship, to limit the number of looms, to prevent truck and regulate the duties of inspectors. The Bill was withdrawn after a second reading, and to safeguard the clothiers a Suspending Bill was rushed through to cover them until May, 1805, without which the clothiers would have been liable to heavy penalties.

In 1804 the change of Parliament and Ministry brought the discussions to a standstill, and in 1805 the weavers made a last attempt to get a settlement. For a time it seemed they had won and there was great rejoicing amongst them, but as time went on and each year another Suspending Bill was passed, their hopes, as well as their funds to continue the struggle, faded away. It left an aftermath of bitterness which has affected the relationship between workers and management ever since.

The only solution which seemed to offer promise of better things was for the workers to band together; singly, or as small units, any efforts they made were doomed to failure. If they tried to withhold their labour they could be imprisoned for breaking the Vagrancy Act, and where this had already happened the sentences had been so severe that only extreme provocation induced them to go on strike. In comparison with the highly organised trade unions of today the weavers' first attempts to achieve unity appear ineffective. But it is difficult for us to understand the strength of the opposition and the weavers' weaknesses and poverty. The clothiers were fighting for their estates, their wealth and their positions, and used every means, honest and dishonest, to that end, while the weavers, in spite of what had gone before, still clung to the idea that the clothiers must recognize the law as well as themselves.

Unable to bring an action because of poverty against two clothiers who paid partly in truck, which was breaking the law, the weavers refused to work for them, feeling that this time their case could not be denied. The clothiers in general then passed a strong resolution against truck payment. Other strikes in the 1820s came about because the time it took to weave the new fancy cloths decreased wages to below subsistence level. Manufacturers in the Uley district therefore increased their rates and after a struggle of some weeks persuaded the Stroud clothiers to do likewise. But this small success revived the fears of early years, and once more the bogey of 'secret societies', as the early trade unions were known, made them ignore the real injustices suffered by the weavers. The authorities became alarmed and dispatched a Francis Fagan from Bow Street to find out about the 'secret societies'. This man, who must have been either credulous or dishonest, sent back a fantastic report of what went on at the meetings where the workers attended 'complete with scarves, masks, turbans and swords'. One wonders from what pitiful attempts at ceremony and oath-taking he concocted this story. As he would not have been admitted to the meetings, for the weavers took elaborate precautions to keep strangers out, one can only suppose his imagination, or bribed ignorant informers, supplied the highly coloured details.

The local Justices, in their turn, were alarmed at the weavers' obstinacy in refusing to work. On one occasion, acting without proper authority, they sent constables into the homes of the men on strike to arrest them, making the excuse that they were sent to take away yarn and cloth belonging to the clothiers. They were rebuked by Home Secretary Pitt for their over-zealous efforts and the reply of the Justices, dismayed by the reproof when they expected to be congratulated on their prompt action, included this paragraph:

> . . . But we are confident that although the law may not strictly sanction what we have done, our acting in the emergency of the case and under its peculiar circumstances was the means of preventing outrages on the second list of committments which took place and we have the satisfaction of knowing that no personal injury was inflicted.

Evidently the Justices did not regard being sent to gaol

illegally as 'personal injury' for a weaver. The Justices concluded their reply with a hint of a threat.

> The clothiers have applied for other warrants but we consider ourselves restricted from interfering in consequence of your letter.

A week later the Justices reported that everything was now quiet. The arrival of a troop of cavalry had convinced the disaffected people that the magistrates, supported by the government, were determined to put a stop to the strikes, and that the weavers, being in a state of starvation because of no work had lost heart, while eighteen weavers, having been sent to gaol to hard labour, made those remaining at liberty fear a similar fate awaited them. As evidence of the improved state of affairs they reported:

> And also the weavers finding they could not satiate the vindictive feeling of leaving the work to rot on the looms while they went to gaol as the clothiers have in all cases recovered the possession of their property where the wives or friends of the weavers refused to complete the work. . . . We have weighed out justice impartially, eighteen weavers in gaol, one master fined for breaking the law relating to truck. We had a delicate as well as a painful part to act. . . .

This last sentence sickens by its hypocrisy, and though the men who wrote it probably believed they were doing no more than their duty one feels the 'delicate and painful' part related to the one clothier fined for breaking the truck law.

In November 1825 there were serious riots at Wotton-under-Edge at the mills of Messrs Neale. The weavers held mass meetings, intimidated those of their own company who would not join in by attacking their homes and burning the work they were doing in the streets for all to see. The Neale Mill was defended by men with muskets and in the firing that followed twenty-one of the rioters were injured. The mob dispersed before the magistrates arrived, but the injured men were captured and sentenced, while the men who had shot them were immediately bailed out, the court sitting until 8 pm to finish the business. Immediately the sentences on the captured men were known the inflamed mob attacked Mr Neale's house, smashing all the windows, but when they went on to the mill they were checked by constables specially sworn in for the occasion. A troop of the 12th Lancers arrived at

Wotton a few days later and the North Somerset Yeomanry stood by in Bristol ready to assist them, but by this time the riots had subsided and many of the weavers had fled for fear of punishment. It is significant that although in the accounts of the town at this date no items are directly debited to the cost of the riots, seventeen levies of the poor rate in place of the usual four to six occur in 1826–7.

The clothiers of Wotton, as well as the weavers, had their troubles at this time as the many bankruptcies show. Yorkshire was beginning to dominate the trade, or rather their trade of lesser grade woollens had begun to dominate the market, and although the Stroudwater valleys maintained their position, Wotton was almost at the end of her time as a clothing town. The most terrible failure on the Cotswolds was that of Sheppards of Uley, where 1,000 persons were thrown out of employment. The Uley Mill, sold by auction, fetched £2,300, though it had cost £53,000.

The Report of the Commissioners for Hand-Loom Weavers, published in 1840, a monumental pile of documents, gives a distressing account of the fate of the weavers. Their fighting spirit broken by the state of the trade, it was no longer a struggle between themselves and the clothiers but the fact that there was no longer work for them to do at any wage except in a few mills still working. Two Assistant Commissioners, W. A. Miles for Gloucestershire, and Austin for Wiltshire, reported that the labour market was overstocked. Austin, a hard-headed man with no sentimental feelings for the workers, soon became sceptical of those relieving officers who complained of the extravagances of the weavers. 'When they are in work they are not provident, the female spends too much on finery, the young men dress smartly . . . on Sundays some of the young men dress gayly and have watches . . .' complained the relieving officers. Miles knew that few could have been extravagant on the current wage of about 6s a week. He wrote:

> . . . that there is considerable suffering and that many families are in a worse condition as regards food and clothing than the inmates of the work-houses. The master-weaver is worse situated in this respect than the generalities of workmen are. He would not be received until he had sold his loom, and having done so his means of obtaining a livelihood are gone and he becomes an inmate for life . . ..

That they have made great efforts to keep out and have only been driven there by actual starvation the following statement which was made to me by a master of a workhouse will amply prove. He was regretting the nature of the food, its scantiness and some other causes produced great mortality in the workhouses, but as for the poor weavers, he verily believed that their children in some instances died of repletion. They had previously been brought so low that the workhouse allowance was too good for them.

The use of power looms was not the cause of lowering wages—wages had not been reduced—it was because the weaver had not enough work to do that he was poor. Although at the time of the Commission other processes except weaving took place in factories, the hand-loom weavers still carried on to a great extent in their homes. The smaller clothiers, particularly, seem to have respected the weavers' wish to work at home. The manufacturers of the Stroud district were amongst the first to try and adapt power looms for woollens but this proved difficult, the woollen yarn, being weaker than cotton broke continually, and until the machine looms were greatly improved the clothiers on the whole did not feel there was any advantage in using them. When they did come into general use there was considerable opposition at first but towards the last half of the nineteenth century, although the weavers hated the factory system for themselves they were more resigned to sending their children into the factories where wages were more regular and hours shorter. In a factory in 1840 a man, his wife and one child could earn together £1 1s 3¾d a week, while a family of five hand-loom weavers at home could only earn 10s 4d.

During the second half of the century when the majority of clothiers had given up, except those around Stroud who had turned their mills into factories using steam power and the new machines, the manufacturers often tried to find work for the few remaining hand-loom weavers. They were no longer a threat but had become picturesque survivals of the past.

CHAPTER FOUR

Wotton-under-Edge in the eighteenth century

T
he early history of the parish of Wotton-under-Edge is mainly associated with the Berkeley family, but for at least 250 years, from about 1600 to 1850, the town lived on the cloth trade. The 1608 Census compiled by John Smith for Lord Berkeley of 'all the able and sufficient men' fit for military service in Wotton reveals that 142 out of a total of 308 were engaged in the industry. This number included 23 clothiers, 92 weavers and 19 fullers, the rest of the total being made up with dyers and other finishers.

A list of mayors from 1558 to 1886, made in 1872 by the then mayor Mr W. Horace Wright, with additions by E. S. Lindley and others, shows that until 1820 at least 80 per cent were occupied with the trade and many of the remainder came from clothing families. After that date only three clothiers and two dyers appear in the list.

Samuel Rudder in his *New History of Gloucester*, 1779, gives seven to eight clothiers in 1770, but if he had counted in the lesser clothiers he could have doubled the number. In 1831 Bigland records thirteen clothing mills employing 778 families with only eighty-six in agriculture. The startling decline in the population noted in the 1851 census was said by the Commissioners appointed to look into the matter to be due to the decay of the industry. The Health Report published in 1854 gives only three mills in the parish and only 200 employed. It says trade had been at its best in 1813 with fifteen to twenty mills working, but that the dyers still flourished.

In the free-for-all of the late eighteenth century many of the older clothing families, having made their money, bought estates and gave up the business, putting their sons into professions. Some were unwilling to risk sinking their capital in the new machinery necessary to compete with the factories making cheaper kinds of cloth in the north of England, and others had already put their profits into land instead of into their mills. Whatever the reasons—and these were many and complex—the industry had practically died out in Wotton by the middle of the nineteenth century. One small instance of the new gentility that became apparent at the time can be found in the directories where the clothiers are listed as 'gents' without mention of their occupation, whereas the eighteenth-century clothiers had been proud to be called clothiers and in most cases had 'clothier' inscribed upon their tombstones.

When the clothiers took over from the originators of the trade, the master weavers who employed a few looms, and it became big business, embracing all the processes under one management, Wotton parish was found to have every natural advantage for the increase of the trade. It had copious supplies of pure water, a thick strata of fuller's earth between the great and inferior oolite, wool-growing Cotswold hills surrounding it, and a main route to the seaport of Bristol for overseas trade.

West of the town the hills are cut by two deep valleys, Tyley Bottom and Ozleworth Bottom, both having streams fed by the many springs issuing out of the hillsides and both going down into the clay and thus making it possible to construct the reservoirs needed for fulling and dying. It was along these streams, particularly at their confluence with the Little Avon river and its tributaries, that the mills were situated. The number of mills we know to have operated in the narrow valleys seems surprising today, for the trickle of water in the Bottoms does not look sufficient to turn a wheel, but this is because many of the springs are now tapped at their source by water companies to augment their supplies. Until the beginning of the nineteenth century no less than fifteen mills were working in the five-mile length of the stream from the Ozleworth border to Michaelwood.

Eight of these were in existence before the Dissolution, when Kingswood Abbey owned the land and water; three of them were already working when the Abbey was built. There is evidence that some of the Abbey mills were used for fulling as well as for grinding corn, and that some originally used as grist or corn mills were worked for cloth as the trade increased. Grindstone Mill, whose name implies its original purpose, was let in 1650 to a clothier as 'a messuage or tenement and smyth's forge, and one grindstone mill and one fulling mill under one roof'. The poles belonging to the cloth racks were said by an old inhabitant to have been standing there long after the mill ceased to be used.

Today there are only gaunt ruins along the gentle Ozleworth stream, so that we see what John Piper, in another connection, called 'the visible effects of history in terms of decay'. The valley has become a place remote from the bustle of the main roads only a mile or so away, and walking across the fields following the abandoned track along which the stones of Kingswood Abbey were taken by Sir Nicholas Poyntz to build Newark Park one can see among the trees on the stream banks the remains of lost mills, the arch of a water-outlet, a row of gaping windows, walls overgrown with ivy, shrubs whose shadows darken a silted-up millpond, and the stone footings of a ruined building where cattle rub themselves and seek shade.

If the ghost of a dissenting clothier or weaver should walk here, would he remember those terrible words of Ezekiel about the destruction of Tyre that George Whitfield uttered in one of his sermons in the town?

> And they shall make a spoil of thy riches and make a prey of thy merchandise; and they shall break down thy walls and destroy thy pleasant houses; and they shall lay thy stones and thy timber and thy dust in the midst of the waters.

Looking into the history of various mills, one can follow the waxing and waning of the industry as it is reflected in changes of ownership and occupation, particularly around 1700 and again 150 years later when it could no longer be revived.

Taking the mills of the Ozleworth Bottom from east to west, the first one we know anything about stood where the stream received the Seven Springs water just outside the old Wortley tithing boundary. It was called Hell Mill by John Smith, the Berkeley historian; unfortunately he gives no reason for this name. Ell Mill, as suggested by Dr Perry, would indicate the width of cloth made there, but in 1825 two men were convicted of stealing broadcloth from the mill, though maybe by this time it had changed over to broadcloth. If its name was originally Hill Mill, because of its situation near where the valley comes out from the hills, its translation into Hell could have been a rustic play on words which then, as such names will, came in time to supersede the original one. It was evidently a small mill and never played a very important part in the local trade. About 1834 it became a grist mill and by 1844 was closed. Nothing remains of it today but traces of mill channels and a cottage.

Monks Mill, one of the oldest in the district, stood where the road to Alderley crosses the boundary stream at a point where the stream is increased by many springs. Its fine head of water was a valuable asset in those days. It was granted by the Berkeleys to Kingswood Abbey as a water-mill early in the thirteenth century, and is thought to have been one of the abbey mills mentioned in a Papal Taxation of 1291. The monks already had a corn mill, and as the Abbey at that period included an office of fullers it seems likely that it was used for making cloth. There is no direct evidence of this until about 1490, when in a book of rentals it is entered as a fulling-mill with three adjoining grounds leased by the Abbey to John Roborough. He rented another mill in Kingswood from the Abbey and must have been a tenant of some substance.

Monk's Mill came to Lord Willoughby and Sir Thomas Heneage after the Dissolution, but by 1557 it was owned by Sir John Thynne of Longleat who finally sold it to John Bridges after Bridges had worked it as a tenant for some thirty years. By 1612 it was being worked by Christopher Neal and Christopher Purnell, who in 1613 built a new wing. They had two fuller brothers from the Abbey as servants. In 1613 it belonged to Richard Poole of Wotton as part of the Wortley estate and it remained in the Poole family until 1716 when it was sold to Richard Osborne of Wotton.

We glean a little about Richard Poole from the records of the time. He was one of the younger sons of a landowning family put to trade. His grandfather, a rich London linen-draper, retired to Long Newnton near Tetbury, bought property there and set up as a country gentleman. Richard's father married an Estcourt heiress, thereby adding a manor to the family possessions. Whether Richard came to Wotton because of the excellent opportunities it offered in the expanding cloth trade or because the family was in some way related to the Pooles of Painswick we do not know.

In 1620 he married Mary Purnell, daughter of the Christopher who had previously worked Monk's Mill. Richard leased 'Purnells', his father-in-law's house, an ancient dwelling in the Cotswold vernacular which was still standing until about thirty years ago, though by this time it had degenerated into a picturesque mossy-roofed huddle of three cottages and was in such a precarious state that it was described as 'being propped up by its grandfather clock'. There is a picture of it in E. S. Lindley's *Wotton under Edge*.

By 1631 Richard was able to buy the Wortley estate which included Monks Mill for £1,500 from the dowager Lady Berkeley—a sale which John Smith condemned as being for her own benefit and against the interests of her son. Richard, a shrewd business man, made the estate a manor and so increased its value that in 1647 he was able to sell it to Sir Matthew Hale for £4,200. Richard made Purnells his manor house, panelling one room with oak and making other improvements. He also initiated manor courts and, as recorded in the Hale papers, these were continued by Hale. Richard also bought the White Lion, one of Wotton's oldest inns, mentioned in a grant to Thomas Adams by Lord Berkeley in 1610–11, when he was raising money for the restoration of his ancestral estates, as a 'messuage or commone inn in the High Street in Wotton, then the sign of the Goat, nowe of the White Lion'.

When Monks Mill was bought by Richard Osborne in 1717 it was the beginning of a family business which became one of the largest in the district, contributing to the prosperity of the town for over a hundred years. The pity is that nothing now remains of Monks Mill or of Monks Mill House and the cottages once occupied by some of the mill-hands. But there is a photograph taken about 1880, after it had been abandoned. In this picture we see a main range of buildings running east and west for some 400 feet, and at the east end a wing of about 60 feet running south, this wing probably being the one Purnell built in 1613. The wing is of three storeys including the top one lit by typical Cotswold dormers, and it also had its own water-wheel.

The main building was of four storeys, one portion having its roof raised giving it greater height; this portion had dormers and a water-wheel which Lindley says was fed only by the waters of the spring. The rest of the building had its four storeys without dormers but under the same roof level, and this may possibly be the later part built by John Osborne in 1767, when he rebuilt

6. Teazel Tower, Woodchester (Chapter 5)

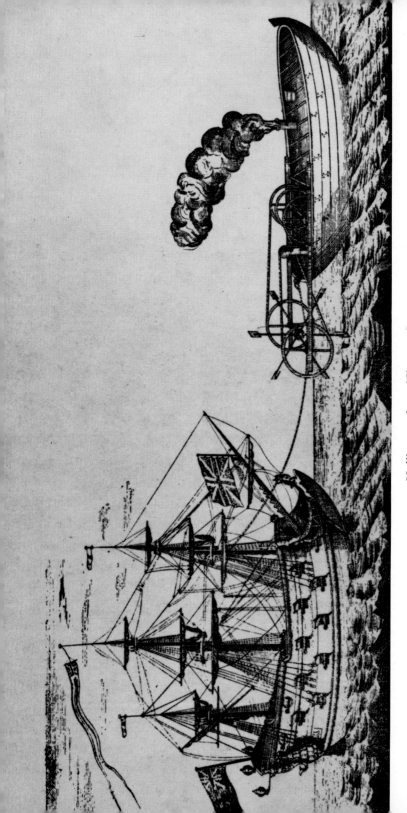

7. Hull's steamboat (Chapter 6)

Monks Mill House, which was origianlly built by Christopher Neale when he worked the mill with Purnell at the beginning of the seventeenth century. The late nineteenth century did not subscribe to the notion that old industrial buildings could be as romantic as ruined castles, and as interesting to future generations, so this range of buildings is lost to us.

We first hear of the Osborne family about the middle of the sixteenth century. William Osborne, in his will of 1584, is described as a sheep farmer and, judging from his bequests, a man of considerable standing. His great-grandson William was mayor in 1675 and in 1682 he was in trouble for displaying arms; being called to account by the Heralds, he was forced to disclaim them.

It was Richard, his son, who bought Monks Mill and raised the family status by his position as clothier. Before he died he saw his son, another Richard, married to Sarah Blagdon of Nind, who came from a family who had held the important Abbey Mills since the middle of the sixteenth century and who were unmistakably 'gentlemen' clothiers until they gave up trade for the law at the beginning of the eighteenth century. Richard's will proves how well he had increased the family fortunes. He was a quiet, religious man not given to ostentation, and he requested a quiet funeral. His memorial in the church shows no armorial bearings.

His son Richard was more conscious of his family's importance, perhaps because of his marriage to Sarah Blagdon. He revived the arms, and when he died in 1749, some six years after his wife, their memorial was made by Sir Robert Taylor, pupil of the well-known Sir Henry Cheere. The epitaph, in Latin, speaks of his having borne severe arthritis for many years with great fortitude. He was a JP and one of the trustees of the grammar school, and he presented the church with an altar frontal and two silver collection plates. He added considerable property in Wotton and the neighbourhood to the family heritage, it being a period when land was considered the soundest investment as well as bestowing the greatest prestige. The family had now become one of the most important in the parish, and the story of its rise is a classic example, not only of the rise of a clothing family, but of the expansion of the industry as the eighteenth century went on its way.

His son John rebuilt Monks Mill House, which probably resembled Purnell's in its Elizabethan character, changing it into the more modern style of Wortley House. He also enlarged the main blocks of the mill into twice their original size, buying eight acres of adjacent land for the new workings and adding another water-wheel, though both were under one roof space. Unlike his father and grandfather, who bought land with their profits, he must have considered it a better investment to put his profits back into the business, where new machinery was needed to meet new demands. He married Elizabeth, daughter and heiress of George White, iron master of Goodrich, who brought extensive property to the marriage. John in his turn brought eleven messuages, barns, stables, gardens and orchards, five mills and 450 acres of land to the marriage settlement, thus proving him a suitable match for the heiress in the eyes of the world, and showing how the family had advanced in wealth and property since the days of William, the sheep farmer.

When he died at forty-nine years of age in 1770 the male line came to an end. He left a widow who survived him by twenty-seven years and four unmarried daughters. Two years after his death his eldest daughter and heiress married Samuel Yeats, of a Quaker family of dyers in the Nailsworth valley. His two youngest daughters went higher in the social scale, Elizabeth marrying Philip Williams of Penpont in Bredon who claimed descent from Sir Thomas Bullen, one of the knights who came over with William the Conqueror, Anne becoming the second wife of Sir Bourchier Wrey, a man of high degree. John's fourth daughter remained unmarried.

Samuel Yeats brought £4,000 into the marriage settlement and the mill continued to prosper under his management and that of his son Osborne Yeats. In 1802 the proprietors of Monks Mill came high on the list of West Country clothiers who were asking Parliament for the repeal of the old statutes that the weavers were using in their attempt to obtain a living wage and to protect themselves from the competition of cheap labour. These included the Act of Edward VI prohibiting the use of gig mills and—the most important—the Apprentices clauses of the Statute of Apprentices. These had been obsolete for a long time but had not been repealed.

The clothing industry had travelled a long way since the beginning of the eighteenth century, and the methods of Samuel and Osborne Yeats were very different from those of the days when the first Richard Osborne worked Monks Mill. Samuel Yeats, anxious to obtain his labour as cheaply as possible, was naturally opposed to State control. It is easy to see, looking at it some 150 years later, how blind the weavers were in hoping they could put the clock back and check full industrial freedom, a freedom that Adam Smith and other economists of the times had, as Dr Lipson put it, 'elevated to the dignity of natural laws whose working no human legislator could hope to arrest or evade'.

The clothiers finally won their case, but the victory did little to help the trade, for the boom was coming to an end. In 1819 Osborne Yeats, who had taken over Monks Mill when Samuel retired in 1812, came third in a scale of contributors to the fund established by the clothiers to fight for their 'rights', and by 1826 after the weavers' riots in Wotton, and seeing the way trade was going, he surrendered his share in the business, auctioned his effects—which incidentally included a cellar of good wines—and retired to Hounslow. To keep the mill going Samuel came out of retirement and took over again until he died in 1829. His last years, if he contrasted them with the years when he first worked the mill and expanding trade coloured the future with rosy hopes, must have been bitter. With his death the rule of the Osbornes came to an end.

The new owner, Penry Williams, who inherited by right of his wife, rented Monks Mill to John Metiver, who, after working it for four years, was declared bankrupt. Hoping to stop the rot, Thomas White & Son took over and put in new machinery. They continued until 1844 when they were followed by Smith's of Sodbury, first Samuel and then Rowland. Rowland Smith installed new machinery and reconditioned the old in an attempt to defeat the drift of the trade to the north. According to E. S. Lindley, the Wotton historian, who had access to the ledgers of the Bennet family who carried out this work, they were estate carpenters, wheelwrights and general repairers in Wortley for many generations. Lindley gives a list of some of the new machinery and describes the reconditioning carried out. The machinery included a warping machine, cutter, gig mill, spooling machine, weaving shop, new brushes for a brushing machine, grinding shears, a new roller, hollow and bowl for wool tuggers and, significantly, a mention of a power loom in 1865.

This kept Monks Mill going until 1869, when Rowland Smith removed the machinery to another mill at Stonehouse where there were modern power facilities; the denuded Monks Mill was left to moulder into decay. It had come to the end of its useful life.

In 1804 its useful value as a prosperous concern had been reckoned as £6,000 in a marriage settlement, but after it was abandoned by Rowland Smith, R. H. B. Hale, one of the trustees of the Osborne family, bought it for £1,500 'at its full complete value'; which tells the story of the eclipse of the clothing trade in Wotton.

One can tell from letters now in the Hale Collection at Gloucester Records Office, written by S. G. Dauncey in 1791 and 1801 to John Blagden Hale, how difficult trade was becoming for the tenant clothier. Hale inherited many mills in the Wotton district. One of his tenants was John Eastmead, a small clothier. Dauncey had sent his cloths to be finished at Eastmead's mill.

> I have been in expectation of his having put his mill in order but I find the small stock only has been repaired and that the great one is in a very bad state, and as my cloths are every day much damag'd and beat in holes I find myself under the necessity of removing my work from the mill.

On another occasion Dauncey complained again, and Eastmead's father wrote to Hale:

> I am sorry that my son cannot Make it anser at your Mill I find He is Half a years Rent behind at Lady Day last past. Now Sr if you will be so kind as to give me Time as soon as can save it I will Pai you the Half years Rent, and if your Brother should Take to the Mill I should be obliged to him if he would be so good as to Employ him to Do it for him for I know it will not answer for him to keep it. My Brother sunk between Two and Three hundred Pounds as he had no family to Maintain. . . .

One of the oldest mills in Kingswood village, situated on the perimeter of the Abbey site, is the Abbey Mills, originally built as a corn mill for the Abbey's own use. Beginning as a corn mill, it was used for fulling and for making broadcloth well before the Dissolution, as is shown by the leases of several of the Abbey tenants in succession.

In 1617 the mill property was part of a trust formed by James I for his son, later Charles I, and in 1618 it is recorded as part of a grant of lands to the City of London, in respect of loans made to

Charles. Through this transaction John Smith of North Nibley held the freehold of the mill, but in 1693 his family sold it to Robert Daw of Bradley.

The Daw or Dawes family had connections with Wotton for at least 250 years. It is difficult to distinguish the relationship today of the many Roberts and Thomases to be found in the family wills, from the first Robarte Dawe of North Nibley who died in 1578 to a Robert recorded by Bigland who died in 1713. There is a mural monument in the church to Robert Dawes of Bradley, who died in 1711, signed by Giles Dance, brother of George Dance who built Guy's Hospital. The family, among the earliest Wotton clothiers, seem to have followed the usual pattern of buying land and becoming gentlemen clothiers, finally not engaging in the trade themselves but letting their mills to tenants. Several became mayors of the town, including Thomas, described as a yeoman, who twice held office, and it was his grandson Robert whose will in 1683 shows that he had bought New Mills in Kingswood from the descendants of John Smith of North Nibley.

The last member of the family to be mayor was Thomas in 1682. Among his bequests when he died in 1712 was land at Bournestream 'for the benefit of the poor'. This was first applied to the Bluecoat School, but in 1720 the trustees decided to build Dawes Almshouses with quarters for six pensioners. The Dawes owned considerable land in the district and for about a hundred years from 1692 were the owners of Bradley Court, which they bought from Sir William Clutterbuck who reserved 'the Little Seat in the church and joint use of the Great Seat'. Sir Robert Atkyns, writing of this property belonging to Thomas Dawes, says 'he gained it by his own industry, and left off his employment when he knew he had enough'. In Atkyns' *History of Gloucestershire* there is an engraving of Bradley Court by Kip as it appeared at the beginning of the eighteenth century, showing a single-span building, a central porch of two storeys and turrets containing spiral stairs. The charming gazebo on the west wall of the garden is a later addition and once looked over the main road out of Wotton before the turnpike road was cut through Haw Park.

New Mills stands where the Wotton-Charfield road crosses the stream; in 1810 it belonged to Humphrey Austin who let it for twenty-one years to Thomas Mercer of Kingswood with millhouse and pigeon-house as well as part of the Abbey corn mill with mill-house. It was burnt down in 1898 and rebuilt as a range of one-storey buildings. It was renamed Abbey Mills in memory of the lost abbey when Messrs Tubbs, Lewis, its present owners, took it over. They do not make cloth but manufacture braid and elastic. They also own Langford Mill and New Mills, built by Humphrey Austin, and are the largest employers of labour in the district.

The Austin family, with the Osbornes, were the most important clothiers in Wotton from the middle of the seventeenth century until 1850. The first Austin we know about was Edward, who died in 1707 and who is described as clothier on the hoary table tomb outside the north door of the church. It was his eldest son John and John's descendants who appear in the town's history, not only as clothiers but in many other capacities concerned with town affairs. John was mayor in 1702 and 1718, and with Richard Osborne supported the master of the grammar school when he filed a bill in 1710 to set aside the leases of all school lands because of George Smith's misappropriation of the school's endowments. Incidentally, a history of Cotswold grammar schools would show many such misappropriations.

Edward, John's brother, went to London, but he kept his connection with Wotton and came home to die and be buried in the churchyard in 1727. Having a brother in business in London to advise on markets and money was a great asset to the family and undoubtedly helped in their success as clothiers.

John's sons, Thomas and Isaac, are on the list of mayors, both recorded as clothiers. In 1766 his grandson Thomas held the office. The most important member of the family was Humphrey, Isaac's son, a man of tremendous drive and diverse business interests, though all the family did considerable buying and letting of properties in the town as well as looking after their own mills. There was probably nothing going on in Wotton from around 1750 until well into the 1800s that the Austins did not control.

The names Anthony, Edward and John crop up again and again, though it is difficult to trace the exact relationship of the sons, cousins or grandsons of John and Isaac. In some instances mills were being worked by Austin Brothers, in others by Messrs Austin. There is an Anthony listed in 1738 as a member of an association of landowners and clothiers formed for mutual protection. When this association was re-formed for clothiers only in

1812, around the time when the weavers' discontent was rising dangerously, the firm of Austin was among those paying the highest subscription. One Anthony did not engage in trade but became rector of Alderley in 1831.

But it was Humphrey and his brother George whose names became known outside as well as within the parish. George was one of the clothiers of the West Country who helped draw up the draft observation for Parliament which emphasised the need for liberty to vary their cloths to suit the varying customs of the countries they traded with, such as Turkey, India, Russia, Portugal, Ireland and America. At this time trade was becoming more and more dependent on foreign markets and George told of the success of the Russian trade, the latest addition to their list of foreign customers. It had become well established by 1813, mainly through the use of machinery which cut costs so drastically that the Austins were selling cloth to Russia at 18s a yard, while the competing French could not sell it below 25s. One senses a certain cocksureness in George's remark 'that it is generally understood that we have had the Market of the world in our hands since the French Revolution'. At the beginning of the nineteenth century George Austin was employing 300 to 400 weavers.

Humphrey achieved the distinction of a nickname in Wotton, for local tradition says he was known as 'Great Humphrey'. This may have applied to his bulk as well as to his achievements and expansive character; I find it impossible to imagine him as small in his person. He was born in 1747, a time when the trade was expanding, and when he died in 1829 he had lived through its most prosperous years and had seen the ominous signs of decay all around him. He was not only a clothier but also dealt in mill property.

He rebuilt the Sury Mill, naming it New Mills, whose façade remains today as one of the finest examples of a late Georgian factory in the county. His initials H.A. can be seen on the west end. Messrs Tubbs, Lewis rebuilt and reorganised much of the building when they bought it in 1850, but it still contains one of the few circular towers for wool-drying left on the Cotswolds, a fascinating relic one hopes will be saved for the industrial archaeologists of the future.

Humphrey, when he built his fine new mill, apparently believed its usefulness would prevail for many generations, and the fact that he let it in 1811 on lease to his niece's husband for twenty-one years at £700 confirms this, if we compare the £60 rental he received for Langford and part of Abbey Mill when he let them in 1801. Rudge in 1811 writes of the New Mill of Messrs Austin that 'it used Spanish wool only and did no weaving'.

Humphrey played as well as worked, or perhaps the two activities were one. He was one of the companions of Frederick Augustus, Earl of Berkeley, who nominated him Deputy Lieutenant of the county. He joined in the beating of the bounds in 1805 after being asked by the earl to organize it and 'muster the recollections of old inhabitants' in advance, and the two days taken up with the perambulations were occasions for much refreshment and jollity. When the earl died Humphrey was one of the pallbearers.

He was a captain in the Wotton Yeomanry in 1797, and even before he received his commission was entertaining the company to dinner at the Crown Inn, and if it was as merry as the following year's dinner which cost Mr Biddle, the mayor, £33, plus £2 8s od for broken glass, it must have been an occasion when many toasts were drunk. In the records of the Yeomanry is one for 'a supper when called out on a riot on 5 May, 1800', which cost £2 15s od, another of those tantalising statements one longs to have elaborated. Were the weavers concerned or was the riot a town affair unconnected with the trade? The Yeomanry must have dealt with it successfully, for there is no further mention of it in the records, and doubtless the townsfolk were reassured and felt their contributions to the Volunteers were worth while as they watched the gallant soldiers riding back to their supper in their gay uniforms and armed with swords, pistols and other equipment as prescribed by the Royal Commission. There is no record that they were called to subdue the serious rioting at Neale's Mills in 1825, though we know that a troop of 12th Lancers reached Wotton a few days afterwards and the North Somerset Yeomanry were held ready at Bristol.

The family also owned Steep Mill, advertised for sale in 1830 'in the occupation of Messrs Austin Bros'. The site had belonged to Thomas Austin in 1763, but at that time there had been no mill, only some buildings in the street. In 1836 it belonged to a Mrs Austin of Cam, for we know that Isaac Pitman, famous as the inventor of a new shorthand, was negotiating with her for part of the building to be used as a new Free Church school. Pitman had been offered the post of headmaster and with his committee, which consisted of most of the leading clothiers of the town, had a little difficulty over the rent to be paid, Mrs Austin raising her demands from 2s a week to £10 a year. Pitman finally signed an agreement for £12 a year for two rooms, which suggests that Mrs Austin was better equipped for bargaining.

Isaac Pitman only kept the post for ten months, his 'unscriptural' views displeasing the committee, and he then opened his own school with his young brother Benjamin in 1837. Shorthand was in the curriculum of the older boys. The fact that the school committee consisted of most of the leading clothiers of the town shows that the high proportion of Dissent in the clothing towns had not diminished since the Rev William Lloyd Baker of Uley wrote to the Bishop of Gloucester in 1793:

> The Dissenters are gaining much ground. . . . They have lately built a meeting house calculated to hold between four and five hundred people and in most respects I believe by far the first in this neighbourhood, at least none but that at Wotton can be at all compared to it.

In 1832 Austin Brothers were declared insolvent. Their assets were assigned to their creditors, but as these seem to have consisted of other members of the family it was evidently a tactical end of their careers as clothiers and not total ruin. This is borne out by the fact that Humphrey's eldest son, Lestrange Southgate Austin, who had no connection with the clothing trade, was invited to become a director of the National Provincial Bank when it opened a branch in Wotton in 1834, and that he was elected mayor in 1848 and 1849. In 1940 Steep Mill no longer belonged to the family, having been bought by the grammar school and turned into classrooms and a carpentry shop, a less inglorious end than that of most of the old mills.

CHAPTER FIVE

The clothier's teazel and other Cotswold plants

It would be an exaggeration to say, except in the broadest sense, that the wild flowers of any district are an indication of its former industries, but one can gather many a clue from the plants of its waysides and waste places. The illumination they shed over the past may be only a flickering candle-power, but this open-air detective work brings its own reward by adding to one's enjoyment of the Cotswold scene an awareness of the past as well as the present, unspoilt by the melancholy of ruin and decay.

The neighbourhood of the little clothing towns of the south Cotswolds is a good region for such a study; long after the mills along the valley streams fell into disuse the plants continued to flourish, living evidence of the trade which once occupied their inhabitants in the eighteenth and nineteenth centuries.

Enormous quantities of the teazel, *Dipsacus sativus*, known as the burler's teazel, were necessary to the clothing industry, the heads with their recurved prickles being used in the finishing process to draw out the loose fibres from the cloth and raise a nap on the surface after the cloth had been fulled.

Originally the teazel heads were set in a frame forming a comb or brush and the dresser raised the surface by rubbing these hand-frames down the cloth, but later they were fixed to revolving cylinders called a gig, thus producing a more even finish. The gig used today is essentially the same as the kind used in the late eighteenth and nineteenth centuries, when the process, known as roughing or raising, began to be carried out in the 'handle-house' and 'dubbing-shop'. One can recognise the handle-house of an old mill by the small openings in the walls to allow free ventilation to keep the teazels pliable. The word handle came from the handle-stocks in which the teazel heads were arranged, the handles then being fixed in courses upon the face of the cylinders. By the end of the eighteenth century these gig-mills were being driven by steam-powered machinery, and it was the use of these machines which caused many riots in the industry. The machines not only did the work more quickly than the hand-raisers but could produce a greater amount of finished cloth. Gloucestershire was one of the first counties to use machine gigs, and they do not seem to have produced the same agitation there as in other West Country clothing areas.

Teazels were grown in Gloucestershire not only in the Stroud-water area but in many other places, and I have talked to several elderly people who can remember seeing small fields of them growing on the hillsides of north Cotswold around Stanway where they were regarded as a chancy crop, rather like the produce from orchards, which might or might not prove profitable according to the weather. White's *Flora of Bristol* says the teazel was still being cultivated about Cheltenham in 1937.

The main source of supply was Somerset, where teazels are still grown and where the soil suits the plant. In the summer of 1966 I saw a photograph of a fine field of them near Curry Rivel and was told they were being grown for a blanket factory. It was interesting to discover that the same family had once cultivated teazels in Gloucestershire. Somerset not only provided teazels for her own woollen trade but also supplemented those grown in Wiltshire and Gloucestershire as well, the chief areas being near Blagdon, Harptree, Hatch Beauchamp and Curry Mallet, not far from where they are being grown today.

When the West of England cloth trade was at its peak home production was insufficient and a large number of teazels had to be bought from the Continent. The majority of teazels used today come from abroad, for it is not a crop which lends itself to England's highly-mechanised farming, being expensive in man-power. Also the teazels are difficult to dry off in the English climate.

Sowerby calls the teazel a casualty crop seldom undertaken except by small farmers and labourers because of the amount of trouble needed and the risk of bad weather ruining the crop. Dr John Leonard Knapp (1767–1845), in his *Journal of a Naturalist*, published around 1830, says much the same thing in his vivid descriptions of rural and agricultural conditions. He tells how the cultivation on heavy soils involved much heavy labour of hoeing and weeding, the plant taking two years to come to flower. A

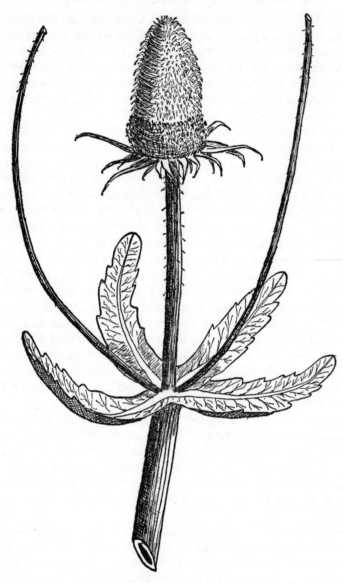

Dipsacus Sativus—the clothier's teazel

period of bad weather could destroy it utterly and this made it a speculative crop that could bring handsome profit or disappointment and debt. The price also varied greatly and was liable to sudden increase if the harvest was wet or the demand excessive, whereas a good season or a falling-off of the clothing trade could produce a glut and a low price. In 1815 King teazels fetched £4 a pack, whereas in 1820 they had dropped to £2. Middlings soared to £8 a pack in 1821, to drop to £4 in 1824. As much as £22 a pack is recorded in the stock books of J. & T. Clark of Trowbridge, but the average was between £5 and £7.

The dangerous period for the grower comes when the teazels are almost ripe for picking and his hopes of making a profit can be dashed almost at the last hour. Where the shoulders of the long serrated leaves meet, just around the flower head below the bracts, a shallow cup is formed where rain and dew collect. In fine weather this soon evaporates, but in wet weather the water stagnates, rotting the stems and heads. Stacking has its problems, for ripe teazels cannot be stacked easily like corn, pressure ruining the spines, while a free circulation of air is essential to dry them thoroughly. The advice to one grower to 'bask them in any sunny gleam that breaks out' suggests that the English summer in the nineteenth century resembled our own.

This continual handling meant much time and trouble, which explains why they were so often grown by small farmers and labourers with a plot of spare ground who were willing to work long hours to make a little extra money, and whose families could help with the sorting and drying. At harvest time, July and August, a special knife is used to cut the heads. Unless cut green the stem hardens into a tough cane-like consistency even more difficult to sever. In 1906 a Wiltshire farmer was advertising in the Bristol newspapers for teazel cutters, and it is likely that bands of travelling cutters went from farm to farm in the teazel harvest season in the same way as reapers and threshers.

When cut, the teazel heads were fastened to poles for drying, thirty going to a stave, thirty staves to a pole. The terminal heads from the centre top branch are ready first and are called Kings, being coarser and larger than the others and used for the strongest kind of cloth. They brought about half the price of the collateral heads—the prize of the crop—known as 'middlings'.

Near Woodchester, once an important centre of the clothing

trade, there is a tall, round stone tower of three storeys known locally as the Teazel Tower which tradition says was once used for teazel drying; the latticed floors suggest that this might be so, though if it had been built originally for this purpose one would have thought there would have been more windows. Usually barns, sheds, shelters of any kind were used. In bad seasons cottagers even stored them in their bedrooms; remembering the large families and small rooms of many a cottage, teazel harvest must have brought considerable discomfort.

Like most plants that have been part of country life for generations, teazels have produced their own folk-lore. Miss Plues, in *Rambles in Search of Wild Flowers*, gives one example. She had watched bundles of teazels being prepared for market in Somerset. 'Country people cut open the heads, where they frequently find a worm. An odd number of these worms, placed in a quill, is believed to charm away sickness.'

The Flora of Gloucestershire, published by the Cotteswold Naturalists' Field Club in 1948, describes the teazel as 'an alien, occurring occasionally as a relic of cultivation'. It is easily overlooked, for to a casual observer it resembles the native teazel, *Dipsacus sylvestris*, particularly in late autumn when the leaves have shrivelled and the bracts have lost their shape. A characteristic of the clothier's teazel is the way the bracts spread outward in a loose ruff below the heads instead of pointing upward as in the wild plant. Also the prickles of the cultivated teazel have fine recurved hooks, while the prickles of the native teazel are without hooks.

For many centuries no man-made substitute was invented for 'raising' woollen cloth. Records go back to the fourteenth century of teazels being brought from the Continent, and in 1327, according to Anne Pratt, they were being grown in Gloucestershire and sold for 2d a thousand. They were probably being used long before that time, though who first discovered that drawing teazel heads across fulled cloth improved its surface without tearing or injuring the material remains unknown.

Not all areas of high Cotswold were suitable for growing teazels; if the soil was too light the hooks on the flower-heads tended to be too small or even to disappear altogether. The richer clay of the Severn valley produced the best hooks. Dr John Knapp, in his *Naturalist's Diary*, published around 1829, says that a piece of cloth needed 150 to 200 'runnings-up' with the teazel-frame, and from 1,500 to 2,000 teazel-heads would be broken in the process. One can see from this what an enormous number of teazels were needed when the industry was at its peak, and why so many had to be imported from other counties and from the Continent.

Three plants used for dyeing cloth are still to be found on the Cotswolds: Dyer's Greenweed, *Genista tinctoria*; Dyer's Rocket, *Reseda luteola*; Woad, *Isatis tinctoria*; most of whose names are a guide to their one-time use.

Most of us have heard of woad, Caesar having told us that the native Britons stained their bodies with it, thus starting the belief, now disproved, that the ancient Britons were savages. The plant itself is not as familiar as its name, though escapes from cultivation were once fairly common. Today the nearest place to the Cotswolds where it can be found growing wild is near Tewkesbury, where it has persisted for many years. Lees, in his *Pictures of Nature*, published in 1856, describes it as 'growing by a tumulus called Mithe Tout . . . the cliff is quite golden with it about the end of May, some of the plants are a yard high, with from ten to sixteen spikes of numerous yellow flowers'.

It was cultivated extensively around Wotton-under-Edge, a clothing town once noted for its dyehouses, and as a result it naturalised itself in fields by the Little Avon and about Wickwar, the last record being 1908. It was also grown at Steanmead or Stonemead near Steanbridge, where the Townsend family of Painswick clothiers had their big mill, for it comes into a dispute about tithes around 1770, when the Rector of Painswick considered that tithes of woad should be paid to him because the dyers were growing woad in fields which had previously grown corn and rape as well as 'lands which had been yielding tythe hay'. This 'tythe hay grew on all such mead as had never been ploughed or broken up', and was known to the local folk by the name of Steanmead. The difficulties were settled by a revisitation of all ploughed and unploughed land in the parish of Painswick by the Rector in conjunction with Mr Edward Wick, the Impropriator, on 10 April 1772, and the Rector received his tithes. Woad, however, had been grown in Painswick at least 150 years before this, for tithes of woad formed an important item in tithes paid to Painswick Church in 1615. Woad was one of the dyes used for the fine broadcloth made by the Stroudwater clothiers. Even the poorer

DYER'S
GREENWEED

DYER'S
ROCKET

Two plants used in dyeing

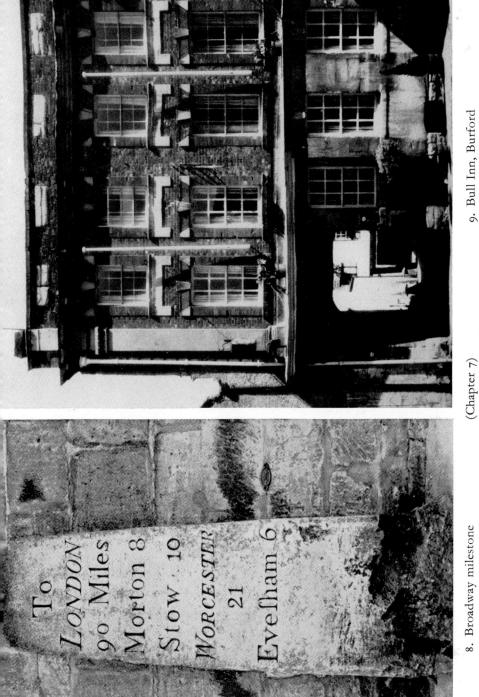

8. Broadway milestone

To
LONDON
90 Miles
Morton 8
Stow 10
WORCESTER
21
Eveſham 6

(Chapter 7)

9. Bull Inn, Burford

10. Burford in the coaching era (Chapter 7)

people tried to have one suit of best black broadcloth, and it was the custom in the nineteenth century for the weaver to wear his best suit when he took his newly-woven cloth to the wool-loft and received yarn for the next piece. For three centuries at least woad had been an important constituent in the making of black and blue dyes.

A monopoly right used by Elizabeth I to raise money was permission to grow woad, one such licence being granted in July 1594 to Richard Leverell and Valentine Harris for twenty years 'to sow a hundred acres of woad in each of the counties of Berkshire, Wiltshire and Gloucestershire for an annual rent of £50'. A good sum, in those days, showing that the profits to be made from woad in Elizabethan times must have been considerable. A large amount came from abroad in the late Middle Ages, when Cotswold and Wiltshire clothiers were selling their cloth to Bristol merchants for shipping abroad and buying in return oil from Spain and woad from Toulouse. And as the clothiers produced more dyed cloth instead of sending abroad the undyed broadcloth, and the home market increased, production of woad at home increased also.

Celia Fiennes, that intrepid traveller, describes the process as she saw it during one of her journeys across the Cotswolds to visit relatives at Moreton in Marsh: it may have been the woad-mill on the Ey Brook near Moreton which the *Victoria History of Gloucestershire* says was working in 1656.

> In the mill with a horse they grind the leaves into a paste, so make it up in balls and drye them in a Penthouse, to secure it from the rain, only the wind dryes it: a plantation of about twelve acres would employ two or three families, men, women and children, and so they generally come and make little huts for themselves for the season to tend it.

To make the paste only the foliage was used, the leaves being picked off when the plant was in flower, the lower ones taken just when they were turning yellow. The gathering was repeated three or four times at intervals of a few weeks. The first picking, being the most valuable, was kept separate from the rest. After being dried a little in the sun, the leaves were ground to a paste which was then sheltered from the rain, but not the air, until it fermented. A cold spell at the beginning of June could delay or even spoil the process. The crust which formed over the paste was carefully protected from breaking, and when the fermentation was complete, in about two weeks given warm weather, the paste was again mixed up and moulded into flat cakes. In this form it was sometimes sold to the dyer who had to break the cakes again and, after applying a little moisture, let them ferment once more. They were then mixed with lime water to bring out the colour. The quality and permanence of the dye depended upon the number of fermentations.

We are told by various writers, including Celia Fiennes, that the smell of the processing was most offensive. Sowerby gives the price as £20 a ton for best quality woad in the middle of the nineteenth century, though by that time indigo had taken its place in the larger dye-houses.

Woad was not used to produce a blue colour but as a mordant or base for a black dye. The introduction of indigo, a superior colour but a less permanent dye, put an end to its general use and to the livelihood of those who cultivated it. These people did not grow other crops but specialised in its preparation as well as its cultivation, a highly-skilled job. It ceased to be successful as a crop if grown for more than two years on the same piece of land, so the woad-growers were travelling people, hiring land in various places and leading a wandering life with their families, only staying long enough to plant and gather and then prepare the paste for market, a tedious, smelly process which stained them and their possessions as blue as any of Caesar's ancient Britons. Like the reddleman, a woad-man carried the marks of his trade on his person, and his image in the districts where he carried on his work was probably used in the same way by parents as a bogey to subdue unruly children.

As the botanists do not consider woad a native plant it must have been introduced well over 1,500 years ago, perhaps even 3,000. It never became a forage crop here as it did in France and Belgium, but was grown only for its dye. It can be recognized quite easily because it is the only *Crucifera* whose pods develop a purple tint when ripening, a hint of the dye it produces. The plants, rather like small bushes with their tough wiry stems, are delightful to see at seed-time. The numerous slender pods dangling on hair-like stems tremble at the slightest movement of the air and have a semi-translucent texture which takes all sombreness from the dark colour.

Withering's *Arrangement of British Plants*, published in 1776, records that it was cultivated at Keynsham, near Bristol, and Mr Fry, in White's *Flora of Bristol*, published in 1912, writes that it was formerly grown at Saltford, a mile or so nearer Bath where 'a field in which it was grown is called Woad Range in reference to a block or range of buildings still standing'. This, says Mr Fry, 'I learned from C. Withers of Saltford, who told me he had often heard his father say that the plant was grown and the dyestuff made from it at Woad Range'. Another field-name is Wadfield, near Winchcombe, the wad coming from the Saxon wad or waad, an indication that woad was formerly cultivated there.

The Dyer's Gild at Bristol regulated the sale and storage of all woad coming into the port. The chief sources abroad were Picardy, Toulouse and Italy. The 'George' of Bristol in 1479 carried an entire cargo of 182 pipes from Bordeaux, and although this was an exceptionally large load, heavy shipments were not uncommon, for the Bristol merchants supplied woollen manufacturers outside their own city. Bristol ships sometimes used Southampton for this trade and the woad was then carried in waggons overland to Bristol. Other dyeing material such as madder and alum were also imported from the Continent.

A burgess of the city was legally entitled to break his own woad, nevertheless the regulations of the Gild strictly controlled its sale, storage and use, the Gild appointing their own officers to break open the tuns. No merchant was allowed to store more than one tun lest he attempted to corner the supply. Stranger merchants and aliens, that is those not belonging to the city, were obliged to sell their woad within forty days of an assay of its quality and were not allowed to sell dyestuffs to each other. The brokers had to be experienced in their job, for it was a tricky commodity which changed its potency if not properly handled, and an inferior quality could spoil the cloth and a clothier's and merchant's reputation.

Dyer's Greenweed, or Woad-Waxen, is a native plant of rough clay pastures. It is more likely to be found in the valleys than on the hills, but it is fairly common in parts of the Cotswolds. It is a tough, shrubby plant with a tenacious root-hold, and its wiry stems, bright green foliage and yellow flowers make it a pleasing addition to the flora of any meadow, though it has no food value for sheep or cattle. As it does not grow in conspicuous abundance or spread rapidly, farmers on the whole do not make determined efforts to eradicate it, and even where old pastures are ploughed for leys it still survives, for the smallest piece of root left in the ground will continue to grow.

The whole plant was once used for dyeing, making a yellow dye often mixed with woad or indigo to produce various shades of green. A local name, dyer's broom, describes it well. Its flowers are smaller than those of the Common Broom and it does not put out the characteristic bundles of stiff angled wands, being altogether a more compact and elegant plant.

Dr Knapp, writing from Thornbury about 1820 says:

> The dyer's broom abounds with us and becomes a perfect encumbrance on clay land pastures. . . . Our poorer people a few years ago used to collect it by cartloads about the month of July; and the season of woad-waxen was a little harvest to them. Women would gain about 2s a day by gathering it, but they complained that it was a very hard laborious occupation, the plant being drawn up by the roots, which are strongly interwoven in the soil. The dyer gave them 8d a cwt—but I fear the amount was greatly enhanced by the dishonest practice of watering the load for the specious purpose of keeping it green; and the old woad-waxers tell me that without the increase in weight which the water gave they would have had very little reward for their labour.

Anyone who has ever tried to pull up a plant of dyer's greenweed by hand will agree that the women of those days earned every penny of 2s a day for their work.

Dyer's Rocket, or Weld, is a more delicate plant than Dyer's Greenweed, not only in colour but in structure. A distinctive yellowish-green suffuses the hollow stems rising out of a rosette of narrow crinkly-edged leaves that hug the ground, and the yellow of the myriads of tiny flowers on its tall spires is lost in the yellowish-green of its general colour. Almost as soon as the plant begins to seed, however, a soft russet tint spreads upward from the base, until by autumn the whole plant takes on a warm glow, as if it had absorbed some of the orange colour of the oolite brash it loves to grow in. Linnaeus observed that its flower spikes followed the course of the sun.

It is a native plant of oolitic and other calcareous soils, a Cotswold plant, though not as common as *Reseda lutea*, often found growing with it. It has a habit of springing up on freshly-made clearings and its tall spires can sometimes be seen on the banks of newly-widened roads, the pale reseda of its leaves conspicuous among the darker greens of coarser herbage. It likes plenty of room to spread its rosettes of leaves and disappears after a year or two, unable to compete when ranker and more rapidly-growing vegetation takes over. The seeds, however, like those of charlock, have the capacity of keeping their fertility and can lie for many years awaiting a favourable opportunity to germinate.

Parkinson, in 1640, mentioned its cultivation in Kent, where 'they used to sow their fields therewith after their barley which abideth until the next year and then gathered'. This was the usual way it was grown in Gloucestershire, the first-year rosettes being left after the barley was gathered to grow into a mature plant the following year. When the seeds began to form it was pulled and tied in bundles and dried in the sun. The bundles were sold under the name of weldcord. In 1814, 28 lb of prepared weld was worth 11s 6d according to a stock book of a Cotswold dyer, and Dr Perry says that 'as late as 1820 the plant was being sold in Bristol by country people at 10s a cwt'.

It is one of the oldest European dyes. Caesar mentions that it was used by the Gauls. It is still used as a dye and prepared by making a decoction of the whole plant, although the yellow colouring matter, luteolan, resides chiefly in the seeds. One reason why it has gone out of favour is the large number of plants necessary to produce the dye.

The colour is strong and permanent and, with the addition of alum, many shades can be obtained. It is sometimes mixed with indigo, or in the old days with woad, to give what dyers call Saxon Green.

The market for home-grown dyestuffs decreased as imports of logwood, redwood and cochineal came in from South and Central America, thus eliminating another harvest-time which had helped cottagers and labourers to eke out their meagre incomes between the hay and corn harvests. In the case of Dyer's Greenweed it had been a harvest they could gather free in the fields.

It is not only in the case of woad, as in the Wadfields and Woadfields seen on old estate maps, that field names can indicate crops formerly cultivated in them. Paradise, the name of a house and a piece of land east of Painswick where the Adam and Eve inn now stands, was not called Paradise because of the beauty of its position, though it well deserves the name for that reason, but because 'Grains of Paradise', the old name for maize or Indian corn, was probably once grown there, perhaps as a hopeful experiment, by the lord of the manor at the end of the fifteenth century. Another of its names, Gran Turco, or Turkish Wheat, was given to it because of the long silky tufts at the ends of the ears being thought to resemble the beards of Turks. Gran Turco from Tripoli was being sold in England in 1453, but this does not prove an eastern origin. It is an ancient plant of the Americas and negative evidence suggests that it was not introduced into the old world until the discovery of the new.

Two other plants with a flavour both literary and culinary are the Common Carraway, *Carvum carvi*, and White Mustard, *Sinapis alba*.

White mustard is fairly common on the Cotswolds, not only as a crop where one small field can illuminate a whole hillside with its vivid yellow flowers, but as an escape from cultivation. Its seeds are ground for the production of culinary mustard, and Tewkesbury mustard has been famous since Elizabethan times. Shakespeare refers to one with 'wits as thick as Tewkesbury mustard', but two hundred years or so later *The New and Complete Traveller in Britain*, published about 1780, referring to a proverbial expression for a sharp fellow, says he 'looks as if he lived on Tewkesbury mustard'. This became changed to 'keen as mustard' until American slang took over and supplied transatlantic expressions in its place.

The Common Carraway is a casual, often passed over as one of those tiresome *umbelliferae* difficult to identify. The occasional plant we see today growing by the wayside is probably descended from a crop plant once grown in a nearby field where it would have been sown with coriander or teazels. The hard-ribbed fruits contain an aromatic oil used in medicine and Sowerby observed 'it is always in demand in the London markets'.

The fruits are used to flavour cakes, though 'seed' cake is not made as frequently today as it was in Victorian times, when it was a favourite delicacy for tea-parties, or to eat with a glass of Madeira. Sugar comfits with their hard sugar coating so smooth to the tongue, a children's delight a hundred years ago, are rarely seen in the shops today.

Like teazels and coriander the carraway is no longer grown commercially on the Cotswolds. The turn of trade from Europe caused the substitution of *Anethum Peucedanum graveolens* for the carraway formerly used in drugs and confectionery. Crops of this delicate little yellow-flowered *umbellifer* came up spasmodically during the war years on Bristol city tips, and are recorded in the lists of alien plants seen in dumping places and waste ground near the docks.

An imposing plant sometimes found growing wild, and which has been used medicinally for many centuries, is the Elecampane, *Inula Helenium*, a plant whose roots were once made into a decoction by Cotswold shepherds to cure sheep of the scab. It was cultivated in the gardens of religious houses before the Dissolution and the plants found wild today are thought to have derived from this source. Most of the places where I have seen it growing have been near the sites of old monasteries and ancient manor houses. *The Flora of Gloucestershire* says it is in all probability an ancient introduction, but J. W. White, the Bristol botanist, believed it to be native in some localities.

Its name, Elecampane, is a corruption of the first words of the line 'Enula campana reddit praecordia sana' from a monastery herbal in which its properties are praised. The Helenium part of the name goes back to Helen of Troy, according to the old botanists, but whether because its tall, fair beauty was being compared to hers or because she used it as medicine or cosmetic legend does not tell us. The plant deserves its name, for it holds itself handsomely. Bold yet subtle, it resembles a small but more elaborately-patterned sunflower, with spreading strap-shaped petals and a fleshy decorative calyx not unlike a soft green flower itself. Indeed, it is the calyx which gives it character. The flower heads are borne on tall thick stems with large lower leaves slightly hairy underneath. It touches the imagination at first sight even if one does not know its associations, and one can understand why the old herbalists, always sensitive to individual characters in a plant, were ready to translate it to human good.

CHAPTER SIX

Two Campden worthies

By the beginning of the eighteenth century Chipping Campden, once a centre of the medieval wool trade, had become a remote country town concerned with its own limited resources and rural problems. The days when its merchants were as much at home in London and the Low Countries as in Gloucestershire were long forgotten. The Civil War brought the burning of Sir Baptist Hickes' magnificent Italianate manor house, and the fact that the house was never rebuilt could be interpreted as a sign that Campden hereafter was to be left to rusticate.

The big landowners still held sway, but there was considerable small-town activity in which they played no part. Whereas before the eighteenth century ideas came from the top, there was now a lower middle class ferment ready to react to change and progress, and out of it came men who were inspired by the opening up of trade and communications everywhere and who wanted to have some share in the new world. This inspiration was not always regarded as a means of making a fortune or of becoming famous. There were the joys of learning and invention for its own sake, desire to add to the world's stock of knowledge, and, perhaps the most potent reason of all, a need to fill their minds with something more satisfying than a narrow provincial existence.

In Chipping Campden there were several men who found encouragement and stimulation from each other, a mutual comradeship that made a buffer between themselves and the jealousies, derision or indifference of their neighbours. One of these men who never achieved fame in his own town—nor is there any local memorial to his memory—was Jonathan Hulls, the first man who attempted to employ steam in propelling a vessel in water. He was baptized in Blockley Church on 17 December 1699, his father being Thomas Hulls of Hanging Aston in Blockley parish. Thomas Hulls was named weaver in the leasebook of the manorial estate of Campden when he leased a small property in Broad Campden in 1717, but tradition speaks of him as a mechanic, so it might be that he was a maker or mender of looms as well as a weaver. Jonathan probably inherited a love of mechanics from his father.

As a boy he attended the Campden Grammar School, though we do not know for how long. It is certain, however, that he had a better education than was customary for the sons of weavers or small husbandmen, and this was added to by home study all his life. His work shows him to have been a sound mathematician and in later years, with his friends Richard Darby, maltster, and William Bradford, schoolmaster, he became one of the three who liked to call themselves the 'Lovers of Mathematics'.

Tradition has garbled many tales around the fortunes and misfortunes of Jonathan, as it will about any person showing signs of originality. It has said that he and his family were reared and lived in poverty. Evidence shows, however, that from 1730 he was a yeoman farmer, married and settled at Broad Campden, where he was a tenant of the manor holding the leases of two properties, one including a 'messuage for lives of lessee, Ann wife and son Thos . . . and the close of pasture of 1 rood and 1 yardland dispersed'. The other lease gives pasture for fifty-five sheep among other parcels of common land of the parish. So it would appear that he was a small farmer in fairly comfortable circumstances.

Another traditional belief is that he was the village clock-repairer, but though, knowing his love of machinery, it is likely that he repaired clocks for a hobby, it was not his source of livelihood. These stories probably arose after the family had died out in Campden. The penniless inventor was a conventional romantic figure of the times; the stories were put about by people who had no knowledge of the family except gossip that time had exaggerated into fantasy.

Jonathan Hulls was never a wealthy man. As far as one can tell from the known facts he had little of the sharp business acumen that goes with the making of money on a big scale, but this is not evidence that he or his family were ever on the poverty line. Indeed, neither his father nor himself would have been able to pay the premiums to the manor estate for their holdings or have been allowed the leases if they had not been able to pay their way. In the will of John Moseley of Broad Campden, proved at Gloucester in 1734, Jonathan received one guinea as an overseer of the poor, and this also disproves the tale. Incidentally it is in the overseers' accounts of disbursements on behalf of the poor that the only autograph of Jonathan known to exist can be found.

A pedigree in the *Harl. MSS* (1450) shows a Hulls family of some standing in Gloucestershire living at Olveston, and it has been suggested that the Hulls of Hanging Aston were descended from the Alveston family. Percy Rushen, the painstaking Campden historian, points out that the Hulls of Broad Campden possessed a panel painted with armorial bearings, though it was impossible to discover if these were the same as those credited to the Alveston family because by the time he saw it the details had become indistinct. One feels that Rushen, a sympathetic champion of Jonathan's endeavours who wrote scathingly 'of the ineptitudes of the Campdeners in the past' to appreciate a genius in their midst, would like him to have had forebears of gentle birth. Whether this is so or not, it is to Rushen that we are indebted for much of the available knowledge of the family, for he pursued his researches in every possible way, eventually discovering descendants living in Birmingham to supplement his own findings.

Percy Rushen was a local historian who dealt in facts, not fancies. He dug his information out of legal documents, making his way unerringly through the involved phraseology to get at the information he wanted and recording it in the same dry fashion. But Jonathan Hulls touched his imagination, and the picture he presents of him comes alive with understanding. I feel Jonathan would have appreciated these qualities in the first Campden man to do him justice. Both had the same integrity and the determination to endure the exacting and monotonous path to knowledge.

One must think oneself back into the period to realize how remarkable it was that a Cotswold small farmer, who probably never had an opportunity of seeing an atmospheric engine at work, for there were no mines where one could have been used in the district, should have understood them so well. His knowledge must have been acquired from reading the scientific journals of the day and from the exchange of information with others interested in the same subject; information not easily come by in a remote country town. The work and thought which led to Hulls' experiment must have been the result of years of brooding over the idea until it finally took shape. He was then frustrated by lack of means from developing it properly.

Two Campden worthies

At this time the steam engine was only used for raising water from the mines and was not capable of use as a prime mover. Cumbrous and slow in action, it was an atmospheric rather than a steam engine, the steam being used to raise the piston into position and fill the space beneath it, that is to say low pressure steam was admitted to a cylinder having a sliding piston, in which cylinder, when the piston was raised to its top, the steam was condensed, producing a vacuum. The pressure of the atmosphere then operated on the piston to force it down, and this movement operated another piston in a pump barrel and so raised the water.

Jonathan Hulls saw how this engine could be made to propel marine craft, and invented a mechanism by which the slow reciprocatory movement of the piston could be conveyed to a rotary paddlewheel which he mounted at the stern of the boat. His idea was to place the Newcomen engine and the propelling device in a special boat, this special vessel to be used as a tugboat to draw ships in and out of harbour. He knew that it would not succeed in the propulsion of large craft in the open sea, for the power obtainable by this means would not have sufficient strength to withstand the force of ocean waters. The device in the diagram shown in his pamphlet *Description and Draught of a New-Invented Machine for Carrying Vessels or Ships out of and into Any Harbour, Port or River against Wind and Tide or in a Calm, for which His Majesty Has Granted Letters-Patent for the Sole Benefit of the Author for the Space of 14 Years*, published in 1737, certainly does not look strong enough to stand up to rough weather. Six paddles in the stern of the tow-boat are seen fastened to a cross-axis connected by ropes to another axis which was turned by the engine, converting the rectangular motion of the piston rod into a rotary motion—the essential principle in steam locomotion whether on land or water. According to De Morgan, Hulls' work 'in all probability gave suggestions to Symington as Symington did to Fulton'.

Few besides marine engineers interested in the evolution of their profession have heard of him, and one cannot help wondering whether if he had had the good fortune to meet with encouragement and the necessary financial aid, he might not have become a household name in the same way as James Watt or Stephenson

As it was, having found a patron in Mr Freeman, of Batsford Park near Moreton in Marsh, who gave him about £160 to patent his invention, Jonathan designed a vessel according to his plans, forwarding models, patterns and drawings to the Eagle Foundry at Birmingham which founded, forged and fitted the various parts. These plans were in existence until the sale and demolition of the Eagle Foundry about 1888, when they were destroyed, there being no person at that time sufficiently interested to save them for posterity—one of those minor tragedies deplored by the industrial archaeologists of today.

The experiment was carried out on the Avon at Evesham, and failed. There was no other attempt to make the steamboat work. The reason for the failure is not known, but it seems probable it was caused by teething troubles Hulls could have rectified if financial aid had not been withdrawn too soon. Disheartened, he let the project lapse. He had a young family to support and he could not let them suffer for his dreams. A less sensitive man would have been more ruthless and would have pursued his vision to the end.

A piece of doggerel circulating at the time reveals local opinion of his abilities. The 'paper skull' refers to the brown paper cap worn by mechanics as a badge of their trade in those days and not to the bone structure of his head.

> Jonathan Hull
> With his paper skull
> Tried to make a machine
> To go against wind and stream;
> But he, like an ass
> Couldn't bring it to pass
> So at last was
> Ashamed to be seen.

When I first read these lines many years ago at Chipping Campden I asked the old saddler, who was a friend of mine, to explain them. He fashioned a hat like a square box out of a sheet of brown paper with amazing deftness for one whose old fingers were crippled with arthritis, and to my delight presented it to me. My delight was even greater when I saw it was after the pattern of the one worn by the carpenter in the Tenniel pictures in my copy of *Alice through the Looking Glass.*

Jonathan must have had previous experience or a foreboding of the contemptuous regard of his contemporaries, for he put a case for himself before the trial of his vessel. In a pamphlet about the machine he wrote:

There is one great hardship lies too commonly upon those who propose to advance some new though useful Scheme for the public Benefit. The World abounding more in rash censure than in a candid and unprejudiced Estimation of Things, if a person does not answer their expectations in every point, instead of Friendly Treatment for his good Intentions, he too often meets with ridicule and contempt.

His fears, unfortunately, proved that the world did abound, not only in 'rash censure', but in never giving him full credit for his genius.

Nothing more was heard of him publicly until 1750, some thirteen years later, when with Richard Darby and William Bradford, he published a treatise *The Maltmakers' Guide for the Use of Maltsters and Excisemen in Gauging Malt*.

Richard Darby was a maltster, but he must also have operated as a carrier, for he is described as such in a letter from George Ballard, the Campden antiquary, to Mr Joseph Ames in 1737. Darby lived in the Market Square at Campden, in premises later occupied by Messrs Vinn and Bennett. Rushen, in 1911, records that the malthouse was still in existence, 'in the same condition as left by him, although it has not been used for malting these last 90 years or more'.

Darby's will, dated 22 April 1774, shows that he was worth at least £2,500, a considerable sum in those days. The will also shows what might have been another bond between Hulls and Darby, for he left among other property land in Hanging Aston, the birthplace of Hulls and the home of his family for many years.

Soon after *The Maltmakers' Guide* appeared the same three men published *The Traders' Guide*, printed by H. Berrow, of *Berrow's Worcester Journal*. This period must have been the happiest in Jonathan's life. His family were growing up and doing well, his friendship with Darby and Bradford stimulated his inventive mind and he was old enough to be philosophical about minor disappointments.

In December 1753 we find Letters Patent (No. 686) being granted to him together with Bradford, for an instrument for *Discovering and Preventing Frauds by Counterfeit Gold*. In March 1754 came a new sliding rule and a thirteen-page pamphlet with another long title.

By virtue of His Majesty's Royal Letters Patent granted unto R. Darby and Co, of Campden in Gloucestershire for their new invented instrument for detecting frauds in counterfeit gold.

This describes the device as being 'as portable as a penknife and by a late improvement made so easy that a child may use it'. It gives four addresses where it could be obtained wholesale and retail: R. Darby & Co at their warehouse at Campden, Messrs Henry and Cave at St John's Gate in London; S. Ans in the High Street in Birmingham, and at the Printing Office in Gloucester.

Although only Hulls and Bradford took out the patents it is obvious that Darby was also involved. The three men issued another pamphlet *The New Art of Measuring Made Easy by the Help of a New Sliding Rule,* which was printed at Coventry.

William Bradford died in 1771, three years before Darby and thirteen years after Jonathan Hulls. His headstone in Campden churchyard stands south-east of the church. The inscription is now difficult to decipher but Bigland records it as:

> To the Memory of
> William Bradford
> late writing master of the Free School, in this town, which office he discharged with strict Vigilance and Diligence for upward of thirty years. He was eminent in Figures and Erudition; and departed this life with Christian patience and Resignation, with a steady reliance on his Redeemer, in hopes of a blessed Immortality, April ye 11th, 1771, aged 67 years.

An engraved portrait of Jonathan Hulls in Stuart's *Anecdotes of the Steam Engine,* published in 1862, with the words Inventor of Steam Navigation, 1763, shows him with long curled hair or wig falling well over his shoulders, a high forehead, dark eyes, thick, dark eyebrows, straight nose and heavy jowled cheeks, the face of one who might have been doctor, lawyer, schoolmaster or a member of any responsible profession. The picture from which this engraving was made has never been found, nor has any original portrait of him been known to exist, but because of the strong family likeness the authenticity of the portrait has been accepted by the family. Jonathan was a quiet man, a Quaker, and one, I imagine, who seldom indulged in talk about himself, and it may be that on one of his trips away from home to patent his inventions a picture was made of him known only to his immediate family and forgotten when he died.

Tradition, which seems to have had its sport with Jonathan, tells a harrowing story about his last days and death, and this would appear to be part of the earlier false romanticism. Penniless and ruined, he is said to have moved to London where he died unknown and unmourned. Another less distressing story of his burial concerns a family of Hulls who lived at High Wycombe, engineers of good position proud to be associated with Jonathan's name, who believed that he left Broad Campden to settle at High Wycombe and was buried in the Friends' Burial Ground there.

It is possible that Thomas, Jonathan's father, was an offshoot of the High Wycombe family, and that is how the tradition arose. In the *Records of the Society of Friends* at High Wycombe several children of that name were given as being baptized between 1737 and 1747, but during these years there are records in the parish registers at Campden of the baptism of Jonathan's six children, Rebecca, the eldest, in May 1719, who died a few weeks later, Margaret, 15 December 1720, another Rebecca who was born 10 December 1724, Thomas, born in March 1725 and Jonathan, born in June 1732.

The marriages of these children are also recorded in the Campden registers, and it is interesting that Thomas married Mary Keyte, a member of a well-known Campden family, several of whom lived in Broad Campden. There were Keytes at Broadway and other neighbouring villages including one, Charles Keyte of Snowshill, known as Schemer Keyte, who in 1824 invented a sewing machine which can still be seen in the Science Museum in South Kensington. A Jonathan Keyte, styled as a wheelwright, is in the rental book of the manor as leasing a small property in Broad Campden in 1703, and a Richard Keyte with a Jonathan Hulls in a list of freeholders voting in the election of 1776. I do not know if this is the same Richard who lost four young children in one year in 1759, for a headstone in Campden churchyard commemorating William, son of Richard and Ann Keyte, who died in June, aged eight; Jonathan who died aged two, the same day as William; Samuel, five weeks old, who died in May of the same year, and Ann, aged five, gives only details of sex and age with no explanation of why they died within a few days of each other. There are occasions when records of the past leave so much untold, and as Campden does not seem to have encouraged the growth of local poets or versifiers in the eighteenth century not even a few lines of doggerel on this pathetic loss have come down to us, though it must have been talked about at the time.

Jonathan Hulls died in 1758, and Rushen suggests that his will was executed on his deathbed because of the almost indecipherable signature. He calculates the date as between 17 May and 7 June, on the basis that the will was proved by the executor on 14 June.

The fact that he was not buried in Campden churchyard may have helped the story that he died out of the county, but this is disproved by the discovery of his will in the Gloucestershire records. It is thought that he must have been buried in the little burial ground belonging to the Friends at Broad Campden, in use at that time. Unfortunately the records of this burial ground have been lost. This could explain why the confusion arose, the Friends' Burial Ground at High Wycombe being substituted in local tradition. In his will Jonathan left the farm and the house to his 'loving wife, Ann Hulls' and all his goods except the 'middlemost house in the Row at Broad Campden'. This house he left to his son Jonathan, who married in that year and was a builder. His son Richard also followed this occupation, adding to it the profession of architect.

Richard prospered and became locally well known for his work. He was responsible for much of the rebuilding and restoration work in the neighbourhood including the east and part of the north wall of Blockley Church in 1838. He constructed the machinery of a carillon to replace a set of chimes by Sleight of Pershore, a piece of local handicraft worthy of a grandson of Jonathan Hulls. An inscription on this set of chimes tells that it was erected at the expense of the parish in 1816.

The great barrel is made up of thin sheets of oak segments put together with excellent craftsmanship. The four tunes were set by Isaac Warner, who was a musician as well as a mechanic, and played *The Blue Bells of Scotland, Taffy was a Welshman,* the *Belle Isle March* and the noble tune of *Hanover. Taffy was a Welshman* was discarded in 1890 and *Holy! Holy! Holy!* put in its place.

In 1829 Richard pulled down the cottage in Broad Campden that had been left to his father by Jonathan and built two houses on the site. He left no children when he died in 1841, although he had been twice married, and the Hulls family died out in Campden with his death, though his widow resided there until she died in 1865.

Thomas, a younger son of Jonathan, moved away from Campden when a young man. One of his sons, William, was a blacksmith at Pebworth and in 1911, when Rushen wrote his history of Campden, some of William's children were still living.

A contemporary of Jonathan Hulls, the inventor, was George

Two Campden worthies

Ballard, born in 1706, some seven years later than Jonathan, and who in his own way showed the same determination and courage to make more of his life than earning a meagre living in a little country town. Although we have no direct evidence that the two men were friends, it seems likely that they must have known each other more intimately than the casual acquaintanceship inevitable in a small community. Both were interested in things of the mind, and both in their own way must have aroused the curiosity of their neighbours because of their unusual pursuits.

George Ballard, however, does not seem to have aroused their hostility. Perhaps the citizens of Campden regarded the study of Anglo-Saxon, antiquities and numismatics as being more respectable than attempts to make boats go by steam when the good Lord had ordained they should be propelled by wind or labour at the oars. Also Ballard's religion was more orthodox whereas Hulls, as a Quaker, would be regarded with suspicion.

Ballard's struggles against poverty and ill-health in his early life, as well as the valiant efforts of his widowed mother to support her family by midwifery, may have made people more kindly disposed towards him; and as he seems to have been of a gentle, kindly nature this may also have won their regard. He was more fortunate in his period than Hulls, and more fortunate in his patrons, or perhaps had a manner which made patrons more willing to help him. It was a time when country gentlemen were interested in numismatics, and if not antiquaries themselves cultivated those who were and liked to be associated with them. Jane Austen in *Emma* describes how Mr Knightly, when putting out 'Books of Essays, drawers of medals, cameos, shells and every other family collection within his cabinets' not only had done all in his power for Mr Woodhouse's entertainment, but was also displaying the usual interests of a country gentleman. The new science of mechanics savoured too much of trade to be generally popular. This does not take away anything from the courage and self-discipline Ballard showed by his attempts to educate himself under tremendous difficulties, for it was because of the knowledge so gained that people who were able to help him became interested in his achievements.

When George Ballard's father, a chandler of Chipping Campden, died in 1710, he left seven young children. George was delicate and was apprenticed at an early age to a stay and habit maker, this being considered an occupation suitable for a delicate child. Almost as soon as he could read he became fascinated by coins and Anglo-Saxon; whether one subject stimulated the other we do not know, but we do know that his collection of coins began when he was very young, helped, probably, by his neighbours, who when they dug up or otherwise discovered strange old coins brought them to him either as gifts or for a slight reward.

Unable to afford a copy of Browne-Willis's Anglo-Saxon Dictionary, he borrowed one and copied out the whole book, adding as he did so some 1,000 words he had collected himself. His study time was at night when he had finished work at his trade, and, knowing the hours of work in those days, he must have studied late into the night to acquire the knowledge he craved.

Oxford was his goal, and even before he reached manhood he was visiting Thomas Hearne, the antiquary, to discuss and show his collections of coins. Hearne records in his diary, shortly after Ballard's first visit to him at Oxford in 1726–7, that Ballard was an 'ingenious curious young man', and that he was attending the Campden Grammar School to learn Latin. One would like to know more about this. I doubt if they had evening school in 1726, so it must have been private tuition or else George was taking time off from work and learning his lessons at school with much younger pupils.

He corresponded with various antiquaries about coins, especially when he added an interesting one to his collection, and in this way won the respect and friendship of many well-known antiquaries of his day, common interests breaking down the difference in social position, though I suspect Ballard had a suitably modest and respectful manner. Hearne became his good friend and it is from Hearne's *Letters* that we learn most about Ballard. He also seems to have been willing to undertake research for his friends. Among other things he is said to have helped Mr Joseph Ames with a *History of Printing*.

In 1731 Ballard wrote an account of Campden Church, and as late as forty years afterwards it was being read by Dr Morrell to the Society of Antiquaries. Since then most writers on the Cotswold churches have used this account, though not always at first hand. With other Ballard manuscripts it is now in the Bodleian Library.

We know, too, that his mild nature could be roused to action as well as anger by vandalism. Posterity has him to thank for saving the monument in Campden Church to Thomas Smith, lord of the manor in the late sixteenth century, from being destroyed by the Rev Nathaniel Weston in 1735. Why this clergyman wanted to destroy the monument is not very clear, though we know only too well how many interesting ancient monuments in churches, as well as church fabric, have suffered from the passion of zealous clergy for obliterating the past. Perhaps it was meant as a tribute to the Earl of Gainsborough, then lord of the manor, whose chaplain he had been. Whatever the reason, having received permission from the Earl to go ahead, it was only by Ballard's quick action that the memorial was spared.

He wrote at once to the squire of Saintbury, a Mr West who was one of his patrons, and Mr West persuaded the Earl to let the monument remain, probably pointing out that it would not look too well for one lord of the manor to demolish the memorial of another who had held the manor before him. Ballard's letter is still in existence, and it expresses his feelings forcibly and with less circumlocution than was customary.

> What can infuse such Monstrous Barbarism into his Capricious Brains to demolish such an Elegant Monument of so worthy a man I can't conceive. . . . I know your powerful interest can very easily stop Mr Erostratus in his mad career. I hope, Honoured Sir, that the great affection you bear to those curious remains of Antiquity will not only put a stop to this scandalous proceeding, but likewise pardon the trouble that is thus given you, Sir,
>
> Your most obedient, etc.

This 'beautiful and curious' freestone monument can still be seen in the north-east corner of the chancel in Chipping Campden Church. Beneath a canopy lies the recumbent lifesize effigy of Thomas Smith in knight's armour with a chain about his neck. His two wives, thirteen living children and two who died at an early age and who are represented at the knees of their respective mothers, are shown in relief in the compartments between the pedestals under the columns carrying the canopy. The arms of the family and a helmet carrying a crest appear in the pediment over the entablature, and against the wall under the canopy is an inscription in Latin recording that Thomas Smith was attached to the court from his boyhood, that he was of the King's Council of the Marches of Wales and twice Sheriff of Gloucestershire. His first wife was Elizabeth, daughter and heiress of Eustace Fitzherbert Esq, his second, Katherine, daughter of George Throckmorton, knight, 'with sons and daughters as here appear'.

It is from Ballard's notes on the church that we know what happened to the old font; Rowland Smith, a churchwarden, mutilated it in 1727 'to make room for his tenants to sit in'.

Although Ballard was in humble circumstances it would seem that the family was not, as Percy Rushen put it, 'of immediate plebian origin', but had fallen on bad times, Ballard's father's early death being another disaster that helped the fall. John Ballard, his great-uncle, was a physician who left a benefaction to the Campden poor. Another great-uncle gave a carillon erected in Campden Church tower, and his grandfather, Thomas Ballard, in 1685 left a comfortable little estate. This, however, had to be distributed between his wife and nine children. George's father, Samuel, according to his will proved at Gloucester, left £10 to his wife and the residue to be divided between his six children, and it is possible that George's share went towards paying for his apprenticeship to the stay and habit maker.

George, however, patiently pursuing his studies in his spare time, was at last able to give up this occupation, though his *Memoirs of Learned Ladies*, a work of some 472 pages, which he published in 1752 with a second edition in 1775, while it brought him considerable prestige amongst the gentry of the district, could not have brought him great financial reward.

He had a 'learned lady' for a friend. This was Elizabeth Elstrob, sister of William Elstrob, the scholar and antiquary. Elizabeth wrote *Rudiments of Grammar for the English-Saxon Tongue*, and Anglo-Saxon was their common interest. She lived with her brother at Oxford, and after his death found herself without means and set up a school in Evesham, where it is said she had so many pupils 'she had scarcely time to eat'. As her scholars only paid one groat a week she still found it difficult to live even on a very modest scale. Sarah Kirkham, daughter of the rector of Stanton and friend of John Wesley, was introduced to Elizabeth by George Ballard, and being a woman of 'extraordinary understanding, lively imagination and humane disposition', Sarah wrote to Mrs Delany, then Mrs Pendarves, who was in attendance on Queen Caroline at court, telling her of Elizabeth's struggles to study and maintain herself at the same time. Mrs Pendarves showed Sarah's letter to the Queen, who immediately ordered £100 to be sent to Elizabeth Elstrob. Wits in the past and present have made great play with Queen Caroline's patronage of indifferent poets and writers, but this act shows a truly benevolent spirit.

The story of the friendship between George Ballard and Elizabeth Elstrob has a strangely idyllic quality and was apparently divorced from any other desire than a mutual love of Anglo-Saxon and similar studies. Both had to struggle for a bare existence, both were dependent upon the capricious goodwill of patrons to be able to study, both were untouched by a need for worldly possessions apart from their books, most of which they were content to borrow from libraries, and both had apparently never considered marriage as within the scope of their activities.

In 1750, with the help of the Vicar of Kineton, Mr Talbot, a recommendation to Dr Jenner, President of Magdalen College, and an annuity of £60 given by Lord Chedworth and others, Ballard achieved his life's ambition, to become a scholar at Oxford. It is said that he was originally offered £100 a year but told his patrons that £60 would be sufficient. He was appointed one of the eight clerks of Magdalen College, an appointment carrying with it furnished chambers and board. By the good offices of Dr Jenner, who recognized his worth, he was afterwards elected one of the beadles of the University.

He was forty-four when he went to Oxford and he stayed there for nearly five years. One can feel certain that for a man of his inclinations the access to libraries, the congenial company, the glow of being in the right place must have given him great satisfaction as well as a sense of achievement. Always in poor health, illness caught up with him early in June 1755, and he returned to Campden to die on 25 June. He was buried in Campden churchyard a few days later.

A tablet to his parents, erected by him, can be seen against the exterior wall of the church, though one must refer to Bigland for the now undecipherable inscription. But there is no memorial in the church or churchyard to Ballard himself. Nichols, in his *Literary Anecdotes*, gives a flowery Latin inscription supposed to come from a tombstone, and he states that Ballard was buried at Campden in 1755. If this stone was ever erected it must have disappeared before 1790 when Bigland compiled his *Collection*; it is impossible to believe he could have missed it. The puzzle remains. Where did Nichols see the stone? The inscription is clear enough, as the following translation shows:

> George Ballard is buried here. By no means an ordinary ornament of Campden, who though oppressed by the exercise of homely arts, sought daily notwithstanding to produce a mind polished by a liberal training. Called at length by the fame of his learning into celebrity and friendship with literary men, and enrolled in the Academy of Oxford, he flourished at leisure. Neither ignoble or usless to the literary world, he as author has commended himself to memory for ever, as is shown to a great extent by his writings on British Ladies, but intent on his studies he died suffering from the stone in the year 1755, indulged too short of time in the retirement of life.

A potted biography, it tells the whole story and if, as seems possible, Ballard wrote it himself, the pity is that he could not ensure its continuance to testify to his ambition when he was dead.

Unlike Jonathan Hulls he has his column in the Dictionary of National Biography. A collection of his MSS, including the MS of his *Memoirs of Learned Ladies*, is in the Bodleian Library.

CHAPTER SEVEN

Burford in the coaching era

The eighth edition of Cary's *New Itinerary, or an Accurate Delineation of the Great Roads, both Direct and Cross, throughout England and Wales,* published in 1819, gives a good idea of how the coaching towns of Cotswold had developed by the first quarter of the nineteenth century. They were at this time at the peak of their prosperity. The amount of information in this fat book must have kept many people employed gathering it and then reducing the bulk by the use of abbreviations as frustrating to the coach passenger seeking quick information as any modern A.B.C. to the passengers of today, but it leaves no doubt that most small towns and large villages were included in the network of coach services available. The proprietor also 'earnestly solicits those who may do him the honour of making the Book their travelling Companion' to have the goodness to 'transmit any additional information for the Improvement of the Work'. It is difficult to imagine our public transport companies including such a request in their time-tables!

Coaching inns at Cheltenham, Gloucester, Stow on the Wold, Northleach and Burford are listed. Burford was an important stopping place for many coaches, being on the main road from London to Oxford, Gloucester and South Wales, as well as a junction linking Stow and Chipping Norton in the north and Cirencester and Faringdon in the south, all these places being on other main routes across the country.

There were two coach routes from London to Burford, one via High Wycombe, the other via Henley, so that it was well used by travellers from the south-east. One of the first to run from Burford by way of Witney to London was started by Thomas Castell of Burford in 1761. He opened up what later became a much-frequented route to Cheltenham, Gloucester and South Wales by way of the Chilterns, Oxford, Burford and Northleach. Before this travellers had gone by roads south of the Thames, but better methods of road-making and field drainage and a new road bridge over the low-lying marshy ground between Eynsham and Oxford made this new route possible and the coaches were quick to take advantage of it.

When one tries to imagine the Burford of those days one must remember that the main road (A40) which today passes the town at the summit of the hill was only a rough farm track and remained so until almost the end of the coaching era. In those days the main road left the ridge as soon as it entered the parish of Burford and then turned down White Hill, to come into the town along Witney Street, leaving the town again on its way to the Cirencester road through Sheep Street, then turning down through Priory Wood to rise steeply at the end of the wood to the top of the hill again, an exhaustingly steep ascent and descent for the horses and an explanation of why one of the oldest coaching inns, The Lamb, is situated today out of the main stream of traffic.

Until the early 1800s all the coaches coming through Burford took this seemingly devious way, and this was probably the cause of as many complaints in the local inns and councils about the trials of inheriting ancient road systems as one hears today on the same subject. An amazing number of coaches took this route. The Magnet from Cheltenham on its way to Oxford arrived about 9.30 in the morning, with the Berkeley Hunt, a green coach, soon after. Another pair, the Regulator and the Retaliator from Gloucester arrived about eleven o'clock, and at one o'clock the famous Mazeppa from Hereford. The Mazeppa had a rival, as indeed most of them had, called the Rapid, and they would go galloping down Witney Street with horns blowing to warn people in that narrow street of their approach.

In the afternoon they would come through on their return journeys, and then at seven in the evening the first of the night coaches would arrive, for it was a round-the-clock traffic and passengers on the mail coaches had to be prepared for departures as well as arrivals at any time of the day or night. Stage coaches mostly ran in the daytime only. The Champion from Hereford and the Paul Pry from Aberystwyth were night coaches.

The Gloucester Royal Mail, one of the most important, arrived in the small hours, the up coach at 1.30 am, the down at 4.30 am, so that the courtyards of the George, the Bull and the Lamb, as well as other inns now gone, were alive night and day with fierce rushes of activity and then lulls while the innkeepers replenished their sideboards in readiness for the next invasion and the ostlers attended to tired horses and made fresh ones ready for the change-over. There was great competition at the best inns to have every-thing ready, particularly for the famous 'fliers'. Their pictures have come down to us and the fame of some of their coachmen. Travel-lers' tales, both long and short, suggest that the breed of traveller in those days was considerably tougher than that of today and one journey across England could provide sufficient horrifying adven-tures to last a lifetime.

By the time Mr Cary printed the eighth edition of his *Itinerary* the roads had improved, but for many travellers in the eighteenth century the risk of poor accommodation at the inns, of being be-nighted on desolate heaths or overturned in the mire in some marshy waste must have made many a cross-country journey as hazardous as any undertaken by Cook or Vancouver. One often finds the words IF GOD PERMITS on the handbills announcing times of departures as late as the last half of the century.

Bad roads were the chief obstacle to a quick and safe passage. It was the state of the roads which prevented the Hanoverian army from coming to grips with the Jacobites in 1754—and as always war was the spur to the making of better roads. Acts for the maintenance of highways passed through Parliament at an increas-ing rate; there were over 450 between 1760 and 1774. This did not mean immediate improvement. Actual work on the roads was slow and thousands of miles outside the main highways remained un-changed, so that, as today, it often took longer to travel a few miles across country in public transport than the long distances between towns.

The opening up of the country brought not only easier travel but other benefits; better roads spread ideas and fashions as well as dust and mud. The Cotswolds awoke from the doldrums which had set in after the decline of the wool and clothing trades and once again were in close communication with the outside world. As Horace Walpole said: 'Good roads and postchaises were the agents of civilisation.'

As well as the coaches of countrywide fame there were those working shorter distances or supplying the links between cross-roads. These were generally small family concerns worked by local men who knew the district intimately. No wonder that Burford's population had reached 1,500 in 1801! Workers were needed to staff the inns, and there were subsidiary occupations connected with the coaching trade. The farmers had a market at hand for their oats, hay and straw, the farmers' wives for their poultry, eggs, cheese and butter. Saddlers, blacksmiths, wheelwrights, laundresses, cooks, chambermaids, ostlers and others were in demand. With regard to saddlers and the makers and menders of harness, Burford had a reputation dating from the Middle Ages for this kind of work, and in 1701 Dr Plot noted saddle-making as one of Burford's industries. He also remarked on the great number of inns in the town for its size. Mrs Gretton in *Burford: Past and Present* gives at least fifteen in the early 1800s, so that Burford was in good shape to cater for the coaching trade when it began.

In 1800 John Lenthall, who inherited the Priory from his father William Lenthall, Speaker of the Long Parliament, and who was called by Anthony Wood 'the grand Braggardochia and Lyer of the Age', did at least one service for Burford. In 1800 he diverted the coach route westward out of it so that this no longer turned down at the Lamb and went through Priory Wood towards the river and then up again to the Cirencester road. Now, passing Kit's Quarry House, it could take a more direct route.

In 1812 the farm track along the top between the White Hill turning and the Cirencester road was made into a surfaced road so that the coaches could keep to the ridge without coming into Burford at all. Two inns were erected, The Ramping Cat at the top of White Hill and The Bird-in-Hand at the top of Burford High Street to serve this short stretch of new road. While making the journey easier for through traffic, this new piece of road took away considerable trade from the coaching inns at the Witney Street corner and others in the town itself. It also meant that passengers from Burford had to get themselves and their luggage to the top of the hill; Mrs Gretton tells how her husband's uncle, Dr Wace, later Dean of Canterbury, coming to the vicarage as a pupil in 1851, walked down the High Street with his luggage following on a wheelbarrow.

I have been told several times that the many stone arches in the High Street are the remains of coaching inns, although anyone looking at them must see they are not wide enough to take a coach and horses. These arches, however, date from a much earlier period and mode of travel and came about in the rebuilding of Burford in stone in the 1400s. Before this rebuilding, the archway from the street led into a paved passage through which the pack-horses carried their bales of wool and other merchandise to the wool lofts and storehouses, and on either side of the passage were doors leading into the house proper. These houses, mostly made of timber and plaster, were easily partitioned into two dwellings when the premises were rebuilt in stone. The archways are practically the only parts remaining of the half-timbered burgess dwellings and are an interesting link with the packhorse trade before coaches and turnpikes were introduced.

By 1830 Burford was on the route of thirty mail coaches daily and was the centre of an intricate posting system. Forty years later its streets were empty, with grass growing in the courtyards of inns once clamorous with the bustle of changing horses, busy ostlers and demanding passengers.

In 1813 Stephenson's locomotive travelled at six miles an hour; in September 1825 the Stockton & Darlington Railway opened; the Manchester line began to run in 1830. The North was ahead of the South, but the little towns of Cotswold depending on coach travel did not see the menace of the 'nasty, wheezing, gaspin', puffin' monster, always out of breath, with a shiny green and gold back like an unpleasant beetle' until well after the middle of the century.

Northleach, some nine miles west of Burford, did not receive the full benefit of the coaching trade until about 1779. Arthur Young described the road from Witney to Northleach as 'the worst turn-pike I ever travelled in', and complained bitterly of the way the road was mended 'by filling in ruts with loose stones as large as one's head'. Although he wrote that 'he knew not in the whole range of language terms sufficiently expressive for denouncing what is called by vile prostitution of language a turnpike' he seems to have done quite well in expressing his disgust. The roads in the vicinity of Northleach in the damp Leach valley were particularly atrocious, resembling the by-road leading to Jawleyford Court as described by Jorrocks in Jack Spraggon's journey, 'deeply spur-lingered clayey-bottomed'. The fliers for many years preferred to use the ancient green road that kept to the hills just north of the town and Hampnett village.

This must have been an exhilarating ride when the north-west wind cleared the air and opened out the view to the farthest horizons. Once the turnpike had been improved, however, the coaches took the route through Northleach, bringing a much-needed prosperity to the town. It was in the coaching era that one of the old warehouses remaining from Northleach's busy days as a wool town was turned into the Lamb Inn.

The narrowness of the Leach valley road through the town had always been a drawback to its expansion, and might be so regarded today, because although its main street is the busy A40 it is still a transit town, the heavy industrial traffic from Gloucester, Oxford and London keeping up a perpetual roar as it rattles by. There is little reason for it to stop, today's road speed having brought Oxford, Cheltenham and Gloucester much closer together.

As one café owner said to me: 'The noise and the smell is about all we get except in summer when visitors come to look at the church, and most of them bring their own food.'

The noise of a heavy articulated lorry grinding past made conversation impossible for a few moments, then when it had passed, he added: 'If the traffic wants to stop it can't. It has to keep going. It's as much as your life's worth to cross the road sometimes.'

Only one inn is given in Cary's *Itinerary*, The King's Head, while Burford has The Bull and The George. Cheltenham has three, The Fleece, The George and the Plough, and Gloucester has The Bell, Booth Hall and The King's Head. These were not all the coaching inns catering for travellers, however. Like the motor-coach drivers of today, the coachmen as well as the firms which employed them had arrangements with various inns advantageous to both concerns. The most important inns were the stopping places of those aristocrats of the road, the mail coaches, which travelled with an official guard and were not obliged to pull up every few miles to pay tolls at the gates across the road. The firms dealing with traffic running shorter distances had their headquarters and booking offices in smaller hostelries, often in charge of the same family who ran the coaches.

Long after the stage coaches ceased to run and the railways had become part of the English scene, carriers' carts continued to play an important part in rural districts poorly served by railway stations. Carriers continued well into the middle of the twentieth century, though by this time the horse-driven vehicle had been replaced by the motor-van or small coach. I remember an ancient Ford in

Cirencester which had replaced the horse-drawn carrier's cart used by the carrier's father and grandfather before him. Travelling from Northleach to Cirencester in it was an exciting trip because of the groans and grinding noises it made going up hills and the possibility that bundles and passengers might be hurled out going down them, as it was the impetus of the downward rush which helped the engine to make the first half of the next rise. As the route was a hilly one, like most Cotswold routes, a ride to Cirencester in the carrier's van was as hair-raising as any trip on a switchback railway at an old-fashioned fairground.

On one occasion, going to the yard to book seats for our weekly excursion, we were accompanied by an old gentleman staying at the same house. He was so horrified by the appearance of the van that he declared it would be suicide for us to ride in such a rickety contraption and gave us a bright, golden half-sovereign to take a car. We were young enough to accept this generous tip, particularly as our friend was leaving next day and would not be able to question us about the journey. And I do not remember that our consciences troubled us very much as we discussed how we should spend this unexpected windfall as we rattled along in the van the following day. Some time later we tried to bring about a similar situation with an elderly aunt who was staying with us, but although she was doubtful of the van's roadworthiness, instead of a tip she gave us a lecture on the lack of stamina in young people who were too lazy to walk when they could ride.

The business of carrier tended to be a family concern, handed down from father to son often for several generations, and sometimes from father to daughter. I know of one instance where a carrier's business went back to the days of the stage-waggon, the poor man's substitute for the stage coach, particularly for local travel. This type of vehicle could seat twenty people with their parcels, and the driver delivered parcels and livestock en route. As its wheels—nearly a foot wide—groaned and creaked over the rough roads they were sometimes set on fire by the friction, and buckets were always carried so that water could be poured over them at intervals to keep them from bursting into flames.

Progress was barely more than a mile an hour on average, but as it could not be expected to carry valuables the stage-waggon was safe from attack by highwaymen. The interminable journeys were enlivened by halts at villages and hamlets, and refreshed at the village ale-houses by gossip as well as drink while the passengers waited for the driver to deliver his parcels. These waits could be lengthy ones, for the driver was expected to deliver the latest news from along the way as well as his parcels, but as the passengers knew what to expect and came provided with food the journey must have been a kind of pilgrimage with every small incident stored up for future telling.

I once found the remains of one of these great lumbering waggons in the garden of an old, dilapidated house near Stow. This house belonged to an old woman who seemed to have an ever-changing colony of daughters and grandchildren about the place. She still worked the remnants of a carrying business between the villages with the aid of a pony and cart as aged and battered as herself; she was the last of a long line of family carriers who had served the area between the north Cotswolds and the Evesham valley for generations.

Embedded deeply in a tangle of nettles and overhung by a ragged elder tree, it was like the decaying hulk of a ship left stranded on a shore whence the sea had long since receded. It was the size and thickness of the timbers which attracted me, though as I touched them I felt their rottenness. But even in ruin it was still possible to imagine what a large, cumbersome vehicle it must have been. The wheels were mostly rotted, but some rusty iron remained to help calculate their size, and surprisingly there were still traces of once bright paint on the sides. It lay among sordid litter, for the old woman and her family had never seemed to destroy anything but had just thrown out unwanted and broken articles to lie in the dirt, and as I tried to reveal more of the old waggon, helped by a rabble of ragged children, the old woman told me it had belonged to some long-departed member of the family who had come from Evesham and started the business 'a long time back'. It had always been a ruined hulk as long as she remembered it, but her grandmother had told her that when she was a child it had still been used to take parties of children on outings, drawn by four carthorses, though when originally used as a stage-waggon eight to ten had pulled it. There was a tradition in the family that oxen had been used when the Evesham valley roads had been too muddy to take out the horses. 'And with all them pulling it it din't go no faster than I do,' she added with a grin, showing me she could also enjoy the local joke that it was quicker to walk than ride in her cart.

One can imagine the superior smiles and the jeers of the passengers in a stage or mail coach passing one of these waggons on the road, but the heavy stage-waggon rumbling along on its broad creaking wheels was less likely to turn over or tip out its passengers on a bad stretch of road. They probably had to get out and walk the steeper Cotswold hills, and coming down a wooden shoe fixed as a brake to the wheels kept the waggon from descending too fast.

A well-known carrier of Cheltenham was Thomas Haines Junior, who operated from the Royal Hotel every day except Sunday, his fly-waggons going through Northleach, Burford, Witney, Oxford and Wycombe to the Blossoms Inn, Laurence Lane, Cheapside, and taking two days on the journey. An old handbill issued by him, still in existence, shows a picture of his fly-waggon, looking not unlike the covered waggon used by American settlers, a low, long, ungainly vehicle with a rounded canvas-covered body on a heavy wooden framework, drawn by four pairs of horses. The fact that it only took two days explains why it was called a fly-waggon, for that was good going for a distance of about 100 miles with the necessary stops for changing horses.

The handbill also gives a picture of a fly-van, with particulars that it left the Royal Hotel Coach Office on Tuesdays, Thursdays and Saturdays at 12 o'clock, going through Oxford and Wycombe to arrive at the Blossoms Inn the following day. Haines' fly-van was a rectangular windowless coach, its two front wheels smaller than its back wheels. It had a guard perched at the back, exposed to the weather, and a coachman in front with a long whip. FLY VAN is printed in large letters on its side and it is drawn by two pairs of horses. An amusing touch is that the horses of the fly-van are drawn to represent speed, while those of the fly-waggon are only pulling sedately.

When Mr John Palmer showed the Postmaster-General how to speed up his mails and his new mail-coach halved the time of the journey between London and Bristol in 1784, this also had the effect of speeding up the rest of the coach traffic and making the Government as well as the coach proprietors interested in improving the roads. By 1820, the *Gentleman's Magazine* tells us, at least 300 coaches passed through Hyde Park Corner daily. Coaching had developed into big business. Rival firms appeared on every route and competition was keen. Time became important. As it was impossible to make the horses go much faster, for they were already pushed to breaking point, time had to be saved in other ways. The celerity with which horses were changed became a source of pride and rivalry between the ostlers, the coachmen and the various owners. It was a quick-change act, with everything ready and everyone alert the moment the coach was heard coming along the road; and the movement of a coach was no silent passage. Some of the changes were timed to the half-minute.

By the beginning of the nineteenth century coaches had begun to conform to a pattern. The earliest ones had no doors or windows, only wooden shutters to keep out the weather or occasionally leather curtains. The passengers sat on slatted benches, which must have been a considerable trial on a long rough journey, though one must remember clothes were more voluminous in those days. Even in their heyday coaches were built for endurance rather than comfort; they had to stand up to continual rocking and jolting hour after hour.

They presented, however, a gay appearance, picked out in red and gold, blue and white, or whatever combination of colours the proprietors fancied for their trademark. The finish of the coach-work was a highly specialized job, as Hugh McCausland describes in his *English Carriage*. It received many coats of paint before the final one, after being varnished six times, was finally rubbed down with powdered pumice to produce a glass-like surface able to stand up to the mud and flying grit of the roads.

The interior and the benches on the roof for outside passengers did not receive the same thorough treatment, though some of the more important coaches were fitted with padded benches. Towards the end of the era the vehicles became well-sprung according to the standards of the period, but a journey by coach still remained a physical ordeal for a delicate or elderly passenger. With amusing snobbery, or so it seems now, De Quincy wrote about 'a tawdry thing from Birmingham, some TALLY-HO or HIGHFLYER, all flaunting green and gold', and goes on to point out the contrast to the mail coach in which he was travelling with 'its royal simplicity of form and colour . . . the single Ornament on our dark ground was the mighty shield of the imperial arms' while 'the tawdry thing from Birmingham' had 'as much writing and painting on its sprawling flanks as would have puzzled a decipher from the tombs of Luxor'.

It was laid down by law that they were to keep to the limit of 10 miles an hour; the average was said to be 9·9 miles an hour.

11. End of the lines (Toddington station) (Chapter 7)

12. Ash plantation (Chapter 8)

13. Cotswold beeches (Chapter 8)

Burford in the coaching era

The names of the coaches run by private companies were often an indication of the kind of country they traversed. Those going through Burford and Chipping Norton—hunting country between Oxford and Birmingham—bore Nimrod, three Tally-hos, a Harkaway and a Tantivy. The Mazeppa, which also ran through the Cotswold, was named after Byron's poem, beginning to run the year it was published. I cannot recollect any trains being named after well-known poems or poets. Defiance, Revenge, Self-Defence and Retaliator tell of the competition between rival coaching firms, though the passengers in the Annihilator as it rattled along at a spanking pace may have thought the name a trifle ominous. The Hirondelle, which went from Cheltenham to Liverpool, could have been so called to suggest an airborne passage, but it soon became changed into the Iron-Devil by the less genteel Liverpudlians and this was probably more appropriate as it rumbled over the cobbles, rounded as cannon balls, of the Liverpool streets. One finds the most elaborate and high-sounding names belonging to the less important vehicles on minor routes, a not uncommon phenomenon in other aspects of life.

Memoirs and journals of the coaching era make bitter or amusing play on coach names. For one coach traveller the Magnets were without attraction, the Regulators uncertain, and the Fliers crawled. Railway passengers did the same at a later date; the Somerset & Dorset, for instance, becoming the Slow and Dirty, though this may have implied an exasperated affection as well as a criticism.

In spite of the fact that some 302 separate Acts of Parliament for the making of better roads and bridges were passed in the eight years following the success of Palmer's new mail coaches, the sufferings of the passengers could still provoke the wits of the day, as these verses show.

> To Palmer many thanks I owe
> For his most rare invention;
> My bones will ache from top to toe
> Whene'er his name they mention.
>
> May he (to wish it is no sin)
> When he to Bath approaches,
> Be pummel'd just as I have been
> By one of his Mail coaches.

As late as 1914 most of the Cotswold roads between villages were still being surfaced with stone from local quarries and were thick with dust in summer. In his *Footpath-Way in Gloucestershire*, published in 1924, Algernon Gissing describes an old man from Saintbury, on the northern edge of the Cotswolds, who combined the jobs of parish clerk, sexton and parish roadmender. The old clerk had a regular wage as roadman, but in addition to this he was paid tenpence a cubic yard for breaking stone.

Gissing used to visit him and take a hand in breaking stones as they talked together, the old man sitting on a block of stone with a sack for cushion as he cracked away with his small hammer. 'If the day was windy or liable to be stormy you would find him at some more or less sheltered heap near home down by the trees, where he was, as he said "in the burrow".' The stones for repairing the roads came from nearby quarries, there was no need on the Cotswolds for them to be carried any distance to distributing points. The cubic yards were measured from the stacks of waste in the quarries and left in heaps for the stonebreaker. Every village had its own road-men, called length-men.

Stonebreaking was a subsidiary occupation, and when the stones were collected from the fields by local women—who were paid miserably for the job—and dumped by the roadside, the stone-breakers grumbled, for Cotswold stone which has been exposed to the air for any length of time is harder to crack into small pieces than the new yellow brash from the surface quarries. Mending the road was a simple business of tumbling in as many stones as were necessary to fill the potholes and leaving the wheels of the carts and farm waggons to roll them in, and if the roadmender was careless or his stones were not broken small enough the result was no great improvement, for the wheels of passing carts displaced as many stones as they rolled. A conscientious mender, or one whose length was not too out of the way and likely to be visited regularly by the overseer, would also shovel small grit and fine dust into the holes with the stones, knowing that the rain would help cement them into place.

My memory of those dusty by-roads between the wars was of stifling dust in summer when the farm carts could be seen moving in a white cloud for quite a distance, and a sticky yellow morass in winter spraying mud all around as one walked.

Tales of accidents to coaches and their passengers can be found in the local newspapers of the period, and reading them today it is obvious that these became more than nine days' wonders and were remembered as great catastrophes in village history. There were doubtless older folk who bored their children with tales of the night of 3 December 1839, when the Gloucester and Stroud mails collided in thick fog. It was at a junction where their routes converged, and to make it more remarkable it is said they were the only two vehicles on the road at the time.

The Cotswold hills must have been treacherous in bad weather for these great unwieldy coaches, and this inspired several inventors to produce ingenious devices to minimise the perils of accidents. One was a tripping hook which released the horses from the shafts immediately a coach capsized; the terrified horses, plunging and kicking, were a serious hazard in all coach accidents. But this Patent Quick-Detaching Slip Hook was never taken up by the Postmaster-General or any firm of coaching proprietors, nor was there a rule prohibiting drunken drivers from taking the road, though if the novels of the period can be believed the amount of hot punch, gin, brandy and other fiery liquors consumed by the coachmen must have made them practically inflammable.

In Burford, at least, the effects may have been neutralised by the famous Burford 'bait', the name given to the gargantuan meals served in the coaching inns, though Burford had been famous for its meals before the coaches came to town. Haunches of venison, venison pies, venison roast and boiled provided by the deer in Wychwood Forest, at first by legitimate hunting and later by poaching, always played a big part in the diet. Charles East, who was born in 1837 and who was still living in Burford in 1934, told Mrs Gretton that when he was a boy he had seen half a dozen deer hanging in a Fulbrook back kitchen, and venison was on sale in the town at twopence and threepence a pound, poachers being almost as common in Wychwood as deer. He also told her that there were always postboys ready spurred waiting in the archway of the Bull.

The newspapers of the early 1800s tell of heroic deeds performed by coachmen and guards. These were rewarded, if at all, in a niggardly manner by the Postmaster-General. John Jelfs, the guard on a mail coach from Oxford to Gloucester, walked the remainder of the journey through snow and icy water with the mail-bags on his back when his coach got into difficulties because of snow and floods near Cirencester. He was given an extra five shillings wages that week, it being the policy of the Post Office to show their appreciation but not in too lavish a fashion lest it attracted the wrong kind of man to take the job. The official who reasoned out that piece of mean-fisted logic, one feels, was probably responsible for fining a guard, Thomas Sweatman, a shilling because the Chester mail was late. The reason for the delay was that Sweatman had been obliged to spend four hours up to his waist in water rescuing passengers and carrying out repairs when the coach stuck on a flooded road, 'after which it froze severely, and he came in that condition to London'. His passengers were a little more generous. They prepared a citation which earned him ten and sixpence.

Anyone who has travelled on frozen roads on Cotswold during a bad winter and felt the force of the icy wind across those bleak uplands will feel a pang of sympathy for the guard of the Gloucester Mail, whose fate was recorded in a Gloucester newspaper.

> The Gloucester Mail, which should have been in by 5 o'clock yesterday afternoon, was obliged to stop on the road, and the guard reached this town only at 1 o'clock this morning, having brought the bags along the beach. He was, however, so affected by the cold that he now lies in a dying state.

They were made of valiant stuff, these guards, and took their responsibilities seriously. Yet they never seem to have become idols like the coachmen, who caught the popular imagination from the beginning, being more highly-coloured in all aspects including their complexions. Their job was arduous enough, needing skill, courage and endurance to keep to the advertised schedules whatever the weather, and these men, who have been described as a mixture of 'gruffness, great-coats and old boots' took a tremendous pride in their timekeeping.

George Borrow, Washington Irving, Charles Dickens amongst others who described the coachmen of their day give the same composite picture. 'He has commonly a broad, full face, curiously mottled with red, as if the blood had been forced with hard feeding into every vessel of his skin; he is swelled into jolly dimensions by frequent potations of malt liquor, and his bulk is further increased by a multiplicity of coats, in which he is buried like a cauliflower....'

'He rolls about the inn-yard with an air of absolute lordliness,' wrote Washington Irving, while George Borrow gives a picture of 'the bang-up coachman', whose insolence was so great that he was hated 'by all the minor fry connected with coaches along the road, especially the ostlers'. Dickens gives a more intimate picture in Sam Weller's father, a coachman who, whatever his manner when in charge of his coach, was henpecked at home.

Hooper, a well-known coach-builder who must have known the coachmen well, gives a kindlier picture, calling them 'the life of the road' and 'professors of their art'. On the whole they treated their horses as hardly as they treated themselves, urging them on mercilessly when the coach was running late.

> I've heard an experienced coachman say
> It costs him more in whips than hay.

Certainly contemporary prints show the horses straining every nerve and muscle, with the coachman using his long whip to lash the leaders or his short 'tommy' urging the wheelers to greater efforts. Many a team of coach horses must have broken their hearts on the hills out of Burford, Cirencester and Stow, and the steep ascent to Birdlip.

There was little alternative employment for the coachmen when the railways finally swept the stage and mail coaches off the roads. A few could be absorbed into private service, but as one of them said: 'A coachman, if he really is one, is fit for nothing else.'

The romantic novelists deplored their passing. 'I wonder where they are, those good fellows,' wrote Thackery. 'Alas, we shall never hear the horn ring at midnight, or see the pike-gates fly open any more.'

The remark of the man in the Bull and Mouth inn yard lacked the sentimental touch when he was asked what had become of the coachmen. 'Some drive buses, some have crept into the country, but, like dead donkeys, we sees nothing on 'em.'

The redundant coachmen, ostlers and innkeepers would feel revenged today could they see Toddington station at the foot of the Cotswold escarpment amongst the orchards, fields and parkland. Not many years ago this was a pleasant country station where milk churns rattled and a leisurely porter attended to passengers and parcels. Now it is a desolate collecting-ground for superfluous railroad property brought here from the dead railroads of the district to await buyers, though it is hard to imagine who will find use for the enormous stacks of lengths of rail looking like the toys of giant children waiting to be fixed together, huge dumps of angle irons and other fitments whose names and uses are known only to trackmen. Monstrous screws and bolts litter the ground among heaps of lamp standards and brackets leaning together in rusty companies; a graveyard of old iron and other metals.

As the crow flies or an engine chuffs, Toddington is not far away from Adlestrop, another country station now derelict where Edward Thomas long ago heard a blackbird singing when his train drew up there

> . . . and round him, mistier
> Farther and farther, all the birds
> Of Oxfordshire and Gloucestershire.

Cirencester Town station opposite Cirencester Park, with its booking hall in mock Cotswold vernacular, is more fortunate. No longer at the end of the line—for the lines have already disappeared—it is being altered and modernized inside for use as offices, its façade also being cleaned and repainted, and will remain a quaint reminder of the railway era and probably, in days to come, a place of pilgrimage for railway enthusiasts who will take photographs of it in the same way as tourists from overseas today take pictures of coaching inns. I can even imagine an enterprising seller of post-cards and souvenirs dressing up a salesman or woman in the old porter's uniform, or on special occasions a station master's, old style, complete with top hat.

The birds still sing around Toddington and it is likely that if the stacks of rails remain there long enough a robin or a wren will build a nest in the gap between the layers. As to the railways, the indus-trial archaeologists have taken their memory in custody and they will be preserved neatly labelled as records of the past.

In the Cotswolds the coming of the railways did not put the smaller coaching concerns out of business immediately. They were still needed in those districts where the railways did not run. They rumbled on, serving as transport between railway stations and for villages whose stations were outside them until well into the twentieth century, and it is impossible to give precise dates when they finally went off the roads, though ironically it was at a time when roads had begun to improve, which would have made their passage easier. Some coaches once used on long runs were reconsti-

Cirencester Town station

tuted into waggonettes, and there are people today who can remember going on Sunday School outings in what was once a fly-waggon or coach.

For the people left unemployed there was plenty of work in the factory towns of the North and Midlands but there was no Welfare State to cushion the removal, and this, added to the countryman's natural reluctance to leave his home town or village, meant that the older workers, at least, relapsed into poverty, their dignity and independence sapped by the harsh Poor Laws and the anxiety of their more prosperous neighbours to keep down the rates. Eleven hundred acres of Burford Field were enclosed in 1795 and of these only about three hundred went to independent farmers, John Lenthall, lord of the manor and the Impropriator of the Rectorial Tithes receiving the rest. When the town was busy with the coaching trade the loss to the ordinary people of their common land and small holdings had not caused much hardship, but when the trade came to an end the loss of 'an acre and a cow', which had helped to feed many a family, became a tragedy.

Northleach, having no other industry, suffered badly also, falling back into an almost moribund state as it had done after the decline of the wool trade, and Stow and Moreton in Marsh were in the same plight. The big towns like Cheltenham and Gloucester could absorb a number of unemployed, Cheltenham with its seasonal influx of visitors coming to take the waters, and Gloucester with foundries and other industries. In the south Cotswolds the coaching trade had been subsidiary to the clothing trade, but it had helped to bring that extra touch of prosperity and recompense a little for the declining clothing trade. Painswick, where the first horse coach from Stroud to Cheltenham had come through the town and where the Plough Inn, now the Adam and Eve, had catered for the coaches, felt the pinch miserably.

In fact deterioration was creeping over most of the Cotswolds at this period, and the little towns and villages were to stay that way through the bad years of the late nineteenth century until the 1914 war gave agriculture as well as manufacture a spur, and the use of the motor-car began to open them up as tourist centres.

CHAPTER EIGHT

Cotswold woodlands

The beech trees of the Cotswolds are one of its greatest attractions, whether as rounded clumps or long narrow belts on the skyline, bringing out the subtle contours of the limestone ridges, or covering a steep hillside falling to a valley. They accord with the landscape at any season and there is always a harmony of colour, shape and texture between the flow of the hills and the upstanding grey columns holding up the green of spring and summer or autumn's rich colour. The pattern they make on or below the skyline gives emphasis to the bare uplands and the sweeping curves of the hillsides. They add strength as well as grace to the scene, and though their shade is dense in midsummer it never casts a depressing gloom. Every part, large and small, has a distinction of form and colour, the long elegantly-pointed buds enclosed in pointed overlapping brown scales, the silky hairs edging each leaf-blade that make haloes of light around them, the great branches coming off obliquely from massive trunks covered with smooth grey bark that glistens like polished pewter. The grey of boles and limbs takes the revealing upland light with as many variations as Cotswold stone. It is Cotswold colour until late autumn sets the canopies on fire and covers the ground at their feet with the same intense russet glow smouldering well into the dark days of winter.

The ash, the other tree most associated with the Cotswold scene also has a bark with a silvery lustre, but as it usually grows in mixed woodland with undergrowth it plays a lesser part in the Cotswold pattern. It does form pure ash woods on shallow soil, as at Witcombe and Stanway and on the steep sides of the small plateau valleys of the Coln and Windrush and, before recent reafforestation, at Chedworth. Ash trees need light and the beech casts a shade which the ash cannot tolerate, so unless the forester intervenes the beech becomes the dominant tree.

Cotswold woodlands

The native Cotswold woods are of the oak-ash-beech type with beech as the climax vegetation, and the Stroud valley hillsides from Chalford to Sapperton are a good illustration of this, showing the gradual elimination of the oak to ash as the ground rises and the soil becomes drier and lighter, culminating in beech on the highest ground.

It is noticeable also how pure beech wood monopolizes the best soil and aspect. Its surface root system and dense canopy enable it to suppress undergrowth and it reduces the shrubs and lower layers of vegetation until only a few thin grasses survive beneath it. And so we get the trunks of the beech reaching upward unobscured by the fret of other patterns to spoil the sculptural effect. This quality makes a beech clump at any season a perfect finish to a rounded hilltop, and the eighteenth-century squires who embellished their estates in this way not only enriched the inheritance of their descendants but enriched us all.

The characteristic Cotswold beech woods are western outliers of chalk down beech woods, and are concentrated on the inferior oolite of the upper slopes and tops of the escarpment. Natural beech is here at its western limit and is only able to maintain itself in any quantity over an area from Birdlip in the north to a little beyond Dursley in the south. Beech woods south of this area are usually found around country mansions and were planted when it was the fashion for landowners to landscape their estates, encouraged by the writers of the day. Fielding, in *Tom Jones,* has a passage which shows how much a part of eighteenth-century country life this landscaping had become.

> . . . In some of these, art chiefly engages our admiration while we admire the wondrous powers of art in improving nature; in others, nature and art contend for our applause, but in the last, the former seems to triumph. . . .

The finest natural beech woods are at Cranham, and it is significant that the high ground between Cranham and Dursley is the wettest part of east Gloucestershire, thus helping to develop a deeper layer of humus and a richer soil. Other trees cannot endure the intense competition of the beech roots which fill the soil with their fine fibres, draining it of moisture so that any other vegetation suffers from drought, especially on shallow soil. So it would appear that rainfall, soil, and their own dense leafage are the reason for this distribution of Cotswold beech woods. That the richer soil of this area is an important factor can be seen by contrasting it with the woods at Witcombe and Stanway Ash, where only a thin layer of humus covers the ground; here ash is abundant.

The planting of trees to improve a landscape or make a new one began to be practised deliberately when a new landowning class took over land belonging to the religious houses after the Dissolution, but it did not reach its peak until nearly two centuries later. The Enclosure Acts were a great spur to tree planting.

Kip's drawing of Dyrham Park shows the Italian influence on seventeenth-century pleasure grounds and is a good example of a geometrical design made up of trees radiating in straight avenues from a centre, and others in rectangular blocks and strict rows, a pattern which became the ambition of wealthy aristocrats when improving their estates. This influence, alien to the English conception of the countryside, soon fell out of favour; the Great Parterre at Blenheim, for example, covering some forty acres, was done away with less than fifty years after planting, to be replaced by a more 'natural' scheme. The romantic landscape paintings of Claude and Poissin helped to bring this about, while the invention of the sunken fence or ha-ha by Bridgeman led the way to an opening out rather than an enclosing of the scene. Not only the area surrounding the mansion had to be landscaped, but the middle and sometimes the far distance as well, to provide a series of vistas in which a single group of trees rather than formal blocks provided focussing points.

Two men who influenced Cotswold woodland at the end of the eighteenth century were William Marshall and Humphrey Repton, whose books were to be found in every country gentleman's library. Marshall wrote *On Planting and Rural Ornament, A Practical Treatise of Planting*; *A Review of Landscape and an Essay on the Picturesque*, as well as books on agriculture. He was more occupied with the details of management of farm and woods, listing rabbits as woodland pests except when enclosed in warrens, and giving advice about soils and cultivation; a practical man less interested in 'good taste' than Repton.

Humphrey Repton saw landscapes as compositions; there were rules to be followed and his clients were expected to understand their subtleties. He wrote many treatises on the theory and practice of landscape gardening, as well as his famous red books with the drawings of 'Before and After'. He was concerned mainly with the pictorial aspect of woodland and advocated planting trees in groupings, disliking the spotted effect of single trees. He favoured uneven clumps underplanted with thorns, slopes covered with trees to emphasize the valleys below them, and broken belts of trees on the periphery of a scene rather than continuous lines, and it is to him we owe some of the more urbane and enchanting parkland still remaining from the eighteenth century.

Every gentleman was expected to be knowledgeable about improving the appearance of his estate and showing natural features to the best advantage, even if it meant moving some of them and importing others. And he was also expected to understand the prevailing rules of taste. The conversations in Jane Austen's novels, particularly *Mansfield Park*, give one some idea of this interest.

As the next century advanced the creative landscape phase began to die out. Rich men found other ways of spending their money. The wealthy clothiers of Cotswold began to feel the pinch as the trade declined. As I have said, not all the results of this planning have disappeared. There are still places where we pay our half-crowns willingly to walk in the wide parkland admiring the noble trees and to wander among the groves and dells so cunningly set with little streams or placid lakes, marvelling that men made this beauty for their own delight and must have felt like gods shaping another paradise as they contrived water-courses and removed, if not mountains, many thousands of tons of rock and earth from one spot to another to fashion a new prospect.

The nineteenth-century explorers and travellers brought home many species of new trees, and as nothing can divorce the Englishman from his planting, and to possess a rare shrub or tree gives pleasure for its own sake as well as by impressing the neighbours, the big Cotswold estates benefited with the rest of the country. At first rare trees were placed singly in the pleasure grounds, with little thought to their place in the scene as a whole, but William Robinson taught that the new must be made to harmonize with the old, and so landscape planting took on a new vision. The day of the great panorama was over; in its place the arrangement of thousands of species of shrubs and trees was the ideal, and nowhere on Cotswold, or on its edge, can this be seen more exquisitely carried out than at Westonbirt.

It was these plantings which saved the countryside from desolation when so much woodland planted in the eighteenth century was felled during the first world war. Much of this has now been re-planted, not always in a manner which has resulted in a true harmony between woods and countryside. There was too much eagerness to plant for quick returns, unlike the old landowners who planted for their great-great grandchildren and were satisfied that it should be so. Also there was no longer the cheap money or cheap labour available.

Forestry under such different conditions and in a modern world impoverished by war had to go through a testing process; and it is only in recent years that a conception of its function, in the broad sense of the relationship of trees to the countryside as a whole, has become accepted. The Forestry Commission has planted over a million acres in Britain during the last forty years, with the pressure for land for other purposes increasing all the time, so that it has not always been possible to fit the woods to the landscape.

The eighteenth-century parkland as its trees grew to maturity has been described as the most beautiful man-made landscape in the world. We shall never again see mansions, each surrounded by hundreds of acres of land, being built for separate families, however wealthy, but new, bold, imaginative schemes of planting in open places combined with public buildings, universities and schools could take their place and become their modern equivalent.

Dr Jones, in a digest of information relevant to British forestry between the years 1790 and 1810, published by the Board of Agriculture, points out that it was not until the last quarter of the eighteenth century that planting of woodland was widespread throughout the country. In the Cotswolds most planting was on a small scale around 'the seats of the gentry', who, having acquired more land by the Enclosures, began to plant windbreaks, ornamental woodland, and cover for game. Many of the long narrow lines of beeches along the roads were planted to take in the excess width of old droves previously unconfined, which over the years had spread out as the surface became too rough and travellers had made a new track beside the old. One of the signs looked for by anyone interested in old roads and wanting to discover if a track existed before the Enclosures is a narrow beech grove. There are fewer today, as in many instances the beeches have died of old age or have been felled and conifers planted in their place, thus giving the scene a less benign aspect than when the tall, grey beech trunks with their changing canopies stood up on a Cotswold skyline.

Cotswold was never forest country. It had the forest land of Wychwood on the Oxfordshire border, the Forest of Dean and areas of Wiltshire forest coming up to its west and northern borders, but high Cotswold was open country, champagne country as the old writers called it. Nevertheless the Cotswolds in the late eighteenth century and throughout the nineteenth were much more wooded than they are today, as can be seen from the early Ordnance and estate maps. Not only were the hillsides covered with beeches and natural forest growth, but there were pockets of scrub and rough woodland, often on thin soil. Many of these were cleared and the ground ploughed during the first world war, and since then most of this marginal land has come under cultivation. The introduction of ploughing subsidies, bulldozers, the general use of artificial fertilizers have played their part.

Not everyone delights in this cleaning-up process. I remember a Gloucestershire botanist telling me sadly how, when he came to look for rare Cotswold woodland plants recorded before 1850, many of the stations had disappeared not only out of sight but out of mind, their names forgotten even by local people. He found one elderly man who knew the name of a small lost wood because a local man had hanged himself there.

On one occasion I was looking for a triangle of coppice near where four upland tracks used to meet, but it had completely vanished. Some fifteen years earlier I had found a rare lily in the coppice. I asked an old man watching me from the gate of his cottage garden how long ago the wood had been felled. 'A lily used to grow there', I explained, knowing that one way to persuade a taciturn countryman to talk is to offer him a piece of information in return. His eyes brightened when I spoke.

'The only words me and my missis ever had was about them lilies. She'd be for ever rushing out chasing the kids away who came to pick 'em. She kind of took care of them. I dug up a clump and put them in the garden when they cut the trees down but they never came up another year. They was wild, see, and didn't take kindly to garden life.'

In an official report dealing with the values and prices of timber in the early nineteenth century, ash and beech, the two trees most common to Cotswold at that time, were a half to three-quarters the value of oak. In the beech woods the timber was often converted on the spot into 'scantlings' for gun stocks, saddle trees, bedsteads and chairs. Beech is a wood for indoor use, it does not stand up to the weather outdoors. Close-grained and hard, it can be worked across the grain and is particularly good for piano-making as less likely to warp under strain or change of temperature. It was used for making peels—those long-handled shovels used for bread-ovens—and the old-fashioned countryman often made his own or inherited one made by his father or grandfather.

In some districts hoops for barrels were made from the ash, and these were exported to the West Indies for sugar hogsheads, this particular market being supplied by those parts of Gloucester-shire easily accessible by road and water to the port of Bristol. The bast of lime trees, known as 'whitten' or 'whitrod', was used for the making of ropes for cider-presses, well-ropes and fishing boats, having the advantage of not stretching or shrinking when wet. It was not, however, a Cotswold trade, but belonged more to those parts of Gloucestershire that border upon Hereford.

Natural woodland, that is woodland that has been left to itself, has become almost extinct since 1916, when all woods suffered from wartime needs and were often felled indiscriminately. Even the pure beech woods of high Cotswold are now under foresters' con-trol. Woods exist nowadays for the primary purpose of growing timber, and much research has gone into finding out what species will flourish in particular soils and how by the right treatment they can produce economic stands.

The first objective after the depletion of war was to lay down a reserve for future emergencies, to plant the kind of trees that would bring in a quick return in cash, not only to pay for the effort ex-pended but to provide capital for future planting. But as the science of silviculture advances it becomes more alive to the science of the amenities, which has its own economics and can be profitable in pleasure as well as hard cash when rightly understood and de-veloped. It is senseless to cover every available square yard with trees when a few open spaces, vistas cut, especially on high land, to reveal the view, can turn a commercial forest into one of changing beauty and interest. In the eighteenth century the landowners created landscape for their own delight and prestige, today they have the opportunity of creating it for everybody. Unknowingly, landscape gardening has been going on in England for ages, and the work of the great gardeners of the late eighteenth century was only a conscious phase of removing all trace of wildness and domesticating the English scene. The latest developments of forest management and control have it in their power to alter the landscape to a much greater degree and very much faster.

A tour around Cotswold today shows how this is already happening; it shows as well that the aim is to keep the character of the Cotswold scene as far as is compatible with utility. In the north, on the exposed edge of the hills near Cutsdean, in woods managed by the Forestry Commission, beech planted in shade on soil with an average depth of only two inches made good growth, but where there was no shade it failed or remained stationary, the young trees not being able to withstand the sun scorch and the lack of water caused by the thin porous soil, driving winds on this exposed site drying up the moisture too quickly.

A few miles north-west of Cutsdean the Stanway estate in 1952–3 planted rows of larch and beech intermittently in an area of scrub on a north-westerly slope where the elevation was 400–500 feet. The planting had been made along the contour line, so that the beech received some protection from the winds coming up from the Severn valley. On the lower slopes it can be seen how the beech has held its own with the larch, but higher up the slope the beech has not done so well, obviously for the same reason as at Cutsdean, lack of shade and scorching winds.

In another part of the estate a sixteen-acre plot of hazel scrub had been planted with beech after cutting back all growth between so that light shade was left, and it was hoped this would prove more successful, though when once established the beech would need more light to maintain proper growth and careful supervision would be needed to keep the hazel in check. The hazel could not be removed by bulldozing because here again there were only two inches of topsoil and bulldozing would expose the rock beneath. Ring barking to kill the hazel could not be employed because the effect would be unsightly, and being on the border of the Cotswolds the estate was fully alive to its responsibilities for preserving the amenities.

It will be seen by this that not only is it difficult to establish new beech woods but that the Cotswold foresters are determined not to spoil the landscape. The Stanway estate includes 556 acres of dedicated woodland, and 400 acres are leased to the Forestry Commis-

14. Cotswold roof showing slates (Chapter 9)

15. Windrush spring, Lower Guiting (Chapter 10)

16. Tortworth chestnut (Chapter 11)

sion. Its woods suffered severely from indiscriminate felling during the two wars and are now beginning to recover.

Of the 4,000 acres of Lord Vestey's Stowell Park, 1,000 acres are woodland. They provide all the timber needed on the estate for fencing, heating, farm trailers and so on, as well as sport and amenity. One of the first jobs to be tackled after the war was the establishment of plantations to screen from the house the remains of a temporary war hospital, not so many years ago an unsightly litter of huts that had been left to fall into ruin. Scots pine, Norway spruce, larch, ash, oak, beech and sycamore were the main species used for this purpose. The site is a dry one, a thin layer of soil over brash with a rank growth of grass intercepting much of the summer moisture, and a breeding place for voles who do considerable damage to young growth. It remains to be seen which trees do best on this ground.

The belt of beech and larch nearly four miles long, planted some 150 years ago along the Foss Way as shelter and to enhance the borders of the estate, is today falling into rapid decline. This long line of trees, familiar not only to travellers this century but to earlier travellers by stage coach as they came up the hill from the Northleach prison crossroads and on to the Puesdown Inn, is also one of the old Cotswold landmarks seen on the skyline for many a mile on all sides. Restocking is with beech again with some larch and Thuja, and a narrow strip of the less decrepit trees will be left for shade and shelter until the new ones are established. Fortunately natural seedlings are plentiful. The narrow strip of old trees will not only help re-establishment of the new but keep the familiar outline of the Foss for a few years longer. There is another mile-long belt of beeches along the Puesdown track shading the way the earlier coaches took above Hampnett to avoid the miry Leach valley and the narrow stony road through Northleach.

Grey squirrels are the enemies of beech plantings. They bark the young stems, killing or deforming them. The job of getting rid of this pest needs constant vigilance and patience. They live and take refuge in the old beech stands which have been left because of their amenity value. When Cotswold foresters get together, sooner or later the talk turns to the way of getting rid of grey squirrels. Deer, who also do considerable damage to plantations, can be fenced out and controlled more easily.

A beech wood is always a joyous sight to a lover of Cotswold, and the woods at Ebworth and Kingscote in the south are two places where they can be seen at their best. Those at Ebworth are mostly about eighty years old. The old trees have been felled, one area providing 50,000 rifle-butts during the war. In another area from which the old trees have been felled one tall beech has been left standing, a splendid specimen that delights the eye with its clean upstanding trunk of some forty-five feet. The owner of the wood, Mr F. E. Workman, a man of imagination, left it standing to remind him of the others which once stood there. One has only to hear Mr. Workman talk about beech to realise his great love and profound knowledge of its management.

Frith Wood, not far away and belonging to the same estate, is a pure beech wood some 170 years old. It is now being thinned out, for it was heavily stocked, there being about 340 stems to the acre according to foresters' counting. This close growth seems in no way to have affected the health of the trees, and to walk along the wide track the owner has made through the middle of the wood is an experience no tree-lover could forget.

Kingscote Wood covers some 200 acres and the main part of it once held magnificent beeches planted around 1810, the young trees coming from the Forêt de Soignes, near Waterloo. Part of it was felled during the first world war and the rest of the trees, except for some thirty acres, went to help make gliders and small fighters in the second world war. Since then the eighteen remaining acres have been closely watched and the growth of the trees recorded. The recording began in 1947, when over a thousand were numbered in readiness and their timber height and volume estimated. In the following years they were again measured and it was shown that the trees continued to grow at a consistent rate of 2 per cent per year by volume. At today's valuation of £1,000 per acre these figures must show how beauty and value in a woodland go together, and that the aesthetically pleasing can be economically pleasing as well.

Lineover and Dowdeswell Woods, east of Cheltenham, cover some 280 acres and are part of the catchment area of the Dowdeswell Reservoir, situated on slopes whose altitudes range from 400 to 900 feet, the soil of the upper parts consisting of the usual oolitic brash covered with a very thin layer of topsoil, the lower parts being of Cotswold sands and lias. As well as limiting the erosion of the soil into the reservoir, the trees add greatly to the attractions of the place and it is the intention of the North-West Gloucestershire Water Board that they should continue to do so. In 1953 a plan of operations was drawn up to ensure this, and the two woods came under an approved scheme.

Before 1953 they consisted mainly of hardwood coppice, growth left after the fellings of 1939–45, and the new plan is to turn this area by degrees into high forest without making large clearings that would denude the ground. Good ash, oak and elm standards have been left and underplanted with a variety of shade-bearing conifers and beech.

A feature of Lineover Wood is an attempt at beech-seed germination from mother trees on the spot, the bare soil being conditioned to receive the seed by having the lop and top of fellings spread over it so that the debris will improve the soil and provide conditions favourable to germination. Already a weed and grass invasion shows that the soil is being enriched, and the result of the experiment is being carefully watched. This method of regenerating beech woods means that the soil must be cultivated as the mast falls, covering it from its chief enemies, pigeons and mice, who find it a favourite source of food.

This is also being tried at Buckholt Wood, Cranham, a National Nature Reserve and a beech wood for many centuries. This is an area where beech grows naturally and has continued throughout the years in the face of common rights. The attempts to regenerate beech woods by natural means is of fairly recent origin, it having been a regular practice for at least 200 years to buy the seed from the Continent and sow it in nurseries. Beech seedlings take unkindly to chalk or limestone soils and need light and shelter if they are to grow into saplings of any size. It is seldom one finds self-sown seedlings more than a year or so old under beech trees. After a good crop of mast hundreds of nuts will germinate, but the tiny plants vanish if the ground has not been prepared for them.

Like all other Cotswold woods, Buckholt and the adjoining Witcombe Wood suffered severely from wartime felling and subsequent unavoidable neglect, and putting the woods in order meant drastic action. There was much local dismay recently because heavy felling was changing the aspect of this ancient woodland, so it was decided not to clear on a large scale but to work in small groups thinning pole crops to favour beech. In 1965 gaps and thickets of ash and sycamore were being planted with beech, the work being undertaken by volunteers of the Conservation Corps of the Gloucestershire Trust for Nature Conservation. These volunteers are mostly apprentices from Gloucestershire factories, students and members of youth organizations led by an experienced woodman. They enjoy the open air and exercise and have the satisfaction of knowing they are helping to keep in existence a national ecological monument. In other words they are enriching the Cotswolds as well as themselves. The necessary felling of overmature trees has left the woods lightly stocked, but in time they will again be filled with tall beeches. As the woods are dedicated one need not fear for their survival.

The hills of the south-west are more deviously cut than those of the north and there are many small valleys where the hillsides are too steep for ploughing and forestry is the only way to utilise them. These slopes have been wooded for centuries, most of them planted with beech in the eighteenth century on the site of natural woodland and scrub. Because of the need for quick cash returns during the farming slumps of the early twentieth century many were cleared and replanted with larch. As this is felled, beech with conifers is again being introduced. Mr John Workman, forestry adviser to the National Trust, shows how these slopes can become profitable and also enhance the landscape. 'On the long scarp banks of the Cotswold valleys wood could and should be cut and re-stocked in well-defined coupes,' he says, going on to point out that the vistas the fellings provide change in the course of years, 'and this itself is a pleasant feature of a landscape in which active forestry has long played a part'.

CHAPTER NINE

Cotswold roofs

The stone-tiled roofs of Cotswold play a great part in the attractive appearance of its traditional buildings. Darker in colour because of exposure to weather and the lichens their coarser grain collects with each passing season, they make the perfect climax to the paler greys of the rest of the fabric. While keeping to a general pattern and laid in sizes according to their position on the roof, their shapes are not mechanically uniform and this breaks up the monotony of the surface so that the eye dwells on it with pleasure, recognizing the right material used in the right place.

Stone tiles or slates usually came from their own quarries, and though every village once had its communal quarry the places where good slating stone was dug were not so common. Guiting and Eyford, near Stow, were famous for their roofing slates, not only in the north Cotswolds but far beyond the region. Professor Thorold Rogers has recorded fissile stones as roofing slates being brought from Guiting to other parts of the country as far back as the Middle Ages.

One must remember that the use of the word 'slate' for rocks that possess 'slaty cleavage' is recent and due to the geologist; the older builders used the word for any stone which split naturally into tile-like layers. The many Roman villas discovered on the Cotswolds were roofed with Cotswold slates, though not all came from the hills. The tiles once covering the roman villa at Wood-chester were made from a dark gritty stone from the Forest of Dean.

All stone slates are heavy and require strong roof timbers and careful fixing on the roof. The stone must also be quarried at the right time of year and in the right fashion and be well-seasoned before use. If these conditions are complied with a stone-slatted roof will last indefinitely. Guy Dawber, in his *Old Cottages in the*

Cotswold District, asserts that houses and barns two hundred years or more old still stand covered with their original roofing.

Stone tile quarries are sometimes mentioned in early manorial records, and Tyley Bottom near Wotton-under-Edge probably got its name from tile pits now overgrown by trees. We know stone tiles were used by the Romans, but E. S. Lindley offers evidence suggesting that they continued to be used after the Romans left Britain, contrary to the general belief that for several succeeding centuries no buildings of any quality were erected. Part of a Saxon charter, defining the bounds of a grant in 'Wudetun'—Wotton—reads:

> Aerest of thaem Aesce and long Aege on Tigel Leage.

Grundy translates this as

> First from the Ashtree along the top of the Ridge
> Slope to the Lea where Tiles are made.

The present-day Ashel Barn could imply the former presence of the mark-ash of the charter, the Ridge Slope being the ridge that was followed by the Old London Road. The valley to the south of the ridge is Tyley Bottom, and Ekwall's interpretation of Tigel Leage is Tyley Bottom. Tile Pitts are often mentioned as a landmark and as being rented in manorial documents going back to 1540.

The main area of the workings is now covered by Tile Plantation, but a big pit is marked adjoining the boundary road, and land on the other side of the road is also pitted. If Tigel Leage is what we know today as Tile Pits—where stone slates or tiles were quarried—then they must have been worked before or at the time the charter was made. Grundy dates the charter about 940, but considers it may be a copy of an earlier document. Though traditional memory is long, the five centuries which must have elapsed between the Roman working of the pits and the making of the charter seems a long time for the pits to have been remembered as a source of roofing tiles, especially when the conditions in the country were so fluid, so it does seem possible that stone was being taken from the pits after the Romans left.

The Roman-British slates were usually hexagonal, but a later and more usual shape has the 'tail' of the slates cut square and the head left a rough oval. They come in several sizes, but according to Professor Thorold Rogers the slates from the famous Stonesfield quarries in the Middle Ages were in three sizes only, common large, middling, and large. He suggests that slate-making was a by-industry of the Oxfordshire quarries and that the quarrymen, when the demand for building stone was slack, employed their time in splitting, dressing and boring such stone as was suitable.

Guy Dawber gives a description of how the slates are obtained from the quarries.

> In October a piece of ground at the quarry is measured off, and the upper eight or ten feet of loose brash is cleared away, this process being called 'riddling'. The 'pendal', as the stone for the slates is called, is then uncovered and wheeled to the top of the ground, laid down flat, and roughly fitted together as nearly as it will allow, in thicknesses varying from two to twelve or fourteen inches, just as it comes from the quarry. It has then to lie and wait for the winter frosts, which swell the beds of natural moisture in the 'pendal', and when a thaw sets in a few blows of the hammer soon separate the layers, which are then cut to the size required and sorted ready for use. But should the winter be mild, the stone has to wait till the following year.

Huntsmen's Quarries along Buckle Street is an example of the rough ground which results from tile-quarrying, an area of uneven hollows and shallow pits where under the matted cushions of wild thyme and rockrose one could still find a debris of broken layers of stone. Many of these areas of 'gruffy' ground, as it is called locally, however, are now being ploughed or used for plantations, but one can sometimes discover an old tile quarry by a field name.

Every village and small town once had its slaters. In John Smith's list of 1608 of all men in Gloucestershire who could bear arms four 'slatters' are listed for Chipping Campden; their job was not only to fix the slates to the roofs but probably to get the slates out of the quarry. This was a specialist job, for the stone must be split along lines parallel to the bedding planes and measured with a 'slat rule' or 'wippet stick'. There were no written measurements, but scratched symbols showed what size of slate had its specific place on the roof. A Cotswold slatter also had to cut his slates or valley stones to a triangular shape and then arrange them with a good overlap to make the swept valleys water-tight.

The tile quarries at Kineton Thorns, near Guiting, go back to ancient times and have been opened and closed many times throughout the centuries. It was here in the 1920s that I found an ancient slate, diamond-shaped like those belonging to the Winchcombe Roman villas. Two kinds of slate were made at Kineton Thorns, one from pendle, the unseasoned stone left for the winter frosts to work upon, and the other from the thin-layered stone which the slatter splits with his narrow pick to make into 'presents', that is tiles which do not need the frost seasoning but will endure without this process if quarried at the right time of year.

The slates are graded, the smaller ones under the roof ridge and increasing in size as they descend. A cubic wooden rule is used for measuring, with a nail at the head corresponding to the nail-hole in the slate. The rule has grooves cut in it measuring inches and half-inches. In the old days each size had a name which varied slightly from district to district, so that it was possible to tell by the names he used which part of the Cotswolds the slatter came from.

In the north Cotswolds the slates used under the eaves were called Cussomes or Top-eaves, those next in size being known as Followers. A slat-rule illustrated in Margaret Westerling's *Country Contentments* gives some twenty-six names for different sizes, most of them bearing a number preceded by Short or Long, but there are also Long Pricks, Long Cuttings, Short Becks, Middle Becks, Short Wivetts and Long Wivetts, and two with the intriguing names of Long and Short Bachelor. Duchesses and Countesses are still familiar today and I was once given Movedays and Cocks by a shy young slater who said he had no idea what they meant but that he had them from his grandfather who had taught him the trade. Wivetts and Bachelors are included in the list of slate-names given by the seventeenth-century writer Randle Holme, but his Rogue-why-Winkest-thou, Jenny-why-gettest-thou, his Farwells, Chilts and Warnetts seem to have vanished from the slate-makers' vocabulary, and it is difficult to imagine anyone using them nowadays without the fear of being thought long-winded and pretentiously olde-worlde.

CHAPTER TEN

Cotswold fulling-mills

One is apt to think that cloth manufacture on a large commercial scale in the Cotswolds began in the second half of the seventeenth century, but there is plenty of evidence to show that it was a relatively profitable and important industry as early as the fourteenth century and even before. Nor was it concentrated entirely in biggish towns such as Cirencester, Gloucester and Bristol, for it was well established in rural areas before the decline of the Gilds and the emergence of the domestic system under the clothiers.

Few traces of the medieval fulling-mills remain, though some of their stones may have become incorporated into the fabric of the mills which came after them; the evidence comes from rental books of religious houses and other old documents still in existence. Painswick, Wotton-under-Edge, Dursley, Minchinhampton and other places in the Stroudwater valley were using fulling-mills several centuries before they became clothing towns of any size, and many a Cotswold hamlet and village situated on a stream was once busy with the fulling of cloth for export to distant places. Today they show no signs of having been employed in anything but agriculture.

Fulling-mills would not be needed for the homespun of the villagers. This was done by treading, or 'fulled under fote' as Piers Plowman put it. The mills would be built in districts where cloth was made in such quantities as would make the use of mechanical devices necessary. Long after fulling-mills were well established treading or walking the cloth was carried on for local use.

The earliest mention of them is to be found in Dugdale's *Monasticon Anglicanum* where one learns that two fulling-mills were built by the Knights Templars at Barton on the upper Windrush near Temple Guiting. Fosbrooke in his *History of Gloucestershire* says that the Templars made them before the year 1175, 'one of which was rented for 32s, the other for 12s', a considerable rent for those days and showing that Temple Guiting must have been an early centre of wool manufacture, just as it was for stone tiles, and played an important part in the economy of the Templars' estate there. It was probably one of the first places on the Cotswolds to have a mechanical process installed. The mills were still working in 1327, when the Bishop of Hereford, then lord of the manor, rendered an account of his stewardship to Edward III.

Fulling was performed by wooden hammers operated by a water-wheel, and anyone who remembers the Windrush at Guiting before the hillside springs which fed it at that place were tapped for a water supply will understand how easily the tremendous weight of water could have served the water-wheels. The hammers beat upon the newly woven cloth after it had been soaped, folded and placed in troughs through which ran the clear water night and day until the fibres of the wool were felted together. All cloth of any quality had to go through this process, cloth that is, made for the use of ladies and gentlemen and for export. A rougher, coarser material for the common folk was not usually subjected to this process but was fulled by being laid in the stream and trodden by the fuller, a slow, laborious task. This being so, a knowledge of the location of old fulling-mills gives a good idea of the distribution of the industry in the Cotswolds; a very large percentage of these were owned by the religious houses and rented out. Many of the monasteries, however, had their own mills and fuller brethren to work in them, making cloth for their own use. There must have been a concentration of spinners, weavers, burlers and other finishers living in the neighbourhood to keep the mills supplied.

Winchcombe was a notable centre of manufacture in the fourteenth century. The *Lanboc*, a mine of information about the economy of Winchcombe Abbey, gives an example early in the century when the Abbey acquired a fulling-mill belonging to Will Aderwyne, of Cotes-juxta-Winchcombe, and by inserting clauses in their tenants' leases that grist mills were not to be converted to fulling-mills, prevented competition with their own fulling trade. We hear of a John Blundell who received 8d damages when the monks diverted some of the water which served his mill to their own, a common cause of complaint in medieval times and a reason for many a prolonged suit. In 1377 tolls were being levied upon alum, woad, wool and teazels, showing that there must have been a considerable manufacture of cloth in the area. Winchcombe's St Kenelm's Fair, held on 28 July, was the occasion for the selling of cloth, and the little town also had a Gild-hall and a Booth-hall. Weavers, dyers and fullers are included in fourteenth-century lists of its inhabitants.

The famous woollen manufacturer of Winchcombe was John Smallwood, or John of Winchcombe, afterwards known as Jack of Newbury, one of the earliest capitalist clothiers, who finally settled in Berkshire, building himself a Tudor mansion at Bucklebury after Henry VIII sold him Bucklebury Manor, some say as a reward for leading a band of a hundred of his own men at Flodden Field. Fuller describes him as 'the most considerable clothier (without fancy or fiction) England ever had'. John Smallwood achieved this position by his own efforts and might be used as an example of a working lad who made good, though his greatest prosperity came after he had moved to Newbury and married his master's widow. His cloths gained a high reputation at home and abroad and Protector Somerset was advised by the English envoy at Antwerp to discharge a debt by sending 'a thousand of Winchcombe's kersies'. His mansion was burnt down in 1830, but the property still belongs to a descendant of the Winchcombe family, and there is a fascinating rebus carved on the wall of St Mary's Church representing a little wheelwright turning a winch and holding a comb. As late as the end of the seventeenth century Jack of Newbury was the chief figure in a pageant of the Cloth-workers of London.

By the end of the thirteenth century cloth manufacture was well established in the Stroudwater district, which was one of the reasons that it became exempt in later centuries when the Gilds tried to prevent the drift of the trade to country areas. Thomas de Rodborough had a fulling-mill at Brimscombe, another at Thrupp and one on the Little Avon belonging to Kingswood Abbey, and there were mills on the Frome at Walbridge and Dudbridge. At Walbridge traces of this early mill still remain, as well as parts of the various clothing mills which followed in the sixteenth, seventeenth and eighteenth centuries, though it is almost impossible to pick them out with any certainty.

The exposition of the Minchinampton Custumal gives nine men who were paying rental of twopence for fuller's earth diggings, and in 1418 John Bygge leased two mills at Walbridge. A new form of short lease for three or four lives of mill-streams in the Stroud-water area gives the names of tenants of numerous fulling-mills in the early fifteenth century. At Beverstone Church, not many miles away, Fosbrooke records that he saw fourteenth-century wall-paintings representing carding devices and other implements used in woollen manufacture, which suggests that the area was greatly engaged in the industry. Woodchester poll-tax records show two fullers and a weaver in 1380–1, while in the manor of Minchin-hampton it was the custom that a homeless weaver might make an enclosure from common land for a house and garden, and the 'weaver's assart' became a recognized part of the landscape there.

There was a fulling-mill at Hawkesbury in 1270, in the Kilcot valley on a tributary of the Little Avon, a forerunner of the many clothing mills which flourished by these waters some five centuries later. Here the tenants were obliged to pay fines if they fulled their cloth at any other mill but the one belonging to the lord of the manor, the income from the mill being a valuable part of the estate. All these instances show a vigorous trade supplying cloth that was not merely for local use.

It is difficult to assess the amount of cloth made outside the city of Bristol from the totals of exported cloth in the thirteenth, four-teenth and fifteenth centuries, but it is plain that not all of it could have been made within the city itself and a considerable quantity must have come from country areas outside. Evidence that there was a large amount of traffic coming in can be seen from the fact that in 1317 Edward III granted to the Mayor and Bailiffs twopence on every trussel of cloth brought in by cart, and in 1334 a half-penny on every horseload. In 1393 Thomas Atte Hay, a burgess and one of the founders of the Gild of St Katherine—a weaver's guild—left the sum of £20 for repairing roads between Bristol and Gloucester and between Bristol and Almondsbury, and as he was an exporter of cloth one can explain that his interest in these particular roads sprang from the fact that he was one of the merchants who bought cloths from the country weavers and knew from the ex-perience of his own journeys the need for road repairs, though as road-making and repairing was one of the pious offerings en-couraged by the Church at that time, this might not be the chief reason for his bequest.

The accounts of the collectors of customs for the port of Bristol give us details of the export of cloth, and those of 1341–2 give the

Margaret of Bristol, *Mighel* of Bristol, *Christopher* of Bristol, with others, as being loaded with cloth only. Bayonne, Portugal, Spain are all named as their destination. The Bristol Records Society in its Accounts of the Custom of Cloth of Scarlet and other Cloth in Grain and Beds of Worsted exported from Bristol, 29 September 1390–29 September 1391, show that Gascony and Aquitaine took 2,143 of the 7,017 cloths exported during the year. Portugal comes next with 1,887 cloths, and Spain only took 155 cloths. Ireland took 1,230 and the remainder went in smaller lots to various destinations. On their return from France the ships often brought woad and were one of the chief sources of supply for this dyestuff.

CHAPTER ELEVEN

The Tortworth chestnut

An ancient tree down the centuries can become as much an object of interest and pilgrimage as any other ancient monument. The fact that it is a living antiquity, even though much 'eroded by the jaws of time', gives it a special claim, if only as a proof of nature's persistency. Age and not beauty makes the appeal.

At Tortworth, about three miles west of Wotton-under-Edge, Cotswold can show an historic tree, the Tortworth Chestnut (*Castanea sativa*), marked as an ancient monument on the 1945 edition of the 1-inch Ordnance Survey map. There may be yew trees older than this sweet chestnut, but no other species in England can show a tree known to have been in existence some four or five hundred years ago and still living. Travellers of old delighted to describe it, and for some 250 years it has gathered legends around itself so that it is difficult today to distinguish myth from truth.

The fourth edition of Evelyn's *Sylva*, published in 1706, is the source of the story that the tree was living in the reign of King Stephen, but this statement arouses one's curiosity for several reasons. There is no mention of it in the first edition of 1664, and its addition later suggests that it was inserted by an editor who took no care to verify his facts. It comes under the heading of Shire-Oaks, and is said to be in Tamworth in Gloucestershire, which of course could be a printer's error for Tortworth. Evelyn also vaguely suggests that it was a boundary tree 'to that Mannor in King Stephen's Time, as it stands up in Record'. But no record exists as far as it is possible to discover. Moreover, the tradition that it was a boundary tree dating from Saxon times has no foundation in fact, for no chestnut trees are mentioned in Dr Grundy's *Study of the Saxon Charters and Field Names,* or in his *Ancient*

The Tortworth chestnut

Woodland of Gloucestershire, though the *Flora of Gloucestershire*, published in 1948, says it is mentioned in Domesday Book.

The first reliable mention comes in Sir Robert Atkyn's *History of Gloucestershire* of 1712.

> There is a remarkable chestnut growing in the garden belonging to the Manor House, which by tradition is said to have been growing there in the reign of King John. It is 19 yards in compass and seems to be several trees together; and young ones are still growing up, which may in time be joined to the old body.

He records the tree as an antiquity, so that it must have been ancient in his time, otherwise he would not have mentioned it, and this takes it back at least to the Middle Ages, though one must remember that the Tortworth Chestnut of today is not a single tree but an aggregate.

Some fifty years later Peter Collinson, a Quaker interested in botany, wrote of it in the *Gentleman's Magazine*, giving measurements and illustrating his words with a drawing by John Player.

> Five feet from the ground it measured 50 feet round . . . the largest part of the tree is living and very fruitful, having on it a great quantity of nuts seemingly of the true Spanish kind. Many young trees are come up and surround the old one. The solid contents of this venerable tree, according to the customary manner of measuring timber, is 1,964 feet, but its true geometrical contents are much more.

So we can be certain it was a living giant some 200 years ago.

The argument now begins as to whether it was one tree or two. In 1797 William Marshall in his *Planting and Mural Ornament* points this out with gentle irony to a Mr Marsham who had published a description of the tree in a paper of the Bath Agricultural Society.

> We will venture to add, that had the day been fine, and Mr Marsham had viewed the field side as well as the garden side of this venerable ruin; had he climbed upon the wall, and seen the gable of the old building, adjoining, clasped in between two stems; and had further ascended to the top of the old stump, which is not more than twelve feet high, and looking down its hollowness, seen its cavity not to the centre of the congeries, we are convinced he would not have suffered so inaccurate account to be published with his signature.

William Marshall had evidently made this rigorous examination.

The tree was again in the news in 1807, when Thomas Martyn,

editor of *The Gardener's and Botanist's Dictionary*, describes how the garden wall which was obstructing its growth had been removed by Lord Ducie and a dressing of fresh soil applied, so invigorating it that it produced excellent, sound, sweet nuts.

Joseph Strutt, author of *Sylva Britannica,* published in 1820, gives an etching of the tree, its size made obvious by the stag sheltering under the hoary boughs, the whole decaying hulk presenting a forester's nightmare. He gave the girth as five feet, two feet more than Peter Collinson's measurement of 1766, and said that seedlings had been raised from nuts produced in 1817.

J. C. Loudon published this picture, after Strutt, in his *Arboretum,* volume three, in 1838, but the information he gives is a disappointing summary of earlier writers, though he did make an original contribution at the end.

> Lord Ducie informs me that the tree is in much the same state as it was when drawn by Mr Strutt. . . . I wish that Strutt had given us a figure of the whole tree instead of the lower part only, for, though the perfect head is but a modicum, or perhaps no part at all of the original head, it yet makes a beautiful object all together.

The interest of the nineteenth-century botanists seemed to have waned after this, until in 1909 Elwes and Henry noted in their *Trees of Great Britain,* volume four, that it was still producing nuts, though a local *Flora* by Witchell and Strugnell, published in Stroud in 1892, gives its measurements as forty-nine feet in girth, with its branches covering a circle of thirty-two yards diameter, about one-sixth of an acre, making it almost a wood in itself. At that time nothing of the old tree remained but 'a decaying mass of wood, but growing up around it are four new stems, the largest of which, on the south side, forming now the most vital portion of the whole trunk'.

The Royal Forestry Society paid it a visit in 1937, and Mr A. D. C. Le Sueur notes in their *Quarterly Journal* that the Tortworth chestnut consisted of three separate trees, the centre specimen one of the finest in the country with a bole forty feet ten inches at four feet above the ground, the height being about twelve feet. He said it showed signs of having been heavily pollarded many years ago. The original tree, a large, hollow and shattered butt, should in his opinion be removed as it was riddled with fungus and a menace to the healthy tree growing up against it.

The Tortworth chestnut

The tree today shows in the centre a gnarled and writhing butt, with a number of good-sized, healthy trees on each side of it leaning away from the main pollarded trunk. We know that on the Continent chestnuts of a great age exist, though they are also an aggregate like the Tortworth Chestnut, but so far their true age has not been made clear. The species has a reputation of longevity and at Tortworth has evidently found a soil and climate to its liking.

CHAPTER TWELVE

Cotswold papermakers

When one looks at Cotswold villages, and the little grey towns that are scarcely bigger than villages, one imagines them to have been remote from industry from the beginning, the only difference between today and a hundred years ago being that they were then less accessible, without modern comforts and entirely given over to the pursuits of country life, except, of course, for the woollen manufacture of the south. The surprising thing one discovers is that in the eighteenth and nineteenth centuries small industries were numerous and, like the rest of the country, the Cotsallers had their share in the general expansion of trade. Not all worked on country estates or farms; many were operatives who used the skills of industry and had the extra advantage of being countrymen as well. Manufacture played as big a part as agriculture in keeping the district alive; it helped to create the villages as they were before retired people and the tourist trade took over and provided the means to build and re-fashion many of the stone houses which delight us today. If one inquires into the past history of many a charming modernised dwelling, one will discover that in the 1800s a small business was carried on in them and some not only supplied local needs but sent their goods to the big cities or for export abroad. Nor did these businesses take away any essential rustic qualities. It never occurred to anyone in those days that industry in rural districts spoilt the amenities. It was chiefly the Victorian romantics, appalled by the grime and squalor the Industrial Revolution had brought to manufacturing towns, who insisted upon a pastoral image for the countryside.

Papermaking was particularly suited to the Cotswolds, for in the early days of the manufacture in England, from about the end of the seventeenth century to the middle of the nineteenth, the essential requirement was water, clear water for the processes of manu-

146

facture and a good supply to provide the necessary power. The introduction of the steam engine banished the water-wheel in many instances but not the necessity for a pure water supply. The Cotswolds had this water, and the abundant springs from the hillsides, streams and small clear-flowing rivers in the valleys suited the industry perfectly. On the streams, waiting to be adapted, were corn, grist and other mills that had been worked for the fulling and finishing of cloth; one finds that the papermakers often took over unoccupied mills, converting them to their own purpose.

These early mills cannot be compared in size or output with modern papermills, and very few have survived to evolve into the highly mechanised firms of today. Their story throws a fascinating light on local history as well as personal endeavour in that period of expansion of trade and population and growth of literacy. Twenty-nine mills were working in Gloucestershire during that time, and there may have been a greater number, for not all the records have come to light. They were to be found from the Burford area on the Windrush in the north to its most southern borders, and if we extend the Cotswold area as far south as Bitton near Bath, we find papermaking on the river Boyd in several places, one of which, The Golden Valley Mills, still functions, following the modern pattern of one big firm emerging and the others falling off as the twentieth century advanced.

Winchcombe, situated where the river Isbourne comes down from the north Cotswold hills, had at least three papermills in its vicinity, as well as a firm of paper-mould makers to serve them. Two have disappeared, one near Stanway about which little is known except that its name is remembered in Paper Mill Farm, and the Sudeley Mill. The latter made gilt-edged paper, highly prized by ladies for special notes and invitations, and had a watermark Lloyd James, Sudeley Mill, 1841. This was also the date when the mill closed down. Nearly a hundred years after it was made I was shown a piece of this paper. It was yellowed a little with time and keeping, but its surface still invited a pen, or better still a quill, to fine handwriting.

The Postlip Paper Mills of Messrs Evans, Adlard & Co Ltd, has produced paper on the same site for over 200 years. Isaac Taylor's Map of Gloucestershire, 1777, shows three mills between Winchcombe and Postlip, all of which at one time were used by the firm. The business is now carried on, enlarged and modernised, in what was originally Upper Mill. Rudder, in his *New History of Gloucester-shire*, 1779, tells us that fine writing-paper was made there, and in 1789 Simon Moreau, in his *Tour of the Royal Spa at Cheltenham*, wrote that 'At Postlip is one of the most considerable Paper Manufacturers in the Kingdom. . . . Writing paper is made there. . . .'

It stands just off the main Cheltenham road about a mile south-west of Winchcombe. A private road leads down to a complex of stone cottages and mill buildings tucked away out of sight and sound of the traffic roaring along the A46. The cottages, with their little gardens bright with flowers, give it a pleasant, almost domestic appearance. Several thorough modernisations from the eighteenth century onwards as new machines and techniques were introduced has changed the original layout, but unlike many old mills in the Stroudwater valley where the discarded remains of buildings and machines are left to moulder into ruin, a tidying-up process after each renovation and the trimness of a modern façade make it difficult to trace its beginnings. The hidden stream, however, still uses the old channels, gushing through sheds in a dark hollow, while the broad, clear expanse of the mill reservoir with Cotswold slopes reaching up to the woods and hills on the skyline make a delightful background to the whole.

A lower road winds east from the buildings, a road now having a metalled surface but which was once a rough track along which the mill-workers from Winchcombe used to walk mornings and evenings. The road passes a small stone building standing alone, purposeful in design, but the eye dwells on it with pleasure because of the silvery grey Cotswold stone of its walls and an outside flight of stone steps leading to a drying loft.

In about half a mile the lower road passes a willow-hung reservoir which the years have made so much part of the landscape that it is hard to believe it is not a natural lake. Ducks and other water-birds are at home on its tranquil waters, nesting in the reed-fringed margins. Shrubs, clumps of tall willow-herb, kingcups and other marsh plants have taken over the foreground here, and behind them stand the remains of Middle Mill, a derelict, single-storey, long, stone shed and a squat wooden drying tower whose slatted sides are still in a good state of preservation. Around the upper part of the tower the wooden slats are so arranged that apertures can be opened in varying amounts to admit the air necessary to dry the sheets of paper. Wind, weather, time of day and humidity could affect the drying and the process needed much experience to dry out the paper correctly. It is now a lost skill, superseded by more easily-controlled modern methods. A small stone plaque on the stone shed has the date 1834 and the initials G.N. enclosed in a thin, moulded circle.

There have been corn mills on the Isbourne at Postlip since Saxon days. Domesday gives two water mills taxed at 15s, one at Postlip Hall and the other where the present mills stand at the confluence of the two streams which form the river. It was not until centuries later that it was discovered that the waters of the Isbourne were free from iron and suitable for making fine paper, or would it be more correct to say that it was scientifically analysed? In the old days local people knew that the waters contained special properties because, unlike the other Cotswold rivers that flow eastward, the Isbourne runs north into the Warwickshire Avon, and local folk-lore tells that water that 'runs against the sun' must have particular properties and healing power.

During the first world war special filtering paper, which before that time had been imported from Sweden and Germany, began to be made at Postlip. From this beginning the firm began to manufacture filter papers for use in industry, laboratories and hospitals, indeed for practically everything containing liquid components in its manufacture, ranging from tiny circles to huge sheets used for 'dressing' great metal presses for the filtration of oils and fats. Germination seed strips, litmus papers, base papers for impregnation in the plastic industry, and glass-fibre paper for clear-air installations are included in its list of manufactures. The firm has always specialised in good blotting paper, one sideline in the nineteenth century being the manufacture of black blotting paper supplied to banks for security reasons.

There is none of the squalid litter and grime of manufacture to be seen around the main mill buildings; even the water, after going through the mill in a yard-wide course, returns clear and sparkling, ninety per cent flowing into the large reservoir and ten per cent into the smaller one. The nature of the industry demands the absence of dirt and dust, outside as well as inside, but one feels also a response to its position in the heart of undefiled Cotswold country.

Facts and figures about production and management are not the only ingredients making the history of a firm. A number of extraneous circumstances have given Postlip Mills a special place in the industrial life of the Cotswolds. This has been true at least since 1849, when the Adlard family became associated with it and it became Messrs Evans, Adlard & Co. It still keeps an urbane eighteenth-century atmosphere, the suggestion of an old-fashioned family concern, without loss of efficiency. Tradition, so often a stumbling-block to good management, here mellows the whole conception of the industrial image. Summarising one's impressions, it is the kind of local industry which has its roots in the place, an industry not imposed upon it from outside but one which has grown up from its native elements, taking on the characteristics of each decade and then, when they became outmoded, passing on from one method of production to the next in a continuous progression. If charm seems an absurd word to use in connection with an up-to-date business, a visit to the mill, added to a knowledge of its past history, will prove this is not romantic nonsense.

Much of the history of Postlip Mills in the past was bound up with the history of Postlip Hall. In Domesday Book two water mills are listed, one a flour mill at the Hall, the other at the confluence of the two streams making up the Isbourne, where the present mill stands, which belonged to Winchcombe Abbey. Sir William de Postlip built the little Norman chapel of St James adjacent to the Hall, a Jacobean building in the Cotswold style, gabled, dormered and steep-roofed, with a stone lamb as finial to one gable, and inside a stone fireplace carved with two conflicting female figures. On one side a Catholic has her heel on a Protestant neck, on the other a Protestant is behaving in the same way to a Catholic neck. Evidently the original owners of the Hall, the Broadway family, had a foot in both camps.

A small stone effigy of Sir William de Postlip stands aloft on the roof at the west end of the great Norman tithe barn, so weather-worn and time-battered now that it is difficult to imagine it was once cut out of new stone from one of the hillside quarries. Legends have been woven about it, including the familiar one that it descends to drink at the wishing well near by when it hears the midnight chimes. I was first told this story some thirty years ago by an old gardener with a twinkle in his eye and an obvious delight in the telling, and I last heard it in 1966 as one of the tourist attractions of Winchcombe; this at least shows that the story is still alive.

William Gates Adlard, who worked the papermills in the nineteenth century and lived at the Hall, kept a silver mug at the well for visitors to quench their thirst and gain their secret wish, a whimsicality maybe, but showing he enjoyed the historic and legendary background of the place where he lived and worked. With Belas Knap less than a mile away beyond the woods and fields of Corndean Farm, it is hard not to be conscious of the presence of antiquity in this district.

The little chapel has a Norman doorway and a poor soul's light in the belfry, to remind the living to pray for the dead. The chapel fell into ruin and was used as a farm building for many years, with its chancel roofless and its floor covered with farm tackle, but in 1892 it was restored and re-dedicated to Roman Catholic worship when Mr and Mrs Stuart Forster bought the property after the Adlard family built Postlip House nearer the mills and the family connection between Hall and mill was broken.

This connection between Hall and mill had lasted well over 150 years, for the Durham family, who were working the mills in 1729, also lived at Postlip Hall. The fine writing-paper sold by them to London merchants was imported from Holland, like much of the writing-paper used in England in the early eighteenth century. Nevertheless it carried a patriotic watermark showing Britannia in a helmet holding aloft a Cap of State on a long staff in somewhat belligerent fashion, with a lion rampant holding a sword in one front paw and in the other a bundle of palings from the gated fence at the bottom of the device which half encircles Britannia and himself. Below the Cap are the words Pro Patria with the name Durham above and a simplified arms of England enclosed, first in a square and then in a circle. Churchill's book on papermaking gives this and other illustrations of the watermarks used by the Durhams.

A glimpse of the kind of manufacture carried on at Postlip can be found in the records of a lawsuit of 1752 in which John Durham was a witness. In this lawsuit John Burnham, papermaker, described the various ways of making scaleboard from beechwood, pasteboard from 'coarse linen raggs' and white Mill board from 'cordage, old tarr ropes and coarse raggs'. In this report William Whiteing of Wotton-under-Edge, Exciseman, explained to the court that 'scale boards are used for the making of hall boxes, band boxes, wig boxes and in bookbinding for the covers thereof and is liable to a duty of four shillings and sixpence to His Majesty.'

As Eleanor Adlard comments in her *Winchcombe Cavalcade*, 'this seems a pretty stiff tax with money the value it was in George II's reign—practically a duty of 4s a cwt'. It was not until after the middle of the eighteenth century that writing-paper was produced at Postlip.

Memorials to the Durham family are in Winchcombe Church. They contributed generously to the church and were the donors of the Durham Charity, and as late as 1837 the Misses Durham are recorded as presenting a communion cloth and two napkins. The first Durham to work the mills began the tradition of acting in the threefold capacity of squire, patron of the church and chief employer of labour in Winchcombe, which was afterwards carried on by the Adlard family.

The Durhams were succeeded by the Lloyd brothers, Nathaniel, high bailiff of Winchcombe, who also owned the Sudeley Paper Mills at the east end of Winchcombe near the castle, and Edward, who subsequently became Mayor of Worcester. An entry in the *Gloucester Journal* of 17 February 1812, reads:

> On the night of Tuesday last a most villainous attempt was made to destroy by fire the paper manufactory of Messrs Lloyd at Postlip in this county. A piece of timber close to the Mills was set on fire but fortunately was discovered in time to prevent its communication with the buildings.

A reward of £50 was offered for information about the fire-raiser, but as far as I can discover the perpetrator of this 'most villainous attempt' remained unpunished if not unknown.

Two years later the *Gloucester Journal* of 4 July has a more cheerful item of news about the mills. Like the rest of the country, they were celebrating the end of the war with France and Napoleon's defeat. The interesting thing about this celebration is that the workmen gave the dinner.

> On Friday night last the workmen employed at Messrs Lloyd and Co, paper manufactory, Postlip, met at the George Inn, Winchcombe, to celebrate the happy return to Peace, when an elegant dinner was provided to which their employers were invited as a token of respect. The day was spent in the greatest mirth with the ringing of bells. . . .

This contradicts the usual impression that the workpeople of those days were downtrodden, and it also shows that a happy relationship existed between workpeople and management; this was fostered by the Adlards when they took over some thirty years later.

In 1824 the Earl of Coventry sold Postlip Hall and the mills to William Searle Evans, the announcement of the sale reading as follows:

> Capital estate and Paper Manufactory, Michaelmas next, that excellent estate, Postlip Hall and 521 acres. All that long established and well-known Paper Manufactory and three paper mills called Postlip Mills used in the making of the finest and other papers. Also all stock-in-trade, implements etc, used in the Manufactory. A most advantageous business has for a long series of years been carried on at the above Mills which are now in full employ, the connection established therewith most respectable and of long standing.

The three mills working were the Upper, now the main mill, the Middle Mill, lying farther east and just below Postlip Hall, and the Lower Mill at Coates, near the junction of Cheltenham Road and Corndean Lane. The Lower Mill became a corn mill for some years and was then converted into a farmhouse. The Upper Mill made fine writing-paper, the Middle blue or sugar paper and brown or packing paper, and the Lower Mill the blue sugar paper once so familiar in grocers' shops. All these papers were handmade until the middle of the century.

In 1848 Evans, Adlard & Co rented the mills and finally bought them outright in 1876. When the senior partner, James Evans, died, the firm consisted of William Gates Adlard and his sons William and Edward. It was Edward who became the great figure in the firm's history, William going to Birmingham where he founded another branch of the business.

William Gates Adlard left the family business in London and took over Postlip Mills on account of his health, and it says much for Cotswold air and country life that he lived to be eighty-five, making his home at Postlip Hall until 1870. He kept horses and carriages in the mill stables to take him the mile or so of rough track to and from the Mill each day, and this, I think, sets the picture of a rural industrialist of the period.

William Gates Adlard was a forward-looking man of humane and liberal interests, and as well as his work in the mill and his social activities in Winchcombe he supported Mrs Malleson of Dixton in getting the Married Women's Property Act passed. He also advo-cated the District Nurse service, in those days considered a dangerous, indeed almost revolutionary measure by the local gentry, who believed working people would be ruined by this 'coddling' and thus cease to be properly grateful for charity.

It was while the mill was under his management that the firm first experimented in making filtering papers and the red and salmon-coloured paper used for wrapping filter circles.

When the Adlards took over in 1848 the papers made were mostly coloured, with an annual production of seventy-three tons, the power supplied by a water-wheel that was one of the largest in the county. Power produced by water could be a chancy business in years of drought, and in 1850 particularly the books showed loss of profit for this reason. After the first steam engine was fitted in 1854 production was doubled and there was an increase in the variety of papers made. The self-blue paper is still manufactured for the packing of Seidlitz powders, and a fine purple-dyed paper, free from acid, for the packing of needles to keep them from rust, the dye for the needle-paper being produced from Honduras logwood imported to Bristol and finely ground before it is sent to the mills.

Under the old system of power by water-wheel the paper machine could only work eight or nine hours a day, but the steam engine could work twenty-four. Daily production had increased to two hundred and twenty-two tons by 1854. The production of blotting paper had also increased and by 1860 had become one of the main established lines.

A new speciality began in 1870, tub-sized paper, every sheet being hand-sized and loft-dried. These papers were made in several colours including yellow-buff, deep blue and self-blue, and were used by merchants for displaying samples of coffee, raisins and other commodities from bulk shipments to prospective buyers. The size for the paper was made by boiling down animal hides, not in their original state as they came off the carcass but after the hides had already been used in the cotton mills.

A few entries from the firm's books reveal occasions when the whole firm spent hours of recreation together. On 4 January 1860 we read 'tea Party in Salle', and in August of the same year 'Work stopped for picnic'. In January of the following year 'Club Supper' is recorded, and on one day in October 1882 a laconic entry 'Work still. Worcester Exhibition' calls up a picture of them going on an excursion together and the preparation and excitement it must have caused.

In 1884, when Edward Adlard was in charge, the mill was closed for the day, the entry reading; 'Treat to Cheltenham Cricket Ground', and this must have been a fine sight as the waggonettes were loaded and they set off for the journey over Cleeve Hill and down into the town. Edward Adlard was a great cricket enthusiast, being captain of the local cricket club whose players were often recruited from the mill. As a boy he used to practise cricket in the long attics of Postlip Hall, which were reputed to be haunted, though none of the Adlards were ever troubled by ghosts during the years they lived there. Later occupants, however, were evidently more sensitive to this kind of influence or were unable to keep their servants, for when the chapel was re-dedicated Mr and Mrs Stuart Forster's chaplain held a service to lay the ghost.

By the last quarter of the eighteenth century it was no longer necessary to have paper watermarked in Holland. In the Tovey family of Winchcombe the firm had excellent makers of Dandy rolls to call upon, the most famous being George Tovey, usually known as 'old George Tovey', a local character of some renown and regarded by the townsfolk with a humorous affection and respect.

Dandy rolls are the wire rollers which hold the moulds imprinting the designs on the wet paper, making the pattern translucent when the finished product is held to the light. It is necessary for makers of fine paper to keep a large number in stock, as banks and other businesses often require their paper to show individual devices, and George Tovey was a craftsman who took great pride in his work and was invaluable to the firm. One gets a picture of him in Eleanor Adlard's *Winchcombe Cavalcade*. 'Old Mr George Tovey, wearing a tall silk hat, and, having fortified himself for the walk, steering a somewhat uncertain course, would carry his precious dandy rolls through Winchcombe and up to the Paper Mills,' and one can imagine that the progress of this Dickensian figure through the streets gave rise to affectionate grins from his fellow townsmen. His workshop in Chandos Lane was closed many years ago, but members of his family still live in Winchcombe, and one of them, Mr Tovey, the bookseller, is still warmly remembered by those who wrote books on the Cotswolds before the second world war because he would always display them in his shop.

A subsidiary trade carried on in connection with the mill was basket-making. Every year bands of travelling basket-makers with their shaggy ponies and tilted carts arrived to set up camp in the vicinity of the mill. Their first job was to cut the withies growing around the reservoirs, then the bark would be stripped and the withies soaked until they were sufficiently pliable to be woven into large two-handled baskets. These were used by the workers in the mill to carry pulp, paper and rags; a good example of adapting the natural material to hand instead of importing it from outside, and which also saved the bushy heads of the pollarded willows from growing top-heavy and falling into the water.

When new machinery and new methods made the use of the baskets obsolete, the countryside and the country roads lost another community of travellers who had pursued their picturesque way of life for many centuries, though as this was a time when the preservation of game was taken seriously their passing was probably not lamented by the owners of country estates.

Another custom went out of fashion about this time, the wearing of litle square paper hats by the mill workers. They were made out of sheets of blue sample paper, and were a headgear as characteristic of papermakers as the brown paper hats worn by the mechanics of the times as a badge of their trade.

In 1879 a new Fourdrinier machine was fitted in the mills and fifteen years later an extensive five-year plan completely re-equipped them. New buildings, new boilers, new washers, two new steam engines and a water turbine were installed. Trade was increasing generally, and Postlip was not the only place aware of the increase. A number of other papermills were also working in the district, a small mill at Sudeley specialising in a fine writing-paper including a gilt-edged paper popular for important occasions. There was also a papermill at Overbury and another at Stanway. All of these have now ceased to function and the premises are converted to other purposes.

I doubt if one realises today the number of small industries, carried on in country districts during the late eighteenth and early nineteenth centuries, which have now completely disappeared, or their variety and the skills they employed. Most modern developers and their opponents appear to regard the countryside as new territory for industry. The difference between the old and the new is that the old industries grew up because of some natural product or geographical condition or position that made them possible and the workers were local people, pursuing a rural as well as an industrial way of life, whereas modern industry, with its greater resources, can be put down almost anywhere and workers brought in from outside.

William Gates Adlard retired in 1881 and his son Edward took over the management. Like his father, Edward Adlard took a wide view of his responsibilities, combining the duties and pleasures of squire with those of mill-owner. Eleanor Adlard, in her *Short History of Postlip Mills*, says that 'Edward used to count amongst his blessings in life the fact that he worked in an office a stone-throw from which he could shoot a cock pheasant in the bordering wood, hunt a fox there or catch a trout in the mill pond—all of which pleasures he enjoyed to the full.' These were the golden days that the first world war was to bring to an end.

The firm became a limited company by the end of the century, the mills being completely modernised and employing eighty to ninety people, half of whom were women. Some 400 tons of paper were being made each year, and until the beginning of the first world war there was little change in the types of paper produced. They included seventy-five per cent blotting paper, and the rest filtering and tub-sized products with a few other specialities.

Some idea of the friendly spirit of Postlip Mills and the contentment of its workers can be seen in the fact that many of them stayed with the firm throughout their working lives. One of the oldest, Mrs Nightingale, walked to and from Winchcombe to the mill daily for sixty-six years. The Lishmans, father and son, put in over a hundred years, the father for sixty-four years and his son Alf fifty-five years. It is said that Alf was the last to wear the paper cap of blue sample paper. Many names of old Winchcombe families appear on the list of employees, including Okey, Sclatter, Mason, Keys, Yeend, Nightingale, showing how the town's life at that time was bound up with the prosperity of the mill.

Edward Adlard, keeping to ancient tradition, built a row of alms-houses for old mill workers. He also built and converted many cottages for his workpeople, believing that decent housing meant decent living. He retired in 1929 and died in 1933.

Since then there have been many changes. The steam engines in their turn have become outmoded, the machinery now being worked by electricity. The workers who used to walk the mile or

Cotswold papermakers

so from Winchcombe up the fields by the river are now fetched and taken home by bus. Lorries have taken the place of the horse-drawn waggons carrying bales of rags the six miles to Cheltenham with its stiff climb of Cleeve Hill, and old Sam Atwood, the carter, has long been laid to rest.

CHAPTER THIRTEEN

Two Cotswold quarries

One cannot go far on the Cotswolds without seeing ground that has been disturbed by quarrying, though this may be nothing more than shallow depressions in the soil or old, gruffy ground now masked by young conifers fringed with beech. The larger quarries on the hillsides, even when overgrown, can be recognised by their shape, and a search around a village will often reveal its ancient communal quarry which provided the stone for most of the old buildings in the locality.

Most quarries of any size began as an area roughly the shape of an arc being cleared of its top level of soil and the few feet of disintegrated rock lying immediately below the surface until the solid rock was revealed. I do not know if the medieval quarryman discovered the best place for his quarry by trial and error or by a subconscious knowledge of the lie of the land, but I do know there are some men who can find good stone without any aid but instinct or intuition.

As stone was taken from the opening the original area would expand, eating into the hillside until after a couple of hundred years the result is a fine amphitheatre overhung by a cliff often fifty feet or more high. In this type of quarry a cartway of easy gradient grows naturally from the mouth as the sides deepen and widen, leaving a broad level floor where the quarried stone can be stacked and measured. As a result of this activity the floor becomes covered with grains of stone fine as sand, while larger fragments, falling away beyond the level floor, make a scree where miniature plants find roothold and cling to the ground in close rosettes of leaves bringing forth flowers bright as alpines in their season.

I remember seeing many years ago a quarry of this kind stacked with stone built into rectangular piles, the corners sharp, the sides evenly walled, ready to be taken away. The quarryman told me that the stone was sold in solid yards. The quarry was about to be closed down and he remained in charge until the last loads had been carted away. Then it would be left to the birds and the plants and the small mammals who had found refuge there. Some of the stacks were of newly quarried stone of a warm yellow colour, others showed a range from pale honey to yellowish grey that would have served as examples for anyone investigating stone-weathering. There were a few small lots of darkest grey, the remains of ancient quarrying that had been left over, but because of its use in restoration work this was now the most valuable of all.

I have often wondered how the smaller pits, disused and almost obliterated today, and pointed out to me as one-time quarries, could have provided sufficient stone for the buildings known to have been erected with stone taken from them. These pits are usually situated in a corner of a field with easy access to a road or farm track, as if the builder needing material dug in a place convenient for cartage, knowing that wherever he dug stone would be found just below the surface. This is so, but it is the quality not the amount which varies from field to field, from hillside to hillside.

It is the larger quarries that are being taken over by firms who crush the stone for making artificial stone-bricks. They need standing room for lorries and bulldozers and enough space for the giant grabber to work tearing out the stone, good and bad alike. All is gathered in, and the ancient skills of the quarryman are not needed for this kind of work.

I have discovered a surprisingly large number of elderly men, particularly those who worked on big estates, who have had training as masons and quarrymen while not regarding themselves as belonging to the trade. As one old man who was coming up to his ninetieth birthday said to me: 'There wasn't none of that keeping to your own job all the time. You had to turn your hand to anything from building a cowshed or a wall to digging the stone out of the pit when it wasn't fit to get on the land to plough or reap. There was always some older chap to teach you, with the back of his hand as like as not, and you was glad to listen and be proud when you'd learned the job, not like the young 'uns today who thinks a machine knows everything. I suppose they'd call it labouring, but you had to know what you was doing all the same.'

I went to see another old man who I had been told had been a

17. Small reservoir, Postlip Paper Mills (Chapter 12)

18. Drying tower at Middle Mill, Postlip (Chapter 12)

19. Scabbling axe (Chapter 13)

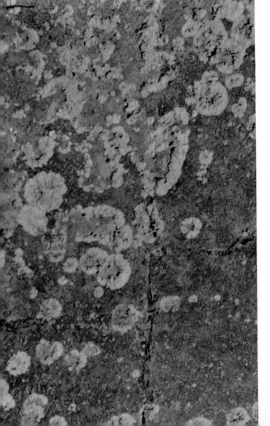

20. Lichen on oolithic limestone
(Chapter 13)

mason of some repute in the Campden district. I found him in the lane near his cottage leaning on his stick, a disapproving scowl on his face as he watched a young man repairing a drystone wall by fixing the toppers in a bed of cement. An old army overcoat made for a much bigger man hung in drapes about his withered shanks, and a crude caricature of his face with its overhanging eyebrows, deep eye-sockets and nutcracker chin would have served a medieval mason as a model for a gargoyle. His expression and the terse comments he was making to the young man warned me he was easily inflamed by the stupidities of the modern world, so I approached with caution to ask my questions. But he answered them as if it were a relief to talk to an interested stranger.

'I did a bit of everything . . . I've built stables . . . cart sheds . . . I helped repair a private chapel . . . that was a good job . . . plenty of time to do it and no skimping. . . .'

'You learnt the mason's trade as a boy?'

He considered this question with head bent while the young workman gave me a quick nod and wink expressing relief that the old man's attention had been turned away from him.

'It was like this . . . you didn't larn it, you just got to know, working with the stone it larns you itself in the handling of it the right way and the wrong way and what it'll do and what it won't. That is,' he added sourly, 'if you're not too big-headed to let it larn you.'

When I left him he was still struggling to express his frustration because seventy years of hardly-earned and poorly-paid experience was buried, wasted and useless in his mind. Whatever philosophical ideas I could have offered him would have been cold comfort.

The district around Burford has been renowned for its stone since the Middle Ages. Its most famous quarries are those at Taynton, on the northern side of the Windrush valley, just above the village quarries whose special qualities have been recognized by English architects since the twelfth century; according to W. G. Hoskins and W. M. Jope 'stone of the Taynton type can be seen in over three hundred surviving examples of twelfth-century masonry'.

Local tradition still holds that it was used for the original St Paul's built in the eleventh century and for its thirteenth-century additions, and it is likely that this tradition was kept alive by masons who went from Taynton to work on Sir Christopher

Wren's St Paul's nearly four centuries later. They would naturally examine what remained of the old building, and as a good mason can recognise stone, whatever its age, from his own quarries, discovering Taynton stone in the old St Paul's would be a matter of intense interest to a local man and a topic of conversation when he returned home. Country people, being interested in anything concerning their own locality, would remember and pass down this information.

The booklet *Cotswold Stone of the Burford Area*, issued by the Tolsey Museum, Burford, in 1966, gives the reason why Taynton stone acquired a bad reputation in some quarters. The builders of Eton College chapel in the fifteenth century and Oxford colleges in the sixteenth, not being able to obtain a sufficient quantity of Taynton stone, used with it a poorer quality freestone obtained nearer to hand, and it is this inferior stone which deteriorated and thus spoilt the buildings.

In the churchwardens' accounts of Thame church for 1444 there are entries concerning Taynton stone, giving the price and cost of transport and showing that transportation was a much heavier burden than the price of the stone. This could be one reason why inferior stone, obtained nearer the building site, was often used. The price of the stone bought at 'teynton' was 3s, while the cost of carrying it 'from Teynton to Oxsynforde' and then 'from Oxsynforde to Tame' was 25s 2d. That the cost of transport was split in this way shows that it was sent by river to Oxford and then by road to Thame. Taynton and other stone from the Burford area was conveyed for centuries along the Thames from Radcot Bridge to Oxford and London. Before Radcot Bridge was reached, at least eight miles had to be traversed laong the rough unmetalled roads of the period, the heavy waggons drawn by horses or oxen grinding along in dust or mud according to the season, though generally such transport was impossible in very bad weather. As well as avoiding road travel as much as possible, it was necessary to reduce the manhandling of the heavy loads and to choose routes which kept it to the minimum.

This must have been the way taken in 1396 for the building of New College, Oxford, bell tower, though Headington stone from nearby quarries was also used on this occasion, the Taynton freestone, because of its stout quality, being kept for the important quoins. The tower is still in a good condition after five and a half centuries.

We know from the notebooks of Christopher Kempster that this was also the route taken from the Upton quarries with stone for the new St Paul's. Kempster, however, spells Radcot 'ratcat', a pronunciation of the name still used by local people.

Sir Christopher Wren chose Portland stone for the bulk of St Paul's because it was not possible to obtain a sufficient quantity or a steady flow of material from Taynton, the quarry not being able to supply the large amount he needed. Cost of transportation also entered into his calculations. Portland stone could be cut from the coast quarries and lowered into boats waiting to take it all the way to London, and journeys by sea were much cheaper than road transport and saved much handling of the stone. He used Taynton and other Burford stone in the crypt, corridors and such places, where its yellowish colour would not be too conspicuous against the white of Portland stone.

Dr Plot, a man of 'rather shaky science' as Geoffrey Grigson called him, the Keeper of the Ashmolean and author of *The Natural History of Oxfordshire*, published in 1705, says that the chief uses for Burford stone were 'Columns, Capitels, Bases, Door-cases, Cornicing, and Mouldings. . . . But it yet is not as hard as that at Taynton. . . .'

Again about Taynton stone . . . 'Yet it endures not the weather as well as Heddington, by reason I suppose of a salt it has in it, which the weather in time dissolves, as may be seen by the Pinnacles of New College Chappell, made of this stone, and thus melted away.'

Dr Plot's 'melted away' describes vividly stone carving that has been exposed to weather-scouring for centuries and has lost definition. What Dr Plot did not say, however, was that beneath the weathering the stone remains hard and firm, harder than when it was first quarried; if a carved detail can be protected from wind and weather by overhanging eaves or any other shelter it will last for centuries. It is the nature of Cotswold stone to harden with age, and an experienced mason knows that it is wrong to clean the stone and remove the outer layer or 'skin' which has taken the force of the weather. The King's Beasts of St George's Chapel, Windsor, had to be replaced in the seventeenth century because their position, standing high and bearing vanes, exposed them to the winds which scoured the grain and ruined the decorative detail.

Eighteenth-century builders may have been influenced by cor-
rosion, but the writer of the Tolsey booklet tells us that Taynton
stone would have been used in the recent restoration of Oxford
colleges, but the quantity required for the work was beyond the
working capacity of the quarry, repeating the circumstances of
four hundred years past. 'Once again the builders made use of the
second best,' says the writer of the booklet.

In his *Natural History* Dr Plot gives some facts about the use of
Taynton stone for other purposes. It was known to 'endure the
fire, and of it they make malt kilns and ovens'. Taynton stone
also made·

> Troughs and Cisterns, and now of late Mesh-vats for Brewing;
> First hinted, 'tis true, by Mr Bayly of Ducklington, but practiced by
> one Strong, a Mason, which it seems did answer Expectations so well,
> that it has since obtained in many other places . . . one that holds
> about sixty-five Bushels, drawn home with no less than one and
> twenty Horses . . . there was one single stone dug in this quarry,
> containing no less than three hundred Tuns. . . .

The Strongs were a family of masons who owned property in
the district, and one, Thomas Strong, freemason of London,
erected a causeway across the damp water-meadows of the Windrush linking up Great and Little Barrington villages.

Some of these great troughs made out of a single block of stone
can occasionally be seen today in Cotswold farmyards. They are
used for watering cattle or placed under springs to catch the
water as it emerges from the hillside. A new use for them is as
sunk gardens for rock plant enthusiasts, and they can be bought
for that purpose from dealers in old garden ornaments at a price
that would amaze the masons who fashioned them long ago. I
once heard a farmer in a pub describing an encounter with a lady
who had tried to buy one from him. She had only recently come
from the town to settle in the country and had not yet learned to
estimate the local character. She had come keyed up to bargain, so
that she was rather taken aback when the farmer offered to give
her the trough. The entrance to his farmyard, near where the
trough lay, opened into one of those precipitous, deeply-scoured
one-time packhorse lanes near Bisley and he knew only too well
the difficulty of moving any heavy load out into the road.

'You will at least let me pay you something for the delivery,' the lady said.

The farmer smiled. It was the moment he had been waiting for. 'You must arrange that yourself. My men aren't experienced in handling heavy blocks of stone. You'll need a crane and chains. Bit of a job it'll be. I remember my Grandad telling me how it was brought here on a sled by a team of cart-horses, and how the horses strained and the men shouted. A mistake of judgment in the handling and they'd have been crushed to death,' he told her.

Then to the company listening to his tale: 'She never sent for it. And I'm glad she never did, for it's been part of the place as long as I remember, though I don't use it now since I had the piped water laid on.'

Taynton stone was used for the bridges over the Evenlode when the Oxford to Worcester railway was constructed, the stone being taken from a quarry afterwards known as Railway Quarry. This quarry also provided the material used to rebuild Magdalen Bridge towards the end of the nineteenth century. At that time it was being worked by the Pittaway family; a pittaway is the name for a stone slat-pick, a tool used for extracting and splitting stone roofing slates. Does this mean that the family had been quarrymen over a long period and derived their name from the kind of work they did?

In 1920 the quarry was being worked to provide stone for estate work at Great Barrington, but the nature of the Taynton quarries has always made carting difficult in bad weather. Although the best beds are fairly near the surface in most places the clay rises, producing a tenacious, clogging mud. The troubles of transporting the stone the two miles or so from Taynton to Great Barrington induced the owner to open another quarry above the Windrush road and to sell the Railway Quarry and the land to the Lee family.

The old method of taking stone from the quarry was by first clearing the top soil and debris until a clean block of stone was revealed. A chain was put round the block and it was hauled out by two men using winding gear. It was then hoisted on to the waggon up strong planks and wooden rollers, the waggon being firmly wedged so that it could not move. The stone gradually slipped up the planks as the men turned the wheel of the windlass and then fell gently into the bed of the waggon. This was a tricky job and one to be undertaken only by experienced men. The block would then be conveyed to the stone yard or shed to be dressed.

Today the owner of the Taynton quarries uses a crane and a diamond saw, and on occasions a bulldozer is brought in to pull the blocks out of the earth. But, as in the old days, the quarryman has to dig carefully round his block until he can see its size and possibilities. The ability to make this assessment is gained by experience and understanding of the way the stone was laid down, and although machinery can supply the power a quarryman still needs knowledge of his craft and a wide experience, both geological and practical.

If the block partially uncovered is right for the job on hand, a block weighing two to three tons can be brought out by mechanical means, a great saving in back-breaking labour and very much safer. Brash at the top, layers of clay, hard weatherstone and ragstone must first be cleared away before the valuable stone of the base bed is reached.

It is this base bed which yields the best freestone used for carving and ashlar work. Stone from the weather bed shows a marbled veining when sawn, and it was this type of stone which provided a veneer, five-eighths of an inch thick, used to line the new Bodleian Library. Exposed to the weather the softer layers of weatherstone scour away but the heart remains sound. When protected from the weather its faint patterning makes a delightful surface, and on outside surfaces that need not necessarily be clear cut it weathers to a picturesque antique grey, moss and lichen appreciating the rougher surface. Many of the mossy eighteenth-century headstones seen in Cotswold churchyards, with their cherubs and thick mouldings, are made of the coarser-grained, hard weatherstone.

If smaller blocks of freestone are to be taken out, or if the master-quarryman decides to split a large block before moving it, he must work with the natural line of cleavage, making a line of holes with a mechanical drill and then tapping home with a feather and wedge until the stone splits true. There is nothing more fascinating than watching a master-craftsman at work, and on one occasion when I watched this process I was impressed by the ease and confidence with which the quarryman handled his material. The hard stone might have been as tractable as cheese. My involuntary murmur of appreciation as the stone split made him smile. I was then shown how the stone is trimmed with a water-cooled circular saw, and as I looked at the trim, neat shapes when the trimming was done I was told that this good freestone was used for chimneys and fireplaces and special ashlar work. Like all natural products it was a pleasure to look at, even before it was used.

The Taynton quarries also produce walling stone of a good quality and provided the stone for four council houses recently built in the village. Its golden hue and fine texture take the light beautifully and make the reconstituted stone bricks used by some housing authorities look lifeless. It is too early yet to know how this artificial stone will weather, but we know the stone from the quarry will take on the soft, grey patina which gives old Cotswold buildings their special appeal. Fresh from the quarry, it has its own characteristic yellow colour. Given a little protection from the weather, in places where it has been sheltered by overhanging eaves or a porch it changes from quarry yellow to a warm honey tint. When fully exposed its greyness has a purplish bloom. One of its characteristics is being found in large blocks, and to stand up to centuries of wear the stone must lie in the fabric of a building as it was originally laid down, that is with the grain running horizontally.

The Windrush quarry, or mine as it is more properly called, has been closed since the beginning of this century. Today the scars of its workings just below the crest of the hill beneath a belt of trees are only to be recognised by those who remember its existence. The freestone bed runs true for a considerable way on this side of the valley and there is still plenty of stone for the mining, but it would be costly to get out today. In an exhibition at the Tolsey Museum, Burford, held in 1966, the family ledger of the Wright family who worked the mine was on show. The last sale recorded was in 1893, for stone supplied to Mr Charles Pether for Minster Chapel.

The Wrights worked the mine for several generations; it was closed down when new safety regulations became too stringent. The main gallery, according to Mr Arnold Wright, whose father and grandfather both worked the mine, was nine feet high and about seven feet wide and it ran about a quarter of a mile into the hill, with two side galleries branching from it. The beds of stone were laid so true that the men who worked in the galleries knew they needed little propping, but their assurances did not satisfy exacting modern regulations about safety. Demand for the stone also fell off about this time, when it was the industrial districts which were booming and not the rural areas. The demand was for quickly-built, cheap, brick dwellings in the towns to house the families from the countryside unable to find work at home who had migrated to swell the factory population, while new building on the Cotswolds was practically at an end.

Horses pulling broad-wheeled trolleys were used at Windrush to bring down the stone to the road below; one can still see the level path the weight of their passing has made, and there are still traces of a deep hollow or trench and the openings of galleries bored into the hill from this trench made by the Windrush quarry-men a hundred or more years ago.

Mrs Dadge, who once lived in Quarry Cottage, remembers how as a girl she went into one of the galleries. She saw an arch to the entrance and a place just inside which held the troughs for the horses and the chains which secured them. Older people in the village still tell how, before the first world war, the village fife and drum band used to practice in this underground stable on a Sunday morning, taking along a small barrel of beer to quench their thirst. Long after the mine was closed, when the field was being cultivated by steam engine, the ground began to give way beneath the weight and the engines were only kept up by their ropes. At one particular spot it was reckoned there were only ten feet between the surface of the field and the roof of the mine.

CHAPTER FOURTEEN

Some Cotswold masons

And what of the men who worked the stone? When Sir Christopher Wren was building St Paul's he was much criticised for leaving the work for long periods in the hands of his builders, but he had sufficient confidence in at least three Cotswold master-masons to know they would work well without constant supervision. These three men all came from the Burford area. There was Christopher Kempster, Kempster's partner, Ephraim Beauchamp, who worked with him at Upton quarries, and Edward Strong, who was Beauchamp's brother-in-law and who owned quarries at Taynton and Little Barrington.

The Strong family were important quarry owners in the district. The first Strong we know about is Timothy, a Wiltshire man who moved to Barrington at the end of the sixteenth century and bought quarries at Taynton and Little Barrington and who, with his son Valentine, provided the stone for many of the new country houses then being built. They were responsible for the south front of Cornbury and it was Valentine who undertook the building of Park House at Fairford. He died before it was completed and was buried in Fairford churchyard under a splendid tomb of local stone. His name, the year of his death, 1662, and the word 'freemason' are cut on a Purbeck marble panel let into the side. A second panel now missing bore these words:

> Here's one that was an able workman long
> Who divers houses built, both fair and Strong:
> Though Strong he was, a Stronger came than he
> And robbed him of his Fame and Life, we see;
> Moving an old house a new one for to rear
> Death met him by the way, and laid him here.

Valentine's son Thomas was also a master mason. After the fire of London the necessity of rebuilding the city called all craftsmen to go and assist, and Thomas went to London, starting business there to work under Wren. He signed a contract for work on the rebuilding of St Paul's, and the first stone was laid by him in 1675, which shows him a master mason of some standing. He died in middle age and his brother Edward took over his commitments at St Paul's and St Stephen's, Walbrook.

Edward was responsible for the north-west corner of the dome and his son began the lanthorn and laid down the marble floor under the dome. Edward was a good businessman. He soon realised that the quarries in the Burford area, including his own, could not supply sufficient stone for the important buildings being erected in London and elsewhere, so he expanded the family business to include Portland stone and became a specialist in the subject. When Sir Christopher Wren was having difficulties with the Portland quarries Edward accompanied him to Dorset and tackled the troubles on the spot. He also worked with Sir Christopher on the Royal Hospital at Greenwich. Their association lasted many years and was a happy one, Sir Christopher appreciating the integrity and meticulous knowledge of Edward while Edward was proud of the friendship of the great architect. Edward Strong's signature can be seen in St Paul's receipt book, an elegant hand, delicate in its precision.

With his son and his own men he worked at Blenheim until the building came to a standstill because of the political troubles of the times. He retired at sixty-two and went to live at Hide Manor in Hertfordshire, where he spent his leisure writing his *Memorandums of Several Works in Masonry Done by Our Family*, a record which gives us a glimpse into the kind of work performed by the master masons of his time; it also makes it plain how proud he was that his brother laid the first stone of St Paul's and that he himself put the last stone in position on 26 October 1708. He ordered the following words to be inscribed on his tombstone :

> In erecting the edifice of St Paul's several years were spent, even from its foundation to his laying the last stone; and herein (equally with its ingenious architect Sir Christopher Wren and its truly-pious Diocesan Bishop Compton) he shared the felicity of seeing both the beginning and finishing of that stupendous fabric.

As a man who liked everything well-finished this must have given him the greatest satisfaction of his life. When he died nine years after his retirement he left £10 to the poor of Taynton parish, but although his will reveals that he owned property in Burford and Rissington he never lived on Cotswold again once he had set up business in London.

Christopher Kempster, or Kit Kempster as he was better known, never forgot he was a Burford man and Burford has not forgotten him. When I asked about masons in the district his name was mentioned to me again and again, so that it was hard to believe he had been dead for over two hundred and fifty years. His memory is kept alive in the town by his house at Upton, known as Kit's Quarries, where carved over the window are the words: *Christopher Kempster built this in 1698.* He built it for his retirement when the time came to give up his work for Sir Christopher Wren in London and elsewhere. He did not retire, however, until he was eighty, his name appearing in the account of St Paul's for the last time in February, 1707, where it is stated that the dome was finished. It was in this year he finally came home, though, unlike Edward Strong, he does not seem to have spent his retirement writing about the past. But then, I feel, even in old age, he was a forward-looking man.

He had his domestic troubles. His son Christopher turned out badly, but another son, William, must have gratified his father in all his work, even to providing him with a grandson, another William, to follow the family calling and work with Sir Christo-

The weeping cherub (memorial to Christopher Kempster)

pher Wren. He died in 1714, aged eighty-eight, his son William being responsible for his memorial in the south transept of Burford parish church where he was buried. William erected a cherub's head in white marble above the stone on the floor covering his father's body. This is now known as the Weeping Cherub. It looks as fresh as when it was first carved, for like Kit Kempster's memory it is still cherished.

The ledger stone, strangely enough, is not made from the pale cream stone of Christopher's own quarry at Upton but is of blue lias, a stone sometimes found with the oolite and which has a tendency to flake in damp or exposed positions. One can only suppose that William, knowing the memorial would be under cover, thought the lias would stand out better in its surroundings, or that its more funereal colour was better suited to the occasion.

His reason for carving the cherub's head in marble is easier to understand; a marble memorial would do his father more honour as being the accepted material of the period for monuments to the illustrious, and the fact that marble was more difficult to carve was another tribute. The choice of a cherub's head could be interpreted as William's personal mark because of the cherub's head he had carved for St Paul's and which earned him warm commendation from Wren.

Kit's Quarry House remained in the Kempster family until 1884, and when a Mrs Buckingham moved in after the last of the Kempsters had left she found Kit's day book among other forgotten litter in the attic. This revealed how the stone used to be conveyed to London from his quarries in Upton, and other quarries in the area as well, being first taken by road to the Thames at Radcot Bridge, and then making the rest of the journey by water.

With his partner Ephraim Beauchamp Kit was responsible for almost a quarter of the fabric of St Paul's. Wren thought highly of them as we know from a letter sent to Bishop Fell in 1681 concerning the building of Tom Tower, Oxford. Wren wrote:

> My Ld with submission I have thought of a very able Man, modest, honest and Treatable, and one that your masons will submit to worke with because of his interest in the Quarries at Burford and therefore you will have the stone from him first hand. His name Xtopher Kempster he wrought the Town House at Abington and goeing now to the Quarries, I have persuaded him to return by Oxford and wait

upon your Lp. I have used him in good workes he is very careful to worke trew to his designs and stong well banded work and I can rely upon him.

His son William's name appears regularly in the accounts of St Paul's after 1701, working on corridors, stairs and carvings. He became an expert carver of ornament, for we know he worked on the 'Great Freestone Wreath' in the west dome, as well as all the ornamentation of the Great Staircase in the south-west tower and the south door head. An entry in one account for the ornament on the staircase of 'two festoones and Cherubim's Head over the Head of ye Neech, 4 ft long and 2 ft 6 ins broad and 5 ins imbost', reads: 'allow to W.K. for extraordinary diligence and care used in the said carving and his good performance of the same £20. 0s. 6d.'

As well as his skill in the carving of ornament he was also a master-builder of considerable reputation. Repair work carried out recently on the circular staircase at St Paul's, known as the 'Floating' staircase because it has no central newel, revealed the mystery of the unsupported steps. Although each one only extended 4½ ins beyond the wall, the perfect rabbeting or joining of one into the other sent the weight flowing down the well, thus showing that William Kempster had considerable understanding of stresses and strains. When there was trouble in the crypt over the adjustment of the mass of St Paul's, William and his men were given the job of solving the problem.

Whether the making and carving of tombstones and tombs was a specialised branch of the industry before the eighteenth century or part of the general work undertaken in the stone-yards is difficult to discover; few masons have left their names on their work. It seems likely, though, that it did become a specialised job during the eighteenth century and that the masons worked to certain designs then fashionable, for one finds the same type of ornament again and again in Cotswold churchyards, suggesting they used the same pattern books for the cherubs, the swags, shells, acanthus and other emblems and 'anticks'. But within these conventions local memorial masons occasionally let themselves go, as at Windrush village where a table tomb in the churchyard has the flutings of the shell-endings of its heavy rounded top carried on to form the curled horns of a sheep or ram instead of the usual skull or conventional ornament, emphasising the point that this was good sheep country as well as quarry country. I like to think the tomb was made for a flock master and that the mason, as he was about to carve the last convolutions of the shell, could not resist curving the lines into a ram's horns.

Windrush churchyard has a good example of the plain type of headstone which went out of fashion in the late seventeenth century. It is a double headstone carved out of a rectangular block 5 inches thick and about 3 feet high, the heavy moulding at the top divided into two semicircles, one for each person. Carved on each portion are two initials and the date in 1-inch relief, each letter and figure 6 to 8 inches high and 2 to 3 inches wide, so that they fill the space perfectly. The plain letters, angular in design, all parts coming to a widening triangular finish, are placed in a simple moulding as in a frame. On the left are the initials K.F. with the date 1694 below them, while on the right-hand side are the initials R.F. with the date 1704 exactly opposite the date on the other half of the stone. One presumes this is a memorial to husband and wife. It is tantalising that the birth date is not recorded, but it does leave one free to wonder and hope they had many years of married life together, growing to resemble each other as married couples do so that words mattered little between them and that their headstone, in its own way, recorded this.

'The grave is but a plain Suit, and a Rich Monument is one embroider'd,' as Thomas Fuller said, and the burgesses of Burford, who were buried in those heavy stone-box structures in the churchyard of their parish church, liked their tombs well embroidered with every device known in the book, as well as lidded with heavy barrel-hooped or bolster tops.

The moist airs of the Windrush valley have darkened the stone to a sombre grey and patched them with configurations of centuries of lichens one upon the other so that not an inch of space remains that has not been decorated by man or nature. Only under the mouldings can one find a faint reflection of the once pale tones of the stone. The tombs huddle together, heavy and solid, with barely space to squeeze between them, and it is only in recent years they have become objects of interest, though they were useful, tradition says, in the years when the poachers returning from the Forest of Wychwood hid their venison under those barrel-tops until it could be sold and distributed to the townsfolk.

Early guide books describing the church seldom mentioned these tombs and there is no record of the men who carved them.

Two miles or so to the east of Burford a memorial we know was the work of a Burford mason—one of the unique monumental tombs of the Fettiplace family—can be seen in the parish church of St Mary in Swinbrook in the Windrush valley. The church is a small one and to allow for the erection of the Fettiplace monuments the north wall of the chancel was recessed a few feet, thus accommodating two tiers of effigies, each tier containing three knightly figures under elaborately carved canopies. It is the first tier, the earliest one, which is said to have been made by a Burford mason, and was erected by Sir Edmund Fettiplace who died in 1613. The effigies represent his grandfather, son of the original Anthony founder of the Swinbrook branch of the family, his father and himself. They are most beautifully carved in freestone and having been recently cleaned now look as if they had just come from the mason's yard. Unable to use the customary table-tomb form because of the smallness of the church, the mason has used the cramped space at his disposal as part of the pattern of three recumbent figures, each resting on an elbow, one hand on a decorated sword, the other supporting the head, thus giving them a remarkably life-like appearance with none of the solemnity of death in their postures. The hair, features and costume are most delicately carved, and the figures with their family likeness repeated immediately one above the other in a design of decisive lines is like a theme in a piece of music three times repeated. The second and more elaborate tier was made by William Byrd of Oxford with slight differences of armour and costume due to the years between the two groups.

Painswick had a family of local masons in the Bryans whose altar tombs still grace the churchyard today. Two memorials to the Poole brothers by John Bryan are as handsome as any on Cotswold, calling to mind that it is in the Painswick churchyard as well as in the elegant merchants' houses one finds reminders of the prosperity of Painswick's golden age. The variety of shapes and ornament show how ingeniously the monumental masons could ring the changes on a basic box form. Some are square, others oblong, some have buttressed corners and pie-crust edges, others are round or triangular with concave sides. There is a pepperpot shape and one which is six-sided, and most of them were

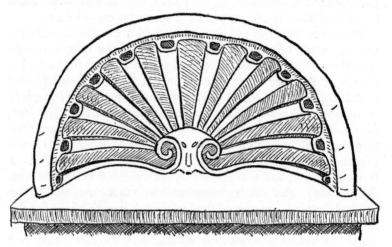

End of tomb—Windrush churchyard

Bolster tomb—Burford churchyard

21. Cotswold quarry (Chapter 13)

22. Cotswold quarry (Chapter 13)

Here

Resteth the Body of
Edmund King of this
Parish who departed th
is life the 21 day of De
cember Anno Domini 1650

His life compleat with vertues manyfold
who now with saints in heaven is infold
his charity to sucколitious was not small
god blessed him and he gave Liberall
where neede requird wt makes our ende to how
our Capt̄ain christ have our enders all
mownd[?]

23. Brass rubbing (Quenington Church) (Chapter 14)

the work of the Bryan family. John, the most famous of them, who died in 1789 aged seventy-one years, took as a model for his own tomb standing among the many others he made, the famous Caius Cestius tomb in Rome, a pyramid of fine-grained stone which still keeps the crispness of its contours. It is not known where John Bryan was trained but his work suggests a strong Italian influence.

There is another tomb in Painswick churchyard to a mason who died in 1731, a humbler man who has the outline of his mason's tools incised above his epitaph. One of these tools, a long-handled scappling axe used for rough dressing has changed little since the thirteenth century, for reproduced in Lethaby's *Westminster Abbey and the King's Craftsmen* is an illustration from a thirteenth-century life of Edward the Confessor showing one of his craftsmen holding an axe similar to the scappling axe still used today.

We do not know the sculptors of these freestone effigies we find in nearly every village church on Cotswold. They date from the twelfth century onward, these knights with the Norman names, the ecclesiastics, the squires and their ladies with their children kneeling in miniature at their feet, the girls as alike as peas in a pod on one side, the boys similarly arranged on the other, with perhaps a babe in swaddling clothes telling the sad tale of an early death. Not many are portraits; in fact the figures are usually made in a central workshop to designs that could be adapted as required. For the men who made them it was a job like any other and it was seldom they signed their names or left their personal mark on them. This applies also to those men who built the Cotswold churches, who carved the Norman doors and the tympani over them. We think of these workmen as being brought over by the Normans but a great number employed on the bulk of the fabric were probably local men working under the direction of a master mason.

Looking closely at the famous north and south doorways at Quenington on the Coln, where every possible pattern and variation has been employed one is struck by the difference between the virility of the decorated doorways and jambs and the gentler unsophisticated carving of the tympani. These have a pathos in their simplicity, the struggle to express piety lifting their crudity into a higher plane. Only the rayed sun enclosing the so-

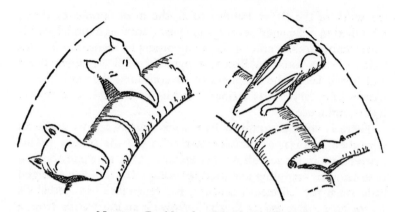

Norman Beakheads—Windrush Church

Details of Norman patterns—Quenington Church

called Harrowing of Hell tympanum over the north door has the emphatic Roman emphasis.

If one wanted a complete contrast to this early Norman ornament, a hint of how the art of decoration had advanced by the end of the seventeenth century, a memorial brass in the floor of Quenington church could supply it, for it is most delicately etched on the plate and has been so well preserved that the finer details are still complete. It is late for a memorial brass, whose best period was some two hundred years earlier, and has no effigy. It is in the shape of a shield and is a memorial to Edmund King who died in 1685. It looks as if the engraver wrote the words without conscious effort, the letters flow so sweetly, and then, not wanting to spoil the effect of his calligraphy by extraneous decoration, he repeated the fine coils of his capital letters in a few economical hair-like curls to complete the design. In their fluidity one forgets the hardness of the material.

The churchyard at Quenington is a pleasant, peaceful place to-day, and though one regrets the loss of many of the old leaning headstones—a few have been placed in a row under the wall—the broad green lawns give it a tranquil air, and the nearby river adds its changing light and serenity to the scene. Around it is a landscape combining parkland, an ancient church, great trees and a backcloth of Cotswold woodlands, a perfect corner of rural England whose foundation rests on the solid rock of Cotswold stone beneath its surface.

Bibliography

Adlard, Eleanor. *A Short History of Postlip Mills*, 1957.
Atkyns, Sir Robert. *Ancient and Present State of Gloucestershire*, 1712.
Baddeley, W. St Clair. *A Cotteswold Manor*. 2nd Ed. 1929.
Bigland's Collections relating to Gloucestershire. (Reprint 1885.)
Black, J. B. *A Gloucestershire Parson's Wife, 1814–1826*, 1913.
Cary's New Itinerary. 8th Ed. 1819.
Daubeny, Ulric. *Ancient Cotswold Churches*.
Derrick, Freda. *Cotswold Stone*.
Flora of Gloucestershire. Edited by the Cotteswold Naturalists' Field
    Club, 1948.
Forestry Commission Bulletins. *Studies in British Beechwoods*, No.
    20, 1952.
Fosbrooke's History of Gloucestershire.
Gloucestershire Notes & Queries, 1881–1913.
Gloucestershire Records Office. D148.980. D1086: Box 22.
Gretton, M. S. *Burford: Past and Present*, 1944.
Grose, J. D. *Flora of Wiltshire*
Hadfield, Miles. *British Trees*.
Hale and Osborne Documents relating to Wortley. Glos. Collec-
    tion.
Harris, Stanley. *The Coaching Era*.
Hutton, Canon. *Burford Papers*.
Hyett, Francis M. *Glimpses of the History of Painswick*.
Knapp, J. L., F.S.A., F.L.S., *A Naturalist's Diary, 1820–1830*.
Lindley, E. S. *Wotton-under-Edge*.
Lipson, E. *The History of the Woollen & Worsted Industries*, 1921.
Paterson's Road Book. 14th Ed., 1808.
Perry, R. 'The Gloucestershire Woollen Industry, 1100–1680'.
    Bristol & Glos. Trans. 1945, Vol. 66.
Plot, Dr. *The Natural History of Oxfordshire*, 1705.
Pontin, K. G. *The Wool Trade Past & Present*, 1961.

Bibliography

Roper, Ida M. *The Monumental Effigies of Glos. & Bristol,* 1931.

Rudder, Samuel. *The New History of Gloucestershire,* 1779.

Rudge, Thomas. *General View of Agriculture of Glos.,* 1807.

Rushen, Percy. *History of Chipping Campden,* 1912.

Shorter, A. H. *Paper Mills & Paper Making in England,* 1957.

Shorter, A. H. 'Paper Mills in Gloucestershire.' *Bristol & Glos. Trans.,* 1952, LXXI.

Smith, John. *The Lives of the Berkeleys.* Ed. by Sir John Maclean, 1883–5.

Taylor, Isaac. *Map of Gloucestershire,* 1777.

Victoria County History. Gloucestershire, 11.

White, J. W. *Flora of Bristol,* 1912.

Acknowledgments

My thanks are due to Mr Roderick Standing not only for his photographs but for his help and encouragement when exploring ruined mills; to Mr Donovan Grose for his picture of Toddington Station; to Mr Ian Forster for his pictures of Cotswold roofs and quarries; to Jane Sturdy for her drawings and her patience on Cotswold journeys. Miss Ann Farwell, curator of Tolsey Museum kindly gave me permission to use the photograph by Miss Susan Macfarlane of the Scabbling Axe from a collection in an exhibition *Cotswold Stone in the Burford Area* put on at the Tolsey Museum during the summer of 1966. I only wish it were possible to thank the late C. E. Montague, who lived in Kit's Quarry House during the 1920's, and who first told me about the discovery of Christopher Kempster's Daybook there.

I am also indebted to Mr Donald Grose for his help with the Cotswold Flora, to Mr Donald Gill who advised me on various forestry problems and to Mr H. Lee Bostock of Messrs Evans, Adlard & Co Ltd for his courtesy and kindness in giving me much interesting material about the Postlip Paper Mill, for permission to take photographs and for lending me his copy of *A Short History of Postlip Mill*. I must also thank the librarians of Gloucester Public and County Libraries for their willing help on various occasions.

Index

Index

Index

Index

Index

McCausland, Hugh, 112
Memoirs of Learned Ladies, 100, 102
Mercer, Thomas, 69
Merchant Adventurers, 39
Metiver, John, 67
Michaelwood, 61
Middlings, 77
Miles, W. A., 58
Miller, Mr, 15
Miller's Long Room, 15
Minchinhampton, 137
  Custumal, 139
Misenor, Thomas, 30, 31
Mithe tout, 79
Monasticon Anglicanum, 137
Montpelier Spa, 15, 18 20
Monk's Mill, 63, 64, 65, 66, 67, 68
  House, 64, 65
Moreau, Simon, 4, 17, 148
Moreton in Marsh, 81, 91, 120
Morrell, Dr, 98
Moseley, John, 89
Mosing-mills, 34, 43

Natural History of Oxfordshire, 163, 164
Neale, Christopher, 63
Neale's Mill, 57, 72
Neville, Agnes, 29
  Charles, 29
Newark Park, 62
Newcomen engine, 91
New and Complete Traveller in Britain, 86
New History of Gloucestershire, 60
Newland, George, 24
New Mills, 37, 69, 70, 71
Nightingale, Mrs, 157
North Somerset Yeomanry, 58
Northleach, 103, 107, 108, 109, 120

Old Cottages in the Cotswold District, 134, 135
Old London Road, 134
Old Well, 12, 13
  Walks, 13
Olveston, 90
Oriel House, 16
Osbourne, John, 64, 65
  Richard, 64, 65, 70
  William, 65
Overbury, 156
Oxford, 98, 100, 102
  Colleges, 162
  New College, 162
  & Worcester Railway, 165

Ozleworth Bottom, 61, 62
  stream, 62

Packer, David, 30, 31, 32
  family, 23, 30
  John, 30
  Richard, 30
Painswick, 79, 85, 120, 137
  Church, 83
  churchyard, 175
  Rector of, 80
Palling, Edward, 25
  family, 23
  John, 25
  William, 25
Palmer, John, 111
Papal Taxation, 63
Paper-making, 146–58
Paper Mill Farm, 147
Papworth Buonarotte, 18
Paradise, 23, 85
Pates' Almshouses, 12
Paving Improvement Acts, 14
Pendarves, Mrs, 100, 101
Pendle, 136
Perry, Dr, 62, 83
Picardy, 83
Pictures of Nature, 79
Pitman, Isaac, 72, 73
  Benjamin, 73
Pitt, Joseph, 18, 20
Pittaway family, 165
Plot, Dr, 106, 163
Plues, Miss, 78
Poor Law, 45
Portland stone, 163, 170
Postlip Hall, 150, 153, 155
  Paper Mills, 147, 148, 150, 153, 156
Postlip Paper Mills, Short History of, 157
Postlip, Sir William de, 150
Postmaster-General, 111, 115
Power looms, 59
Poyntz, Sir Nicholas, 62
Presents, 130
Priory Wood, 104
Privy Council, 42, 43, 44, 45, 46
Puesdown Inn, 129
Purnell, Christopher, 63
Purnell's House, 64
  Mary, 63

Queen's Hotel, 16

189

Index

fever

fever

 1969   NEW YORK

& other new poems
by Bella
Akhmadulina

with an Introduction by

Yevgeny
Yevtushenko

Translated by Geoffrey Dutton
and Igor Mezhakoff-Koriakin

WILLIAM MORROW AND COMPANY, INC.

CONTENTS

v

FOREWORD BY YEVGENY YEVTUSHENKO

> It is difficult to be a woman on this Earth.
> It is difficult to be a poet on this Earth.

And there is something in common between the fate of a Woman with a capital letter and of a Poet, likewise with a capital letter. Not without reason did Pasternak write:

> . . . from my early years
> I have been wounded by woman's lot,
> and the trace of a poet is no more than the trace
> of her movements.

Woman is born for love, for the procreation of human beings who are carried in her womb and then in torment released into the wide world. But from her early years she has to face filth and banality and throughout her life she has to pass before someone's vulgar stares and through someone's clammy, impudent hands, throughout her life she is forced to defend her inner destiny against the daily attacks of the cynical and corrupt world. And the inner salvation of a woman lies in fulfilling the task given from above: in love and in the molding of a new man in herself, just as the inner salvation of a poet lies in love and in the future. And when the woman is a poet—her task is doubly difficult. Life's abominations keep attacking her both as a woman and as a poet, and for this reason her spiritual defense has to be doubly strengthened compared with that of a poet alone.

I hate the word "poetess." It brings to mind something vague and nebulous, rustling with its false wings, something with affectionately sheeplike eyes, awkwardly holding in its chubby little hand a pencil tracing out painstakingly touching things in a little album with a golden edge. Let us agree to call only poets' wives poetesses. But let us call women who write genuine poems poets, because a master is a master and in art there is no allowance for weakness of sex.

In Russian poetry there were a great many poetesses. But one has not the heart to call Akhmatova or Tsvetaeva poetesses. They are poets who occupy their own particular yet valued place along-

1

side the best male poets in Russia. Maybe they are on the summit of a different kind of rock formation, but in any case it is a summit of equal height.

And Bella Akhmadulina is one of the few women who write poems and who possess the full right to be called a poet and not a poetess. Just like other poets she has her detractors (rather of the female sort, naturally), but probably none of them would take the risk of expressing any doubt as to whether she has a genuine, God-granted, poetic gift.

She was born in 1937, the year that is forever engraved with blood upon the long-suffering memory of the Russian people. Later, in her poem "My Genealogy," she was to write, for some well-wisher who commented on her arrival into the world in such a spiritual leap year:

> Why do you force your way in there,
> When there is no way out again?
> You know that you could choose a far
> more lucky year in which to be born.
>
> How easy it would be, how safe,
> away from the wrath of wind or age,
> neither to grow nor accept a face,
> talent, or even a human name.

And still later she returned to this again in her poem "The Night of St. Bartholomew."

> Still a nestling, hardly chirping nonsense,
> still a lamb whose limbs are not yet suited,
> he survived and drew in his first breath
> inhaled from the nostrils of the executed.

But, probably, the great harmony of bloody, disgusting, and yet at the same time beautiful life consists precisely in this, that inside it there is some kind of unrecognized law of compensation for countless losses by innumerable gifts. And life, throwing on one scale the bodies of the unjustly executed and sacrificially killed, lays on the other scale the squealing, wrinkled little bodies of the newly born, each of them containing the possibility of expiating at least partially the mortal sins of previous generations.

Bella Akhmadulina started to publish early; when still a

2

schoolgirl she studied in the literary circle of the Stalin car plant under the guidance of the poet Yevgeny Vinokurov. She was lucky, because Vinokurov, poetically an extraordinarily well-educated man, succeeded in imparting to her the sense and skills of poetic technique. But, although she was noticed right after her first publications and on entering the Literary Institute was immediately recognized as a queen of rhyme, Bella still remained only a poetess. Her poetic world was childishly unstable. This unstableness was felt (when she tried to express it) in the way she expressed that world. Genuine poetry demands two qualities: range, and the confinement of that range in the tight container of form.

Some poets acquire range first and only later master the formal incarnation. Only in some rare cases do both achievements come together. Bella was too young to have any range in her knowledge of the world. She lacked the personal suffering to feel with her own skin "the tragic essence of the world." Of course, she did feel something instinctively, but that did not blend in her with the intimate experiences of a large-eyed girl, with a Komsomol badge and schoolgirl's plaits. But instead she began seriously to study form. In the instability of her gifted sentimental lines something concrete and concise started to appear. Endowed with an amazing poetic ear, Bella grasped the inner law of freshness of rhyme, resilience of rhythm, and delicacy of epithet, and that is one of the most important components of real poetry. She managed to master in only one year as much as I did in at least ten. She learned the charm of grammatical incorrectnesses which creates a special air in a poem. She understood that sentimentality and metaphors alone cannot get her very far if there is a lack of tension and compactness in her poems. Out of her sleeves, like an enchantress from a Russian fairy tale, she produced a sparkling shower of epithets, rhymes, intonations, images. Formerly her verses merely rustled. Now they started to ring. However, the compactness of the form, still combined with the poverty of the content, as yet could not command faith in her future in the minds of many serious people, although it did raise some hopes.

Her name became known among readers, but for the sake of honesty one has to admit that this was due not to her poems, but to some kind of promise which was contained in them, as well as to her participation in the general new wave of Soviet poetry and to other accompanying circumstances.

3

Her first book, *The String (Struna)*, was sold out immediately, but the content of the book did not come up to the reader's anticipations. It was lacking in range, far too many things happening in life and imperiously demanding to be expressed were left outside the limits of the book. The content was too elegant, and alongside the lack of elegance of the knifelike problems which rip one's chest every day, it seemed criminally frail and infantile. But as far as Bella is concerned, the time was not yet ripe for her to speak about those problems. The oratorical intrusion into life peculiar to me at some periods, or the explosiveness of the monologues of Voznesensky, who also appeared at that time, was alien to her very nature. Bella was looking for her own path to the age, or maybe the age was looking for its own path to her. And this path of connecting her personal pulse to the pulse of the age lay through her inner suffering, which life, despite her apparent well-being, fortunately did not grudge her. She was happily gifted with kindness, and although for a while she did not know enough of personal sufferings and sorrows, nevertheless she was able to take part in other peoples' experiences and they became her own. She was always a faithful friend who shared in her friends' troubles and who was ready to defend them.

It was precisely this ability to share in her friends' sorrows which compelled her to write the poem "And once more like the lights of the open-hearth furnace," in which, with a boyish anger surprising in contrast to her former soft intonations, she mercilessly pilloried the murderers of poetry. She did not become a publicist— this was completely outside her talent, but her own nerves, by now independent of herself, became the nerves of the age, and in her apparently most intimate poems, behind the snow, the twilight, the lights, and the swaying of the branches, glared the terrible face of our epoch.

Whatever she wrote, whether about a fellow poet:

> Whether you want to praise or damn,
> there is both prophet and clown in him,
> and the hot world like a frying pan
> burns his hands below the skin . . .

or about a boy who as he pedals his bicycle:

> . . . suddenly looks at the wide world
> and feels serene and sad . . .

or about that "cordial" encounter in a café when:

4

> . . . a murderer in a gray coat came in.
> His victim was sitting not far away . . .
> My friends, what a wonderful reunion! . . .

or about Yelabuga,* who once killed Marina Tsvetaeva and is now trying out her red gaze on other victims.

In all this one can see a great feeling of suffering for herself, for others, for history—and great suffering always was and will remain the basic content of great poetry.

The poem about Tsvetaeva in which Akhmadulina swears to kill Yelabuga became some kind of inner Rubicon, which she crossed, and was then overcome with a nervous trembling of responsibility for everything that was, that is, and that will be. The only imperative responsibility for her was the challenge to all kinds of yelabugas and petty-yelabugas hiding their venomous fork-tongued stings behind sweetly smiling lips. The struggle of Akhmadulina does not look like a struggle, because it is not thundering but lyrical; however, a slender silver flute gives us strength just as much as a bugle in the difficult battle of life. One should not forcibly thrust into someone's hand a musical instrument unsuited to him. But the musician chooses his instrument and the instrument the musician.

And the tragic symphony theme of responsibility started to sound through Akhmadulina's flute, which had apparently been created for chamber music only. This was poignantly uncovered in her poem "Longing for Lermontov." For Bella, as for many Russian poets, Georgia meant something eternally beautiful, which offered healing space and genuine hospitality in the most difficult periods of time. And yet in that country, so generously endowed by God, Bella, suffocating with the happiness of the open spaces, tells herself:

> Stand on the mountain! The more the longing for the unknown,
> a foreign country's mysterious novelty,
> the more furious the temptations of your own,
> the more you need her sweet severity.

"The more you need"—what a prosaic phrase compared to the attributes of poetic grace usually served as a fulcrum in Bella's former poems. And suddenly this "need." It's even strange! And yet this shows her spiritual maturity. Only the feelings of sufferings experienced and shared make you understand that not only is the

---

* See note to poem "I Swear."

...world necessary for yourself, but that you are necessary for the world. And this understanding leads you away from endearments, from tenderness, from beauty, as though you do not deserve them because they are not yet for everyone, it leads you to the temptation of that most sweet severity of unaccomplished reality, it leads you to participate in misfortunes—it does not matter if they are not yours but belong to others, but precisely because of this they are yours and not others'. And the pain spreads through the air and the very air injures your skin. If, when you feel fine, someone else, who breathes the same air as you do, does not feel fine, then you must feel pain.

This astonishingly strong sensation of the air causing injury is expressed by Bella with the greatest audacity and power in her two startling masterpieces, ''Fever'' and ''A Tale About Rain.''

It is as if nothing happens in the first poem. Even the cause of the fever is not explained, but the very shivering, which lashes, drives in sharp tacks into one's skin, cries out how in this uncomfortable world covered with slush the soul feels feverish.

If you are a poet, you may even try remaining motionless, but you won't escape this fever.

> How fast, I thought, I stand but run away!

Listen to the following lines:

> The doctor explained: Your illness is quite simple.
> It would have been perfectly innocuous,
> but the high-frequency wavelength of each tremble
> stops me examining you—I just can't focus.

Indeed, always nervously vibrating, Bella's poetry lays obstacles to examination. (In some cases the poet should be thankful for this.) But Bella herself, despite all the dangers, desperately wants to be seen. She wants to irritate, to be active.

> Wherever I went, always a draft would blow,
> flaring a candle, then snuffing out its flame. . . .
> I blighted everything, I would have been a menace
> to paradise, in the hell of my negation.

From the craving, natural to every soul, for the complete roundness of peace, Akhmadulina forces her way to that most sweet severity where ''there is no comfort and no peace.'' And not for

6

nothing is the prudent neighbor cold toward her when he meets her, even when her fever is seemingly leaving her. The fever is simply hiding inside and every moment it can break out, and because of its trembling the gilded plastic ornamentation on the filthy arches of bigotry will fall down.

In Bella's poems there appeared the resoluteness to doubt till the end, which it is impossible to compare with her former childish formal resoluteness.

Akhmadulina is acquiring what is not simply a boyish impudence but a refined fury armed with the venom of ruthless irony. She wants to tear away the garments of decorum from everything, to tear away everything from her own soul and place it, fearlessly naked and contemptuous, right before the slippery gaze of other people.

> How are you? (Oh, the flashing of the lightning's flood
> dammed in the slender neck of a proud woman!)
> —Thank you—I said—I think I'm still human,
> though I've wallowed in fever like a pig in the mud.
> . . . And you know, here is another detail—
> What appeals to me is to end my days in the gutter.

Oh, how she hates all those who inquire

> —Who is it that endows
> those who have been gifted by God? And how?

Of course, she knows that creative art is not meant merely to delight someone's ear. She knows that it is when you

> . . . fly through the air's verticals,
> smashing your elbows and knees until they bleed
> against the snow, the air, corners of the streets,
> the bed sheets of hotels and hospitals.

Yes, a poet is one who smashes himself against the air. She has understood this. This understanding is maturity.

The Rubicon is crossed and she will never betray her vow to Tsvetaeva to kill Yelabuga. She will never betray the Rain who sat on her shoulder with the trustfulness of a monkey. She will never betray her sacred chill, which like a child invisibly beats inside her asking to be let out. On the path chosen by her she still has a lot to suffer, but at the same time a lot to accomplish. But even if she is

7

predestined not to accomplish much more, just the same she will remain in Russian poetry a poet and not a poetess. And if life breaks her, after all she is a woman, so what—just the same she will be able to use Blok's words about herself!

> Let me die in the gutter like a dog,
> Let life trample me down into earth—
> I know it was God who covered me with snow!
> And the blizzard that was kissing me!

TRANSLATORS' NOTE:
These poems were written after the publication of
Struna (Moscow, 1962), Akhmadulina's only published
volume.

I have attempted as far as possible to follow Akhmadulina's original rhymes and meters and to suggest
something of the complex web of internal rhyme, dis-
sonance, assonance, and alliteration which gives her verse
its musical quality. However, any attempt to follow those
soft, feminine Russian rhymes which Akhmadulina uses
so subtly ends in English in a Swinburnian slop, and so
I have sometimes shortened or lengthened lines to suggest the movement of the original. Likewise the so-called
"new rhymes" so popular with Akhmadulina, Voznesensky, Yevtushenko, and other young Russian poets are
very difficult to reproduce in English, as they rhyme on
the first syllables of words, or on consonantal patterns.
E.g. (from "Verses about Georgia"): plutáli-platány;
sud'bé-dekabré; bazára-bazál'ta; Medéi-meléli; oleándry-
Ariádny (pronounced aleándry-Ariádny).

Bella Akhmadulina was born in 1937. She was married
to the poet Yevgeny Yevtushenko. Her second marriage
was to the short-story writer and screenwriter Yuri
Nagibin.

G. D.

INVOCATION

Don't be sorry for me! I'll still live—
a good-conduct convict, a happy beggar,
living in the North as a frozen Southerner,
or else a consumptive and wicked Petersburger
in the malarial South, yes, I'll still live.

Don't be sorry for me! I'll still live—
like that lame girl who came out on the church porch,
or that drooping drunkard whose vodka breath could scorch
the tablecloth, or that icon painter whose torch
scarce lights the Mother of God, yes, I'll still live.

Don't be sorry for me! I'll still live—
like that girl who has learned to read and write,
who will be my poetry in the blurred future's sight,
whose fringe like mine will catch the same red light,
who like a fool will know that I'll still live.

Don't be sorry for me! I'll still live—
more merciful than a nurse to a hussar
in the mad pre-slaughter recklessness of war,
and living under my own, my most bright star,
be sure of this, somehow, yes, I'll still live!

I SWEAR

To the memory of Marina Tsvetaeva

I swear——
—By that summer photo:
on somebody else's porch,
standing by itself, crooked
as a gallows,
neither leading into the house
nor out of it—
locked
in an all-over armor of furious satin,
high collar hindering the throat's great muscle,
that's how you're sitting—done with song and action,
all the horselike labor of hunger and hustle.

—By that photo:
where you are a child with an astonished smile,
and by the thin angles of your elbows,
irresistibly attracting other children, a child
drawing their faces out of the shadows.

—By the dragging pain of remembering your causes,
when, gulping down the vacuum of grief,

(TRANSLATORS' NOTE: Marina Tsvetaeva, one of the finest twen-
tieth-century Russian poets, was born in 1892 and emigrated
to Western Europe in 1922 to join her husband, a former
White officer. She returned to Russia in 1939 with him and
their two children. Her husband was shot, her daughter ar-
rested, her son killed in the war, and on August 31, 1941,
Marina Tsvetaeva committed suicide in the town of Yelabuga
in the Tatar Autonomous Soviet Socialist Republic. In a letter Bella Akhmadulina says that of course the town is innocent and all the blame should be placed on the small-minded-
ness, cruelty, and indifference that bore down upon Tsvetaeva
in her last days. Nevertheless, Akhmadulina spells "yelabuga" with a small letter, in order to show that the word
symbolizes an animate, powerful, and evil creature, which has
defeated Tsvetaeva. In derivation, "yelabuga" is a Tatar
word, probably derived from "devil.")

and caught in the choking anger of your broken verses
I clear my throat by coughing till it bleeds.

—By your presence : like a shoplifter I bundled you
into my handbag—to steal you for myself,
forgetting that you are somebody else's—you are taboo,
you belong to God, God wants you for himself.

—By all that your drawn flesh had to withstand
from the hunger that gnawed at your coarse orphaned youth,
and by the blessed, holy motherland
which made an end of you with its rat's tooth.

—By that extraordinary African,*
all goodness, you loved as an omen of the bad,
the Negro who was happy watching children,
and by the children themselves, and the Tverskoy Boulevard.

—By your sad resting place in paradise
where you have neither trade nor torment
I swear
to kill
your yelabuga.

—By your yelabuga
so that grandchildren will fall asleep
and the old women will frighten them at night,
not knowing the yelabuga is no more :
—Sleep, my boy or girl ! Hush ! Keep quiet !
Else the blind yelabuga will come in the door.

Oh, when with all her legs tangling around
she begins to quicken her crawl—then immediately
I'll stamp my steel-tipped heel right down
on her tentacles, and swivel silently.

---

* This refers to Pushkin who was, on his mother's side, of African
   descent. The Pushkin monument, on which there is a quotation
   from Pushkin referring to the unknown young generation,
   is in the Tverskoy Boulevard.

And then with all my weight on that one heel
I'll jam it in the back of her head and keep quite still.
The green juice of her cubs will scorch
my soles with the caustic of its venom.
The ripe egg from her tail I'll throw
to the depths of earth because they're bottomless,
not saying a word about the porch
and Marina's deathly homelessness.
And I swear by that.
While in the darkness
the yelabuga measures me with her red eye
and swears by the stench of hell
by the toads from the well
that I shall die.

REMEMBERING SIBERIA

You tell me I don't have to weep,
and maybe it's so, all right, all right,
no tears for me, but I need to leap
into cold rivers and swim at night

and by swimming make the water shift
from my hand as from a curving oar,
in order to make myself the gift
of the freedom of the other shore.

There was no small reason for my sighing
softly in Siberia, far away,
where the close-pressing plants were replying
to all my movements all the day.

How could I give you samples, true
to what was happening to me?
There are objects reflecting a pale blue
shimmering in my memory.

The hidden pool of Baikal
where the salmon swimming by
flash in the slow water each scale
separately to your eye.

And those houses, and those byres
just visible on the far land,
and the tiger lilies' fires
instantly fading in your hand,

and a little, white-striped marvel—
the sudden chipmunk of Siberia,
staring at me, alert as a sentinel,
but in his pupil no trace of fear.

How I was lured, yet made to feel
death in the depths I overcame!
The waters of the river Kieziel
had glinting edges cold as flame.

I remember, as if it had just occurred,
that there, between the earth and rye,
I never said a single word,
not one word that was a lie.

THE WORD

"Caught in the slow sufferings of growing pains,
I lapse into insolence and then disdain,
I write poems: 'Tear them up!' they tell me.
And you simply say the word you have to say,
rhythms love you, each day is your lucky day."——
a boy from Perm wrote this in a letter to me.

In the unfamiliar darkness, fumbling for the light,
blindly disturbing my hosts from their peaceful night,
stumbling as if the air had fallen like a tree,
in my clumsy failure the victim of my own sneers,
over every book drowning my heart in tears,
the boy and the city of Perm came back to me.

And really—in Perm lives a strange child
who can use language, be verbose or wild,
or just mumble. And then, when the conflagration
of all the familiar stars of Perm is stirred
to leaping flame, that child simply says the word
he has to, with a throat not meant for incantation.

How the child speaks! Can it possibly
be true, in me or anyone, that in the dry gully
of the larynx, plunged into obscurity,
there is a clean space for such a bird
to spread its wings in the fullness of the word,
in the whole span of its beauty and purity?

Oh no!—in me a sob or a wheeze is heard,
the daily noise that has taken the place of the word,
there in the lungs where smoke and shade are seething,
and the neck lacks the strength of the ox, to make
light of difficulties like having to take
the bother of the vain habit of breathing.

The rough, iron sound of muteness gasping
tortures my throat, drawing blood with its scraping,
I start to speak—my handkerchief stains with blood.

Buried in silence as if earth was piled
above me, it is strange to know there is this child
in Perm, able simply to say the word.

LONGING FOR LERMONTOV

O Georgia, it is all your doing, your fault
that when the winter closes up its harsh white dress
my sorrow is not utterly distraught,
what I hope for not entirely hopeless.

My only happy love is love for you,
in your face only there is no hypocrisy.
Like two warm stones together, laid dead true,
your hand on my head builds my security.

I won't be able to walk in on you
to surprise you, held already in your keeping.
All that you say, and every whisper too,
you'll whisper for my ears. No need of weeping.

But today I am not so young that I am free
to choose between the North and South so clearly.
Late autumn has come in, a catastrophe,
all that was comforting is cherished now more clearly.

The black umbrella clatters in my hands,
nothing else for my live, dull muscles straining.

(TRANSLATORS' NOTE: In 1837 the Russian poet and novelist Mik-
hail Lermontov (1814–41) was transferred to a regiment sta-
tioned in the Caucasus. On his way to join the new regiment
Lermontov visited Mtskheta, the ancient capital of Georgia.
Lermontov used the cathedral Sveti-Tskhoveli, built in the
eleventh century, and the fortified monastery Dzhvaris-Sak-
dari, built in the seventh century on the mountain above the
town, as the setting of his long poem ''Mtsyri'' (a Georgian
word meaning ''novice''), written in 1839. Below the monastery and between it and the town, the two rivers Aragva and
Kura join, one blue-green, one yellow, their two currents remaining quite distinct. The rivers are mentioned in many
works of Lermontov, and there are also several paintings by
Lermontov depicting the scenery in the vicinity of Mtskheta.)

Do not hold the traveler from leaving for other lands,
let him go. What use is there in his remaining?

I give the umbrella to the gale, do not chase
it, even watch which way its freedom's going.
I am walking across October, pace by pace,
through the water lying and the first snowing.

I don't know why, but in another's house
I've managed to stop the flexing of my knees.
Have you ever tried living in another's house?
It's nice there. That's all. I simply took my ease.

I learned solitude like an alphabet.
I was free to go. But it so happened, living
in that house, inside the bathroom, there was a cricket
which did me a favor, simply by singing.

At that time there was no spirit in me,
and that is why—don't laugh at my way of thinking—
I loved with all my heart, most passionately,
weak though that heart was, that weak singing.

Soon the whole good family got used to it,
that he and I, neither making the other worse,
two of nature's nonentities, would sit
quietly together composing harmless verse.

Thus, here I am. A sleepless star gleams,
I start singing, and there he is answering.
Well, all right. And what about my dreams,
where will they live? Homeless, where are they hovering?

They are still there, where I have been,
where the tallest young man in the world of straight and level
used to stand on the summit of a solitary mountain
between the sun and the clouds, between good and evil.

Oh, there, far down, under the mountain's protection
as in a kiss, the deception of dancing heart to heart,
the two rivers, Aragva and Kura, in the junction
of their currents, are unable to meet or part.

In the cathedral down there, pure and gloomy forces
stir up warlike prayers in its soul.
It holds the thunder of swords, the snorting of horses,
the eternal battle here to gain control.

Where was he standing? Where the monastery still lives,
right here, in the full, fresh, hawk-swing of the air,
where even the smallest hovering stone gives
out the great nostalgia of the monk who lived there.

My little, little boy, my great, great man!
What have you done to me, this resurrection
by my brain's agony, by the darkness my shut eyes scan,
of myself, weeping over you, my little one?

And in this fate, around which God has drawn a line,
in the high torment of your elevation,
I wish the cricket, that cricket of mine,
would sing for you, beloved, in your lone station.

Stand on the mountain! Stay there! Only there!
Don't go where in only four years' time
empty and absolute freedom will fall from the air
and close down over you, however high you climb.*

Stand on the mountain! Following your steps, I'll find you,
under the sun, near the cathedral of Mtskheta.
I'll see nothing else but you, stand behind you
and save you and not lose you, and that will be forever.

Stand on the mountain! The more the longing for the
                                                    unknown,

---

* This refers to Lermontov's death in a duel.

a foreign country's mysterious novelty,
the more furious the temptations of your own,
the more you need her sweet severity.

TO SLEEP

To me—dancing under the moon of Mtskheta,
to me—weeping with every muscle in my body,
to me—turned into an emaciated shadow
too long for the cathedral of Sveti-Tskhoveli,
to me—who like a naked silver wire
am threaded through your needle, Tbilisi city,
to me—who lived like a criminal, till morning's fire
found me frozen in your glasshouse without pity,
to me—unable to fall asleep at night,
seducing my acquaintances by my mad details,
having a horse's pupil in my sight
that reared back from dreams as from the rails,
to me—with the beggars at the bridge, singing:
"Forgive us, O morning, all our mortal sins.
Cover our miseries with gold by bringing
soup for our charred stomachs when the day begins."
To me—jerking diagonally to and fro
in my insomnia, that hollow entertainment,
in a bed like a cradle, slung deep and low,
O Lord, how I wished to sleep and lie content.

To sleep—falling asleep. Waking—to sleep.
To sleep—slowly, like taking a drink in sips.
Oh, to sleep and suck dreams like a sweet,
dribbling the surplus of sweetness from my lips.

To wake up late, not to open my eyes,
tempting myself as long as possible
with the secret of the day's weather still a surprise
hanging over my bed, its greeting not yet acceptable.

How luscious the aftertaste of sleep in my throat!
My hands make fresh, amateurish movements.
My resurrected body is shy, still deep
as the tomb inside the wrappings of indolence.

My brain is blind as an extinguished star.
My pulse is calm as sap in a sleeping tree.
Sleep again! To sleep for all the days there are.
To sleep in the womb of dark security.

VERSES ABOUT GEORGIA

The names of Georgian women . . .

There across the sea sails were straying,
and, indifferent to heat,
plane trees blossomed, lazily
shedding December leaves.

The bazaar's noises were strident,
and on the bald heights
the basalt's interlacing stripes
lay black in the snow's lights.

And a little shop in the park by the sea
stood out white and mute,
and the names of Georgian women vaguely
had the scent of grapes just cut.

They turned into a stream of song
running down to the sea,
and then they swam out like a black swan
bending its neck curiously.

A girl called Lamara ran over the stones
toward the edge of the water,
laughing as she jarred her bones,
her lips made up with wine.

In the water Medeya's hair was streaming,
her hands interlaced
in a waterfall of drops striking
the dry air they displaced.

And flowering over the oleanders,
gathering them into one spray,
for a moment the name of Ariadna
hovered and faded away.

24

Leaning close to the water as a willow,
a mooring by the piles stirred.
"Zissana!" they called down from a window.
"Natela," a voice answered.

IN THE DESERTED RESTHOUSE

To float into unconsciousness like a fruit
fallen quietly asleep among the branches,
not recognizing a single living shoot
of your own flesh, its disorders and mischances.

Here is an apple I found yesterday,
in it there are muscles of moisture, beauty of pigment,
the crush of ripeness, the onset of decay.
To all this the apple is indifferent.

And here, as if part of a crowd of children,
you can't control even your own reactions,
you can't foresee which way you will suddenly run,
you can't pacify your body's warring factions.

In the end it is as tedious as at the start,
to examine yourself, like a doctor a patient's ills,
hearing all the time the thudding of your heart,
distinguishing the ticklish running of the molecules.

And you feel like turning away to other affairs;
now, I really will turn away, but still curiously,
as in a similar way the music playing upstairs
disturbs and fascinates simultaneously.

In the wild forest, where I live like a recluse,
roofed with snow, each day further retreating,
I live alone as if there were two of us—
I live with my lungs heaving, with my blood beating.

Now I smile and now a song makes a little run,
now my pulse is throbbing like a butterfly in the hand,
well, thank God, I think, at least there is someone
in these still walls who does more than simply stand.

There, then, my body, with thanks I give you this reference,
one of nature's little, living animals,

carry on, carry on with your simple existence,
like the sun, like the forest, like the rows of vegetables.

All right, get out and play, forget your dumbness!
Winter's solitary inhabitant,
I'll enjoy myself in the middle of emptiness,
living as my own compact and noisy tenant.

Who knows, whether forever or for a moment
it will be my destiny to wander the earth,
for that moment or eternity's extent
I give equal thanks to the world that gave me birth.

No matter what happens, I do not curse, but bless
the snowflake full of light and light as breath,
the falling star that charts for me your sadness,
the silence of snow and star that is my death.

FEVER

I must be getting something—for three days,
like a horse waiting for a race, I've been quivering.
My neighbor, in the next flat, with his haughty ways,
even he has exclaimed:
          ''Bella, you're shivering!

''You'd better come to your senses! Your odd ailment
is shaking the walls and shooting tremors outside,
stirring my children up into a ferment,
and at nighttime sending my crockery for a slide.''

I answered him simply:
          ''I shiver more and more,
but really, quite without any sinister meaning.
All the same, pass it on to the whole floor,
I'm clearing out, I'm leaving home this evening.''

But my trembling made my shivering worse and worse
so I could not think, my words were puerile,
my moving foot would suddenly dance off course,
my lips could not find each other in a smile.

Leaning over the banister, my neighbor
watched me with disgust but without insincerity.
I tried to give him some reward for his labor:
''Now I'll show you something really pretty.''

My illness was not short of curious features.
What I could make out almost extinguished hope,
the flashing of some wild and foreign creatures
like a drop of water under a microscope.

The shivering lashed at me more heavily,
driving into my skin sharp little nails,
just as the rain lashes at an aspen tree,
punishing all its little leaves with flails.

How fast, I thought, I stand but run away!
My muscles are achieving a mad velocity!
And my body, under some independent sway,
has an insolent familiarity.

It moves farther and farther from where I stand.
And what if suddenly it drops out of my grip
just as a ball slips out of a child's hand,
unwinding the thread around his fingertip?

I didn't like that at all.
                    I told the doctor,
although I was actually quaking in his presence:
"You must realize I am proud, and I abhor
my body's intolerable disobedience."

The doctor explained:
                    "Your illness is quite simple.
It would have been perfectly innocuous,
but the high-frequency wavelength of each tremble
stops me examining you—I just can't focus.

"It's like an object vibrating to and fro
when the speed of its tiny movements is so high
that visually it is reduced to zero
and looks like a weak nebula in the sky."

The doctor connected his golden instrument
to my indefinite distinctive marking,
the sharp waves of electricity went
washing through me, a chill green in their sparking.

And the pointer and the scale were horrified!
The mercury boiled up in furious jumps!
With a splash the glass committed suicide
and the dying splinters drew blood from my thumbs.

"For God's sake, Doctor, quick, look round."
But he announced,
                    quite unconcernedly:

"Poor thing, you're perfectly sound
and everything is functioning normally."

How sad it was! For I alone was aware
that I was part of the very highest normality,
that far above my intellect's narrow stair
extraordinary things were being enacted over me.

And my nervous system, trained to a fine excess
by the multidigital figure of my agony,
bursting out like a spring through an old mattress
tore my skin and twanged back upon me.

The enormous pulse that was crippling my wrist
boomed all the time, trying to free itself forever.
I cried: "To hell with it! Let it exist!
Let me choke with it, like St. Petersburg with the Neva!"

By night now my brain races, but also stops,
my hearing is so keen, so excited by silence
that whenever a door squeaks or a book drops
I think it's a shot, I'm done for, the last violence.

Yes, there were beasts at me that could not let go,
blood-drinkers I did not dare to tame.
Wherever I went, always a draft would blow,
flaring a candle, then snuffing out its flame.

In my pupils hanging over the cliff of my face
tears always shone, without any moderation.
I blighted everything, I would have been a menace
to paradise, in the hell of my negation.

The doctor wrote me out a prescription
in the usual scrawl of a latinate lunatic,
and with wisdom blossoming without inhibition
the girl in the chemist's read it like playing from music.

And now my old home is growing soft and young
with the salubrious kiss of tincture of valerian,

and the insidious medicine with its peppermint tongue
has licked my wounds of their corruption.

My neighbor is in splendid spirits now.
He sends his children round with congratulations
on my remarkable recovery, and how
he has praised me to the local administration.

I've paid back all my debts and all my visits,
answered all my letters. I promenade
in circles, deriving exquisite benefits,
allow myself to keep no wine in my cupboard.

There is not a sound, not a soul around me.
My desk is a desert, my papers dusty plateaus,
my pencils, blunt and illiterate, surround me,
jabbing their little snouts into the shadows.

Each step I take is slow, the reins held tight,
hobbling like a horse being broken in.
Everything of course is fine! But then, at night
I'm worried by a dangerous premonition.

The doctor doesn't see what I've secreted,
he has no idea when I am pulling his leg.
You know, everything he prescribed and treated
I could demolish as easily as breaking an egg.

I'm like a snail hid in its bony coffin,
saved by the blindness and silence that cover me,
but painfully at first, then tickling and softening
my forehead, the horns of aerials rise up over me.

A falling star of myriad dots and dashes!
I call on you, fall down! Let my heart crack,
shivering in the pure silver flashes
of the mermaid's icy tail burning my back!

Fever, beat on my drawn skin with your drumstick,
don't spare me, I'm yours! Without you I am lost!

I am a ballerina to your music!
I am the frozen puppy of your frost!

I do not shiver yet, oh no, not I,
there is no possibility of that.
But my prudent neighbor with the foreseeing eye
looks somewhere else when we meet outside my flat.

MOTOR SCOOTER

How I envy you the flying track
of your wheels, O pink motor scooter!
I watch it without holding back
those causeless tears that flow at the start of summer.

And to the girl, pressing herself
against the rider with a triumphant, fatal smile,
I seem like a snail, pressing myself
to a leaf for an interminable while.

Good-by! Above me your track lies,
fading into the green distance of the trees.
Two rainbows, two bright lights, two skies,
your shameless girl, are burning at your knees.

And your body is visible through your raincoat
like the thin stalk of a flower through water and glass.
Suddenly strange weeping cries float
to me, to freedom, like a bird flying over grass.

That's your voice, faint and slight,
you sing simply, but of eternity.
But you see, the gaiety of your flight
is balanced by my immobility.

For you, on the upswing of the seesaw,
the giddiness at the high point isn't dangerous,
for at the other end I restore
in opposition the downward impetus.

While silence settles down on me
your racket clatters across a distant lawn,
while I tread along heavily
you have spread two green wings and are airborne.

Then shoot past me . . . I'm still here.
Then chatter on . . . my silence is sedate.
And your lift to the stratosphere
is completely expiated by my dead weight.

33

THE WAITRESS

But now a queen is walking by,
her earring slowly swaying.
Humbly each young man lowers his eye
and hears what her foot is saying.

She is rustling with the slide of silk.
Her eyes have moist places.
Suddenly everyone is struck
by the shock of her eyelashes.

How splendidly she walks away!
A waitress, never spilling
an arm-high glass, in the café
under the pale blue ceiling.

The customer reading the menu begins
what she can always expand,
and the snowy lances of the napkins
soar up under her hand.

And the unapproachably severe
starched crown upon her curls
floats over her correct coiffure
as white and cool as pearls.

AUTUMN

Not working, not making a sound,
the beehive drowns into its essence.
The autumn grows more profound,
the soul more round from its experience.

It is involved in the form
the fat fruit takes from the slender sprays.
How tedious work becomes in autumn,
how heavy every phrase.

Days grow more burdensome
with Nature's deliberate opulence,
as idleness that seems like wisdom
overshadows your mouth with silence.

Even a child may ride
a bicycle,
pedaling like mad,
and suddenly look at the wide
world and feel serene and sad.

WINTER

O winter's gesture in me,
with its chilling discipline.
Yes, in winter there must be
some healing, as in medicine.

Otherwise, why then,
so trustingly, does my sickness
suddenly stretch its hand
to it, from anguish and darkness?

O my darling, practice
magic, let your familiar ring
with its ice-cold kiss
touch my forehead with healing.

And stronger and stronger the craze
to confront deceit with honesty,
to be able to bear the gaze
of dogs, to press against a tree.

To forgive, as if in play,
take a running jump, make a quick turn,
and having cleared it that way
to be able to forgive another person.

To take a winter day
and become forever its equal,
managing to stay
within its perfect, empty oval.

to reduce oneself to zero
to be able from behind the wall
to summon not my shadow
but light not blocked by me at all.

SMALL AIRCRAFT

Ah, surely I've got troubles enough
nearly sending me daft—
it really does seem a bit rough
to be dreaming about small aircraft.

They don't mind that in my dreams
they appear now like fledglings who pick at
grains in my palm, now to live like a cricket
in my wall is one of their schemes.

Or one with its silly nose
comes bumping against me, like a fish
making a child laugh, all ticklish,
by swimming into his toes.

At times they crowd in and blind
themselves flying around my light,
stopping me reading, their whispering flight
brushing the edges of my mind.

One thing more: they moan
like tearful children no one calms,
crying, "Take us in your arms,"
not letting my knees alone.

You chase them away—from the darkness
they are back again with you, in high
polish their long bodies float by,
looking sideways like dachshunds.

PAGES FROM A POEM

I

I'll begin from far away, not here, but there,
I'll begin from the end, which actually is the beginning.
The world was like the world. And this means winning
anything in the world of which you are aware.

In that district there was a wood, like a vegetable garden—
not very big, but enough for relaxation.
There, by the chance of a childish miscalculation,
everything was right and wrong, a blessing and a burden.

There was a house like all houses, on a small
clearing of calm. Being interpreted,
this meant that a woman living there shook her head
and the lamps were lit well before nightfall.

Work there was easy as a lesson in composition.
And someone—who it was we ourselves
didn't know—was offering up prayers to the heavens
for the sin of our imperfect comprehension.

He was guilty of equilibrium, of being able
to balance good and evil. And the earth
flew carelessly on, sure of her own worth,
while a candle was burning high above the table.

For ignoramus and liar forgiveness was equal.
What's the difference?—facing the wide
world, allowing us to turn aside,
he made atonement for the guilt of all.

But when the gap in air he left behind
opened around the world, then toward the east

(TRANSLATORS' NOTE: Boris Pasternak lived and is buried at
Peredelkino.)

Nature, slowed down by that shock, released
our bodies and made us light as wind.

The immensity of space, taken by surprise,
watched us, miserably congregated,
and no one any longer compensated
for the dreariness of all our petty vice.

For many people that house was a landmark,
a place to come to. And those two boys in striped shirts
entered the garden without fear of hurt,
with the raspberries around them growing dark in the dark.

It so happened that I also came,
but I am alien to the modern style
of rushing in with the immediate smile
and calling strangers by their Christian name.

It was night when I was there, proud
to be gazing at the house, to address my prayer
to it, to the garden, to the raspberries hidden there—
I didn't dare to say that name out loud.

Autumn was well advanced, it no longer abounded
with proofs of summer, being merely a conclusion.
At that time no one had penetrated the illusion
that the roundness of the year was not rounded.

Avoiding any place where he might go
I went through the trees, toward the fated meeting,
into the space of his face, his slow speaking . . .
But to rhyme in the presence of your name?

Oh no!

Unexpectedly he came out of a wretched thicket of
Peredelkino's trees late in the evening, in October, more
than two years ago. He was dressed in the coarse, clean
rig of a hunter: a blue raincoat, high boots, and white
knitted mittens. From tenderness for him and my own

pride, I could hardly bear to see his face—only the bright white flashes of his hands blinded the corners of my eyes.

He said, "Oh, how do you do! I was told all about you, and I recognized you at once." And suddenly, with unexpected emotion, he begged me, "For God's sake! Forgive me! I must telephone, this very minute!"

He went into a little building, some kind of an office, for a moment, but abruptly came back, and in the pitchy darkness my eyes were struck, as if they had been splashed, by the brilliant pallor of his face, by his forehead, by his cheekbones luminous in the pale moonlight. He stirred an icy-sweet Shakespearean chill in me. Terrified, he asked me, "Aren't you cold? It's getting toward November!"—and, embarrassed, backed awkwardly into a low doorway.

Leaning against a wall, I heard him with my body, like a deaf person. He was speaking to someone as if persistently making excuses to him, surrounding him with attention and love in his voice. With my back and palms I was absorbing the wonderful modulations of his voice— the swelling, foamy phrases, the good oriental muttering transformed into an inarticulate trembling and humming of wooden partitions. I myself and the house and the bushes around were all spontaneously caught up in the embrace of this lovingly rounded, majestically delicate intonation.

Then he came out, and we walked a little way over ground that was overgrown with stumps and twigs and crossed by fences. It was extremely difficult walking. But somehow he easily mastered the rough chasms that thickened around us, as if quite at home—at home with the bulging, cheaply glistening stars, with the cavity where the moon should have been, with the coarsely placed, comfortless trees.

He said, "Why don't you ever come to see me? Sometimes nice, interesting people do visit me—you won't be bored. Do come! Come tomorrow!"

Because I was feeling faintly giddy I answered almost arrogantly: "Thank you, I'll come, somehow, without fail."

From the forest, like an actor emerging from the scenery,
he suddenly brought a splendid gesture out
into the open, with no audience to shout
applause—and stretched out both his hands to me.

He was both theater and himself, combining
in that ancient scene in which the actor rejoices.
It's starting! The lights are going out! Through the voices
the light-blue phosphorus is already shining.

—Oh, how do you do! It's getting toward November—
Aren't you cold?—No more. And that is all.
Always kind to human and animal.
The part he could play without having to remember.

That's how to play one's part—Forever! For the wild
joy of it! Solemnly! Without a trick!
To tears! The way he has played it, like lapping milk,
playing with the world like an animal or a child.

Well, good-by!—it's generally not the custom
to sing this way. But in theaters they sing this way,
they finish this way the soliloquies of that play
in which death and love make up the question.

Already the curtain! In the darkness lights swim!
But it's not over yet—Do drop in! Tomorrow!—
such spontaneous fires of hospitality glow
for no one else but Georgians and him.

Somewhere in the world such a house should have a brother
which I can enter—it's impossible! I don't know.
And because of that, always too wary to go,
I didn't visit him the next day or another.

I was weeping among the stars, the dachas, and the trees,
after the performance, in the stalls lapsing into darkness
where the children, sensing the meaning of first loss,
are crying so hard, a crying nothing can appease.

41

He declared: "Between the hothouses
and ice floes, just south of paradise,
playing upon a children's pipe,
there exists a second universe,
and this is known as—Tiflis."

Eye-scalding, cool in the hand,
my beloved, my source of tears—Tiflis!
from Nature the shape of a concave cornice
where God, abstracted and capricious,
let a miracle stand.

My eyes began to darken,
my mistakes were falling like a projectile
while that city lay in a semicircle
trembling, hovering like the smile
on the blessed lips of Tamara.

I don't know for what joy or ache
it has closed its oval around me,
for life, death, completely
made me forever a captive of Metekha.

Oh, if only I hadn't drunk
the river Kura's water!
And had never drunk
the water of the Aragva!

And had never been stung
by the sweetness of poison!
And had never sunk
face down in those pastures!

And returned with thanks
all those gifts, generous, Georgian!
Too late! The first sip is over,
and the intoxication is forever,
and God sees my dream of you—the river
deep down in the valley of the Alazan.

THE NIGHT BEFORE THE SEVENTH OF OCTOBER

When I was twenty-seven years old
I was lucky enough to enjoy the miracle
of living in the close circle of a household
widened by a garden's lovely circle.

I gave myself completely to the goodness
with which nature, always equable,
watches the withering in the pine forest
or decides the destiny of a vegetable.

I liked forgetting both sorrow and anger,
thought and speech, having no such duties,
tolerant of being cared for by a stranger
whose genius was the innocence of trees.

Suddenly I became healthy as grass,
pure in my soul as other plants in earth,
having no more wisdom than a pine tree has,
no more alive than just before my birth.

At night I used to smile up at the ceiling
at the empty gap, where near and clear to mark,
the obvious god who had wanted to see me smiling
and greeting him, showed whitely in the dark.

Paradise came so surely to my bed,
the great god wrapped such tenderness around me
that I would push the fringe back from my forehead
to make it easier to kiss, and sleep profoundly.

And then for an age, centuries of descent,
I dived down into the earth and trees,
and no one knew at all how great the torment
closed behind the door of my aloneness.

A TALE ABOUT RAIN IN SEVERAL EPISODES

With a Dialogue and a Children's Chorus

1. The Rain had not cleared away from me since morning.
   Oh, leave me alone! I kept on saying rudely.
   It retreated, but followed me again, sadly
   and devotedly as a little daughter.

   The Rain had fastened itself to my back like a wing.
   I reproached it.
   —Useless! Haven't you something better to do?
   In tears a gardener appeals to you!
   Fall on the flowers!
   I don't need what you bring!

   Meanwhile a ferocious heatwave had clamped down,
   the Rain was with me, neglecting all the world.
   Round about me in a dance children whirled
   as if they were chasing a sprinkler round and around.

   Cunningly I slunk into a café.
   At a corner table I sat incognito.
   The Rain like a beggar settled behind the window
   tapping at the glass that it had something to say.

   I went outside and with a supple slap
   wetness punished my cheek, but immediately
   the brave sad Rain apologetically
   brushed my lips with the warm scent of a puppy.

   I am sure I must have looked ridiculous.
   I tied a damp headscarf round my neck.
   The Rain was sitting on my shoulder like a monkey.
   And the town
   was a bit embarrassed by all this.

   Such evidence of my weakness made the Rain grin,
   it tickled my ear with the finger of a child.
   The drought quickened. Things wilted and dried.
   And I alone was drenched right to the skin.

2. But I had been invited to a house,
   people were waiting for what I had to say,
   where over the amber lake of the parquet
   the clear moon of the candelabra rose.

   I thought: What shall I do with the Rain when I call?
   You know, it's got no intention of departing.
   It'll leave marks on the floor. It'll wet the carpets.
   They'll never let me into the house at all.

   Sternly I explained:
   My kindness is often
   commented on, but it's not as big as the sea.
   It's most improper for you to go with me.
   But the Rain was looking at me like an orphan.

   —Oh, to hell with it, in you go!—I decided.
   What downpour of love draws you and me together?
   Oh, damn and blast this incomprehensible weather!
   The forgiven Rain went jumping on ahead.

3. The master of the house, my host, did me an honor
   which I did not deserve, I must admit.
   However,
   drenched to the skin like a water rat,
   at precisely six I was ringing at the door.

   The Rain had formed itself into a queue
   and was breathing pitifully, tickling down the back of my
   neck.
   Steps—the peephole—silence—the turning lock.
   I said, I'm terribly sorry,
   the Rain's come too.

   Would you mind if it stays in the porch and keeps quiet?
   It's too wet and also rather too elongated
   for the rooms.
   —What on earth?—My host was agitated,
   his normal, healthy face was turning white.

4. I must confess, I loved this house for its life.
   Lightness was always dancing in its air.
   Oh, corners would never injure elbows here,
   nor would fingers ever be slashed with a knife.

   I loved it : the way the silks of my hostess, covered
   by a shadowing scarf rustled slowly, quietly,
   and most of all, my sleeping beauty—
   the crystal—in the prison of a cupboard.

   That rosy seven-shaded glowing spectrum
   lifeless but lovely in its coffin of glass.
   But I came to my senses. Ritual greetings passed
   between us like arias and dances in an opera.

5. My hostess, to be absolutely honest,
   might not have looked at me with adoration,
   but the fear of being thought old-fashioned
   checked her a little, though perhaps not for the best.

   How are you ? (Oh, the flashing of the lightning's flood
   dammed in the slender neck of a proud woman !)
   Thank you, I said, I think I'm still human,
   though I've wallowed in fever like a pig in the mud.

   (At this stage something was causing me some pain.
   You see, having made my bow, I wanted
   to say :
   My life is empty, but it seems good today,
   especially so, as I am seeing you again.)

   She began to speak :
   You're the one to blame.
   For goodness' sake ! With such talents !
   All through the rain ! And the distance !
   Everyone shouted :
   Get warm by the fire, by the flames !

   Some time, in some other period of time,
   in a square, amidst the music and the swearing

we could have met, with drums and trumpets blaring,
you could have cried :
To the fire with her, to the flame !

For all of it ! For the Rain ! For then ! For after !
For the black magic of the eyes' blackest berries,
for the sound from lips, for the stones of cherries
flying through the air without any effort !

Greetings to you ! Fly out at me, jump,
fire, my brother, my dog of many tongues !
Lick my hands in your great tender love !
You are also the Rain ! You scorch but you are damp !

Your monologue is somewhat whimsical,
said my host, sounding a little put out.
But what's it matter, long life to the green sprout !
There's a certain fascination in young people.

Don't listen to me ! I admit I'm raving !
I begged him. The whole thing is the fault of the Rain.
All day it has been killing me like a demon.
It's because of the Rain that I've been misbehaving.

And suddenly I saw—through the window, there,
my faithful Rain, getting all blue and crying.
Only a trace of it, left in me, was lying
floating in my eyes like two tears.

6. One of the guests, like a dove over the eaves,
   all nebulous, lifting up her glass,
   asked, a little hostile and capricious,
   Is your husband as rich as everyone believes ?

   Is he rich ? I don't quite know. Well, maybe.
   But he's rich. His work is perfectly easy.
   Do you want to know a secret ?—there seems to be,
   inside me, something incurably beggarly.

   I instructed him in all the witch's arts—
   I was like that, not at all afraid of frankness.

And now he can turn anything precious
to a ring on water, a little beast, or grass.

Here, I'll prove it to you! Give me your ring.
Let's save the star from the little ring that locks it in.
Naturally she didn't give me her ring,
looking somewhere else as if the whole thing were baffling.

And, you know, here is another detail—
what appeals to me is to end my days in the gutter.
(Really, my tongue was getting swollen with rubbish.
Oh, the Rain was dictating over and over again.)

7. Rain, we'll remember it all long after now!
   Another guest, in a contralto voice,
   launched this inquiry:
   Who is it that endows
   those who have been gifted by God? And exactly how?

   Fever shook me like a rattle in a case:
   a slightly old-fashioned god like a professor,
   always ready to laugh with you or bless you,
   is coming toward you, to shade your brow with grace.

   And further—fly through the air's verticals,
   smashing your elbows and knees until they bleed
   against the snow, the air, corners of the streets,
   the bedsheets of hotels and hospitals.

   Do you remember that painted cupola
   of St. Basil's Cathedral, edged with teeth? Imagine—
   smashing against it with all your skin!
   Please sit down!
   She put me in my place in a fit of temper.

8. Meanwhile, for the guests' diversion,
   something was happening, new to me and dear:
   in the drawing room began to appear
   a lacelike, silver cloud of little children.

My dear hostess, forgive me, my wickedness will out.
I have been telling lies and acting like an ass!
An exhalation of unsullied glass
is rising from you as from a glassblower's mouth.

A container filled to bursting with your soul,
your very own child, molded so tenderly!
How precise the outline its contours are extending!
Don't judge me too harshly, it was out of my control.

My dear hostess, your evil genius
Is in despair all day, all night long
over your child, and, over your little son
it droops its great head downward to the dust.

The Rain called my lips toward her hand.
I was weeping:
Forgive me. Please try to understand.
Your eyes are very wise and very clear.

9. Just then a children's chorus sounded nearby:
   Ah, that's the way time flew—
   we need to have a little laugh!
   A certain Jew—
   ha-ha—he had a wife.

   His family had to sweat
   through all the heavy hours
   so that a single kopeck
   could grow to the size of a house.

   O little drop of metal
   full as honeycomb!
   You have arisen, vital
   as the sun in heaven's dome.

   All this is only meant to be
   a joke, our party trick.
   In the twentieth century
   we grow up gay and sick.

We are little children
but we grow up in a dream,
as in banks the copper hidden
takes on a golden gleam.

At our backs—a sweet chill
and the points of two wings.
Frost has begun to fill
our pores with aluminum.

So life will not be too vapid,
art, art for little men,
like someone else's baby
touches us now and then.

We will pay the penalty
for our careless parents. Hurrah!
O banality,
you are our comforting star.

Thanks to you, we will miss
tortures of wrath and pain.
Our queen, we humbly kiss
the hem of your velvet train.

10. Laziness like an illness closed in on me.
On my shoulder a stranger's hand was resting.
In my hand I warmed a wineglass like a nestling.
Its wide beak opened and closed at me.

My dear hostess, when your boy was at rest,
so soon asleep, did you feel a twinge of doubt
or sadness when you poured into his mouth,
into that craving wound, your poisoned breast?

What if in him, like a pearl in its secret place,
a spring of bended music was asleep?
Like the rainbow—in a white bud hidden deep?
Like a hidden muscle of beauty—in his face?

50

What if in Sasha—a Blok about to be?
O she-bear, what made it seem so very sweet
to go hunting with hungry, loving teeth
in the fur of your cub, and pick out God like a flea?

11. The hostess brought brandy, poured me out a nip.
You have a fever. Get warm by the fireplace.
Good-by, my Rain!
What gaiety, how nice
to make one's contact with the frost by tongue-tip!

What a strong smell of roses in the wine!
Wine, you alone are not guilty.
The atom of the grape is split in me.
In me a war of two different roses burns.

My wine, I am your defeated prince
lashed between the two saplings bent down.
Let fly! Don't be afraid! Let the execution
separate us with the sound of ringing.

I am growing vaster and vaster, kinder and kinder!
Look—already I am as kind as a clown,
at your feet, toppled over by a bow!
I feel squeezed already between the doors and windows.

O Lord, such kindness nothing can eclipse!
Hurry up! Pity to tears! Fall on my knees!
I love you. The shyness of a cripple freezes
my pale cheeks and gives a twist to my lips.

What could I do for you, anything, even once?
Humiliate me! Pitiless humiliation!
Here is my skin—naked with anticipation
like a canvas for paints! The space is clean for the wounds!

I love you boundlessly and without shame!
My embrace is rounded as the sky above us.
We come from the same fount. We are all brothers,
My boy, Rain! Please, come here quickly, Rain!

12. Over everyone's back there rippled an icy feeling.
    A horrible scream from the hostess cut the silence.
    And suddenly rusty orange signs
    floated across the expanse of the white ceiling.

    And—the Rain burst in in torrents! They chased
    it with basins, brushes and brooms bit at its legs.
    It tried to break away. It flew at their cheeks,
    rose in a transparent blindness before their gaze.

    It danced an unexpected cancan through the tussle.
    It sang as it played on the resurrected crystal.
    Over the Rain the house like a trap gritting
    its grip had begun to tear away the muscles.

    It bellied across the parquet, leaving wet trails
    and looking up at me with love and anguish.
    The men, hitching their trousers up above the ankles,
    came darting at it, driving in their heels.

    They bundled it up with rags and disgustedly
    wrung it out into the lavatory.
    Tearing my throat, which suddenly
    was hoarse and wretched,
    I shouted,
    Don't touch it! It belongs to me!

    Like a beast or a child it was capable of pain.
    May your children have bad luck and live in torment!
    Why did you dip your blind hands, ignorant
    of all secrets, into the blood of the Rain?

    The lady of the house whispered:
    Mark you,
    you still have got to answer for all this!
    I laughed:
    I'll answer without prejudice.
    I find you quite disgusting. Let me through.

    I looked so wretched passersby stopped in amazement.
    I kept saying,

Never mind. Leave me alone.
I'll be all right. Even this will soon be gone.
I was kissing a drop of water on the dry pavement.

The naked skin of the earth began to wince,
and the skyline around the city was turning pink.
The weather forecast bureau, plunged into panic,
has not promised any rainfall ever since.

WHAT HAS HAPPENED TO ME?

What has happened to me? Why can't I?
—powerless in a whole year-long eclipse
to write one single poem, and when I try,
stones of silence hanging on my lips.

But look! you'll say—there's a stanza already written,
it has four lines, it's ready like a meal.
That's not the point. I already have the habit
of simply letting word after word unreel.

My hand is familiar with the way they go.
That's not the point. But how was it before?
When something more than words began to flow—
not just a line. But what?—I'm not sure.

Yes, that, the other one, it could look after
my voice, do what it wanted, it knew no fears,
all by its bold self, it laughed like laughter
and cried in my mouth the cries that go with tears.

TO A. N. KORSAKOVA

In the spring, in the spring, in its first leaf,
grieving I lived on in distress.
But there in the shadows of my grief
how happy I was, nevertheless,

that in this house I loved so much,
among such loving, gentle folk,
my surplus of love and pain drifted up
into the sky like dangerous smoke.

What we were, each to each,
no one exactly knew—and yet
it was our destiny to reach
a unity like a closed circuit.

And you were here, a splendid watchdog,
you also, the responsible one,
above that friendly dialogue
of the torturer and the physician.

But in this tragedy we enacted
where we lost all we had or would,
the interval saved me, distracted
me like a dream about my childhood,

when my life was uncomplicated
and dinner simply laid before me,
like Alexandra Nikolayevna's
originality and beauty.

When I looked at her I understood:
Oh no, it is not for nothing
that we enter the unending world,
but for some mystery of doing.

Our agonies are always pointless
and one cannot count on what may be won
because our hands can match the canvas
with the colors they lay on.

No, it is not for nothing, the dinner
hot and savory, a break
in all misfortunes, and the children
promising to be good and eat their bread.

In the midst of a feast or on the rack,
now set for glory, now for ignominy,
not for nothing are we red or black—
they are equally our destiny.

MARINA

I love it, Marina, that you, like us all,
Like me
With my chilled throat
I don't say : You—like light ! like snow—
Squeezing my neck, as if gulping down ice,
I try to unfreeze a word : Like everyone else
They taught you music.

                          What a waste of teaching !
It was just as if, while the gods cried and laughed,
They tried to teach a candle the principles of light.
The two equal darknesses were at odds :
The grand piano and you—two perfect circles,
Lost in their mutual deafness-and-dumbness,
Tolerating each other's foreign tongue.
The two of you glared sullenly at each other
In a meeting both insoluble and hostile—
The grand piano and you—the two strong silences,
The two weak voices : of music and of song.
But your being an orphan gave you extra power,
And that settled it. What's a grand piano ?—
Merely the prisoner of silence until its ally
Digs her little finger into C sharp.
You're all alone. You can't expect any help.
And you have some difficulties in learning music,
Not troubling the one who is giving the wounds
To discover in herself the bleeding of the sound.
Marina ! C ! C of your childhood, C of your destiny,
C-D, C of your speech, C
Of all that afterward is shared,
As together we incline our heads
In that attitude common to all children at the piano.
How you, how you, stuck on a stool,
O merry-go-round, O nonchalance of Gedizke,
Unwind the equator whistling round one's head
Which already has whipped one's beret away !
Marina, all of that was planned

For beauty's sake, and I reckoned that with luck
I could satisfy myself with shouting : I'm like you! like you!
And I would have shouted just that, yet—but I'm crying.

ADVENTURE IN THE ANTIQUE SHOP

What for? Why not—as you enter thick aspens, and stop
to enjoy the peace and the laziness of walking
without calculating, without talking,
I entered the doorway of an antique shop.

The old antique dealer looked with scorn at me.
Had he not been weary of guarding the little flowers
of tender shabbiness for two centuries—
he would have never moved to open the door for me.

He had visions of the sudden demolition
of his fragile cups and ailing cut-glass chimes.
To him the bustling meanness of our times
rubbed up too close against him, hostile and alien.

Having chosen me from others, it was enough
to suffer some infamy he could not defy,
and hatred, taking the breath away from a sigh,
sprang up in him with the immediacy of love.

The rest of the crowd was after a good thing,
and a foreigner was trying, cold and clear,
to interpret an old-fashioned chandelier
with his hands making the cut-glass chorus sing.

Discovering that the voice of one pendant had flown
to pieces at some long-since-over ball,
petulantly he took umbrage at its fall,
felt miserable, and began to long for home.

An old woman was brushing a sad bright speck of dust
from the vale of shadows of a vase of glass,
and in her palm the whole weightlessness
of modern life and possessions felt ponderous.

How melancholy!—amidst these gloomy hothouses
to examine the autumnal expiration
of other people's things, in the illumination
of extinct fires and the gaze of lost faces.

And precisely then, in the revealed silence
sounded the cry of a certain scent or color:
An unknown soul's indistinct gesture
was appealing to me to come to its defense.

The little bugler of familiar pain
was blowing a call on the ridge of poetry—
That's how the object insists that it must be
and you run like a dog to the whistle once again.

I know these voices are nobody's of right.
O lament of all things to be glorified!
This mute request, violent with sobs, cried
like the one word "Help!" bursting out of the night.

In despair, having reached the extremity where I
struggled with my mute throat to radiate
all my requests, I rushed to meet this fate
and said, only beginning, "My child, don't cry."

"What do you want?" the antique dealer smoldered.
"Here all is dead, incapable of crying."
He, still hoping for success, was trying
to press me back, pushing me aside with his shoulder.

We stood for a moment, shoulder to shoulder, trembling,
brought close by enmity. I answered, glaring:
"I who have become an open wound of hearing
would like to hear every single thing."

"Go away!" he kept repeating angrily.
And suddenly, through the stupidity of my doubts
an inspiration of genius flashed out,
and let fly the words: "That case, give it to me!"

"That piece of lace?" "The case." "The clockface?" "The
case."
"The chased dish?" "For goodness' sake, the black leather
case!"

He turned pale and shouted: "God give me grace!
Whatever you wish, but not that particular case.

"I beg you, please don't be so enthusiastic!
You're a sweet young thing, you smell of gasoline!
Those modern shops, they'll know what you mean,
With their infinite variety of plastic."

I said: "You're really very kind to me,
but I'm afraid I think that plastic goods are dreadful."
He flattered me: "You're right. And beautiful.
You like the fragility of antiquity.

"I myself serve out its calendar.
Here is a locket, inside, a child's portrait.
Last century. So delicately made
and now, it's yours. It is a present, my dear."

. . . A sad angel with a sick little face.
An unearthly look. A diligent forehead. Limp hair.
A thunderstorm in July. Pneumonia.
He was closed up in the blackness of final space . . .

"I have enough sorrows in my own life
and here you offer me another way
of making miserable the rest of my days,
with his death, and his mother who went mad with grief?"

"Then take the dinner service for twenty-six!"
he cried, some new hope beginning to increase.
"It has a hundred extremely valuable pieces.
Take it for nothing—and then the problem is fixed."

"What generosity! Who could have known?
But twenty-five of all my possible guests
are always in Georgia or Budapest.
The service will be bored with me alone.

"A hundred pieces! How can I entertain them?
For goodness' sake, it's completely beyond me.

61

No, I value an object's unity.
Of course, you're well aware of my meaning.''

"Oh, I'm so tired!" the antique dealer groaned.
"I am two hundred years old. My soul rots.
Take everything! I am fed up with the lot!
It's all yours, everything I own.''

At that moment, he opened the case.
And, set at liberty from its dungeon,
a light shone from the dark passage, and singed
my eyelashes, and it was a woman's face.

Not by its features, but by its darkness
which scorched my mind, by the air thick as cement,
could I calculate its beauty's full extent
even before I could see it, in my first blindness.

With its half-smiling lips, its eyes half in darkness,
her face suggested a simple proposition:
To lose one's mind, to sink into dark perdition,
to ask for her hand and a transfer to the Caucasus.

And there for a lazy sniper to be allowed
his sights on the sparkling vulnerable back of one's head
once and for all—that's that. The shot-echoes are dead,
and in the sky there is either God or a cloud.

"My youth is a hundred and thirty years away,''
the sad antique dealer began to expand.
"Through the green of the lime trees, along the yellow of
the sand,
I used to visit that house and garden every day.

"Oh, I was in love with her for more than a year,
kissing the air and the stones in the garden as well,
when during his journey—to or away from hell—
that uninvited guest was suddenly there.

"Do you remember Hannibal? He was an expert
in all kinds of business, was very high-ranking.

But I'm telling you that Hannibal's great-grandson
suddenly by chance turned up in this spot.

''Ardently exhaling his native darkness
he sprang through the door. Everything was transformed.
The servants made crosses as in a thunderstorm.
My heart fought a terrible heaviness.

'' A strange draft struck. The glass became unstable.
The cupboard answered with broken crockery.
There was a breath of fire, then of icy mockery.
The candle went out. The guest sat down at the table.

''The candle was lighted, the light shone again,
bending toward her, immediately changing,
he lowered his eyes in that universal danger
of African slavery, like a horse just broken in.

''I whispered to her : 'He's odd, let me tell you,
though modest enough in size, that lessens the task.'
'Do you really think so ?'—that's what she asked.
'I think just the opposite is true.'

'' He was their guest for three days, the incarnation
of goodness, any advice he took as an order.
And when he left his eyes flashed like swords
and his laugh came from the fire-mouth of damnation.

''Since then a hint of grief has run like a ripple
across the tranquil surface of her face.
Her forehead shows how hard she tries to trace
its origins, but she cannot solve the riddle.

''When from the depth of warmth, from her dream,
a blind smile slowly broke the surface,
she took fright, as if by itself her face
had contradicted the truth of some well-known theme.

''But no, I did not go to the Caucasus.
I proposed to her. She gave me her answer. No.

I could not accept this, I refused to go,
and made a second and third proposal.

"In that century, in the year thirty-seven,
I think in winter, yes, in winter it was,
she died, without any obvious cause,
and in delirium. I was never sent for.

"Since then immortal with grief and love
I am in charge of this insignificant temple,
and lost somewhere between God and people
I talk with idiots and sell them junk.

"But I am still consoled by someone's comment
that of course he was killed, long ago, in a duel."
"He was not killed, and I am sick of you,"
I said, "even though you are innocent.

"Forgive me the desire of my hand to take
and possess. Let us share this, and that.
Mine the pure object, yours the beauty of the portrait:
as a reward, as a revenge, to please, whatever the
                                        mistake . . ."

The old man asked: "Did I make you miserable
by confessing all those fantastic misfortunes?"
"No, I was thinking of Hannibal's great-grandson,"
I said, "only he was pitiable."

And if suddenly the reader who can comprehend
all sciences, says, from his position of strength:
"All this is false, expounded at great length,"
I'll answer: "Of course, it all is false, my friend."

Our sober life would never be fulfilled
if antique dealers behaved like this to you,
and if things lived like living beings do,
and that other fellow really had been killed.

But no, the portrait is living on my wall!
And the tinkling of glass. And the slippers rustling as they
dance.
And the gloom of the candles. And to all appearances—
Hannibal's great-grandson takes part in it all.

FAREWELL

And at the very end I'll say:
Good-by, don't commit yourself to love.
I'm going mad. Or on the way
to madness pure as air above.

What did your love give me? A taste
of disaster. But not that finally.
What did your love give me? A waste
of ruins, but ruined so clumsily.

The cruelty of blank space. Or, you won't
be forgiven. My body is alive
and wandering in the world I want,
but my body is an empty hive.

My curving forehead still consents
to a little work. But my hands are slack,
and like a little flock, all sound and scents
leave me by an oblique track.

NUMBERS & LOSSES
in the CIVIL WAR *in*
AMERICA

By Thomas L. Livermore

NUMBERS & LOSSES

in the CIVIL WAR *in*

AMERICA: 1861-65

introduction by Edward E. Barthell, Jr.

———

CIVIL WAR CENTENNIAL SERIES

Indiana University Press 1957

BLOOMINGTON

FOREWORD

In his little book entitled *Numbers and Losses in the Civil War in America,* printed in 1900 and here reproduced without excision, Thomas L. Livermore stated that, if reduced to three-year terms of service, the total Union enlistments during the war numbered 1,556,678 as against 1,082,119 in the Confederate armies; and estimated the number of "effectives" under McClellan at the battle of Antietam to number 75,316 as against 51,844 commanded by Lee.

Culled pretty much at random from other sources, we find differing statements as to numbers engaged during the war on the opposing sides, viz:

	Union	*Confederate*
Woodrow Wilson's *A History of the American People* (1901)	1,700,000	900,000
Cazenove G. Lee in Volume XXXII of *Southern Historical Society Papers* (1907)	2,778,304	600,000
Encyclopaedia Britannica (1954)	"more than" 1,000,000	"as many as" 500,000

Similarly, the opposing numbers engaged in the battle of Antietam are differently reported, viz:

	Union	*Confederate*
McClellan's comprehensive report of the organization and operations of the Army of the Potomac (1863)	87,164	97,445

	Union	Confederate
Walter Taylor's *General Lee*		"a fraction over"
(1906)	87,164	35,000
Account of Richmond *Inquirer*		
reproduced in Moore's *Rebel-*	"about"	"about"
lion Record (1863)	150,000	60,000
Comte de Paris' *History of the*		"no less than"
Civil War in America (1875)	66,000	40,000

Discrepancies, of which the foregoing are typical, can never be resolved accurately because full contemporaneous reports, especially of Confederate numbers and losses during the ending phases of the war, were never made. But, by painstaking and intelligent research through the *Official Records* and other reliable sources, Livermore was able to come up with a compilation so nearly approximating verity that it has been accepted for more than half a century and cited by thoughtful writers, both North and South, without too much begrudging. Among those who in recent years have made honored references in their bibliographies have been: James Ford Rhodes in his *History of the United States;* Stanley F. Horn in his *The Army of Tennessee;* William Roscoe Livermore in his continuation of John Codman Ropes' *The Story of the Civil War;* Robert Selph Henry in his *The Story of the Confederacy;* Kenneth P. Williams in his *Lincoln Finds a General;* E. Merton Coulter in his *The Confederate States of America;* T. Harry Williams in his *Lincoln and His Generals;* John P. Dyer in his *The Gallant Hood;* Bruce Catton in his *A Stillness at Appomattox;* Gilbert E. Govan and James W. Livingood in their *A Different Valor.*

Thomas Leonard Livermore was born at Galena, Illinois, where, as a seventeen-year-old youth on vacation

from his schooling at Lombard University in Galesburg, he was inspired to enlist for Federal military service not only by his own and his father's wishes but perhaps also by the examples of his older acquaintances, among whom were Ulysses S. Grant and John A. Rawlins. His "second home," as he says in his autobiographical *Days and Events,* had been with relatives at Milford, New Hampshire, and, hastening to Poolesville, Maryland, by way of Washington, he patriotically lied about his age and was accepted on June 14, 1861 as a private in the First New Hampshire Regiment of three-months volunteers with the army of General Robert Patterson.

After being mustered out on August 12, 1861 he re-enlisted as a sergeant in the Fifth New Hampshire Volunteers and was successively promoted through intervening grades until, at the war's end and before his twenty-second birthday, he had become Colonel of the Eighteenth New Hampshire Regiment—an organization composed largely of conscripts.

The highlights of Livermore's war experiences were many and varied.

As a private: He saw no fighting, but moved here and there in Maryland and in the lower Shenandoah Valley with the rest of Patterson's army in what proved to be the unsuccessful effort to prevent the junction around Bull Run of the Confederate forces of Generals Johnston and Beauregard.

As a sergeant: He was now and thereafter a member of the Federal Army of the Potomac, was on the march through evacuated Centreville and Manassas Junction to the Rappahannock, sailed to Fortress Monroe, waited

out the siege of Yorktown, made camp as a part of Sumner's corps on the north bank of the Chickahominy (where he assisted in building the Grapevine Bridge), and was engaged actively in the second day's fighting of the battle of Seven Pines or Fair Oaks.

As an acting-quartermaster and second lieutenant: He fought in the engagements of The Seven Days' Battles known as the Peach Orchard or Allen's Farm, White Oak Swamp or Frazier's Farm, and Malvern Hill— where he was wounded in the leg. After a short recuperation in the hospital at Alexandria, he returned to his regiment to witness the fighting at South Mountain and to take an active part in the battle of Antietam, where his division commander, General Israel B. ("Old Dick") Richardson, was mortally wounded. His duties as a quartermaster kept him from participation in the actual fighting at Fredericksburg; but he saw the bloodily repulsed charges of his comrades against the Confederate prepared positions and remarked the "strategy" of General Burnside in waiting a month for pontoons while the standing piers of the old bridge over the Rappahannock might have been covered with timbers taken from houses close at hand.

As an acting-quartermaster and first lieutenant: He continued in camp service after the battle of Fredericksburg, and was promoted to captain on March 3, 1863.

As a captain: Neither he nor his company, in Couch's Second Corps, appear to have participated in more than token fighting at the battle of Chancellorsville; but they later were part of an elite group who served as infantry support for Pleasonton's cavalry in their great battle with Stuart's Confederate troopers at Brandy Station.

As a captain and chief of ambulances: He attained staff status as a member of the Second Corps headquarters, serving at the battle of Gettysburg under Hancock until that gallant commander was wounded, and later under Gibbon. Thereafter he continued his gruesome duties of supervising the removal of the dead and wounded of the Second Corps in the Mine Run campaign, during which his new chief—Warren, who had succeeded Gibbon—graciously made a morning apology for overdrinking on a preceding night when they had been together.

Reverting to his active captaincy: He was now assigned with his company to guard Confederate prisoners at Point Lookout, Maryland. He must have demonstrated in this new job his unusual talent for managing men, because he was shortly assigned and performed the task of organizing a regiment to fight for the Union from those of his prisoners who wished to renounce the Confederacy and take an oath of allegiance to the United States.

Appointed as quartermaster: He took over the duties of that office in General Edward W. Hincks' Third (Colored) Division of the Eighteenth Corps, with which he accompanied General Benjamin F. Butler in his occupation of City Point and Bermuda Hundred.

Appointed as acting assistant inspector-general: He again attained corps staff rank with General William F. ("Baldy") Smith, as inspector of the Negro troops in his Eighteenth Corps. While holding this position he had almost a box seat from which he saw not only the explosion of the mine beneath the Confederate defense line at Petersburg but also the sanguinary fighting

that followed, during most of which General Burnside remained under a covered way.

Appointed as assistant inspector-general: He returned to staff rank with the Second Corps under Hancock and was present at the battle of Boydton Plank Road.

Successively promoted to major and lieutenant-colonel: He made a short visit to his home at Galena, but returned to his duties on the staff of the Second Corps, now commanded by General Humphreys, in good time to participate in the Union assault on the Confederate lines around Petersburg on April 2, 1865 and, on April 7, to gain honorable mention in Humphreys' official report for his brave exertions in saving for Union crossing the railroad bridge over the Appomattox river which had been set on fire by Lee's retreating army.

As a full colonel: He saw no further fighting, drilled his conscript regiment around Washington, suffered a bad injury by running his racing horse into an ox at Georgetown, viewed the grand parades of Meade's and Sherman's armies, and was mustered out of service in July, 1865.

After returning to civilian life, still as a young man, Livermore studied law and first engaged in its practice at Concord, New Hampshire. Some time later he became the manager of the Amoskeag Mills at Manchester and continued in the position for seven years before resuming his law practice, this time at Boston. Here he remained until death in 1918, the business hours of his last twenty-one years being spent as Vice-President of the Calumet & Hecla Mining Company.

His business success undoubtedly produced both relationships and opportunities conducive to his produc-

tion of the work here reprinted, for so early as 1881 he was elected Commander of the Massachusetts Commandery of the Loyal Legion, and during his later years he was elected several times to be President of the Massachusetts Military Historical Society, an organization founded by his good friend John Codman Ropes.

As previously stated, the book here reprinted was first published in 1900. It may have been pure coincidence that in the same year the Massachusetts Commandery of the Military Order of the Loyal Legion first published its roster; but it is of high significance that, as active members, the roster named Thomas L. Livermore, Thomas L. Livermore, Jr. and 880 others. When we see also, in the long list of members with whom our author was associated, the names of George H. Gordon, Thomas W. Higginson, Francis W. Palfrey and John C. Ropes—and when we scrutinize his educational, military, and business background—we may rightfully suppose that no mediocre or slipshod work could leave his hands for public inspection.

The steadily increasing recognition by informed current writers of the authoritative value of Livermore's *Numbers and Losses* adds assurance that the book—now scarcely obtainable in its original printing—should be in the library of every student of our Civil War. In making it newly available the Indiana University Press is performing a commendable and discerning service.

EDWARD E. BARTHELL, JR.

Ludington, Michigan
March 12, 1957

PREFACE

THIS volume has grown from an essay which was read before the Military Historical Society of Massachusetts, February 23, 1897. Later research and study have led to changing many of the figures given in that essay. This is notably true of the numbers given for the strength of the armies engaged in the different battles. In the essay the number of those "present for duty" was used, but here, for reasons given in their place, the number of "effectives" is taken. This will explain, and excuse the author for, discrepancies between citations made by others from the former essay and the figures here given.

The articles "Military Training," in the Journal of the Military Service Institution of July, 1893, and "General Thomas in the Record," in volume x. of the Military Historical Society of Massachusetts, were written before the studies for this volume were begun; and while, for the comparisons made in those articles, their figures do not need much if any amendment, they must give place to those given in this volume as an exact statement of numbers and losses.

The author cannot hope that he has found everything in the 129 volumes of War Records that should be considered in a work like this, and it is hardly probable that he has entirely avoided errors in transcribing so many figures and making so many calculations, but he

trusts that the citation of volume and page for every number given will result in the correction of any that exist by those who use this work.

The author earnestly hopes for criticism and amendment of what he has written, wherever they seem to be due, and especially by the survivors of those who were actors, on both sides, in the great events upon which this work touches.

T. L. L.

Boston, June 1, 1900.

NUMBERS & LOSSES
in the CIVIL WAR *in*
AMERICA

ABBREVIATIONS.

W. R. — War Records. The volumes are cited by the " serial " numbers which from volume xxxi. are printed on the backs. It will facilitate reference for the reader to number prior volumes in the same manner.

M. and D. — Messages and Documents of the War Department, 1865–66.

Reg. Losses. — Regimental Losses in the American Civil War, by William F. Fox.

Va. Camp. — The Virginia Campaigns of 1864 and 1865, by Andrew A. Humphreys.

M. H. M. — Military Historical Society of Massachusetts.

Van Horne. — History of the Army of the Cumberland, by Thomas B. Van Horne.

NUMBERS AND LOSSES

CIVIL WAR IN AMERICA

TOTAL NUMBER IN THE UNION ARMY.

THE enlistments in the Union army during the War of the Rebellion numbered 2,898,304.[1] This number includes about 230,000 militia and "emergency men," who served for short terms, and some part of whom were not mustered into the United States service.

The term of service (expiring by the terms of enlistment or by the close of the war), under 1,580,000 of these enlistments, was from two weeks to fourteen months.

The number of individuals under arms was considerably less than the number of enlistments, because of repeated enlistment by individuals. It is probable that many of the 200,000 men who served for short terms in 1861 and 1862 enlisted again. Over 200,000 men reënlisted in the veteran regiments, the Veteran Reserve Corps and Hancock's Veteran Corps.[2]

TOTAL NUMBER IN THE CONFEDERATE ARMY.

It is most disappointing that the mass of records which have been published by the War Department

[1] See post, p. 50.   [2] M. and D., Part III. 58–93.

contains no summary of the number who were under arms on the Confederate side. General Cooper, the adjutant-general of the Confederate army, stated soon after the war that no such summary existed.[1] The officials of the War Records Office, because of the incomplete and fragmentary character of the data in their possession, have never attempted to fix the number. As far as the writer has been able to learn, neither of the Confederate States kept a record of the number of men furnished to the Confederate service, and the statistics which can be obtained from the state authorities are far from complete.

ESTIMATES OF CONFEDERATE WRITERS.

The total number of men in the Confederate armies has been estimated at 600,000 to 700,000 by General Marcus J. Wright,[2] and at about 600,000 by General Early,[3] Alexander H. Stephens,[4] and Dr. Joseph Jones,[5] surgeon-general of the United Confederate Veterans; but, excepting the last-named, neither of these writers gives the source of his figures, and, as will appear below, the largest of these estimates is too low. It is a part of human nature which persuades the losers in war to believe that the result must have come from a great disparity in numbers. The sustained conflict and terrible loss of four years of war placed the reputation

[1] So. Hist. Society Papers, vii. 290.

[2] So. Hist. Society Papers, xix. 254.

[3] So. Hist. Society Papers, ii. 20.

[4] The War between the States, ii. 630.

[5] So. Hist. Society Papers, vii. 289. Pamphlet entitled United Confederate Veterans, published at New Orleans, 1892, in files of M. H. M., p. 6.

of Southern valor so high that exaggerated statements of numbers cannot further exalt it in the estimation of the world. To prove that the estimated ratio of four to one between the two armies is not founded in fact does not diminish that reputation. The result of the war depended much upon the superiority of the North in material resources. This outweighed many men. On the other hand, it would not disparage Northern courage to establish a large disproportion in numbers, in view of the defensive attitude of the South, and the necessity of invading and occupying a constantly enlarging territory which was forced upon the Northern army. This required many more men than mere battles upon equal terms would have required.

Dr. Jones, in arriving at the estimate above mentioned, takes the following statistics of casualties in the Confederate army, furnished by General Cooper : —

Killed in battle, 1861–65	53,973
Wounded, 1861–65	194,026
Captured, 1861–65	202,283

and the following from the returns of the Confederate field and general hospitals for 1861–62 : —

Killed		19,897
Deaths in field hospitals from wounds . . .	1,623	
Deaths in general hospitals from wounds . .	2,618	
Deaths in field hospitals from disease . . .	14,597	
Deaths in general hospitals from disease . .	16,741	
		35,579
		55,476
Total wounded		72,713
Prisoners		51,072
Discharged		16,940

He assumes that the mortality from wounds and disease in 1863–64 equaled that in 1861–62, that 100,000 deserted or were discharged, and that 20,000 died in Northern prisons, and states that "at the close of the war, the available active force in the field numbered scarcely 100,000 men;" and from all these figures he calculates the number serving in the Confederate army during the war at 600,000, as follows : —

Grand total deaths from battle, wounds, and disease   200,000
Losses of Confederate army in prisoners during the war, on account of the policy of non-exchange adopted and enforced by the United States   . . 200,000
Losses of the Confederate army from discharges and desertions during the years 1861–65 100,000
Available active force in the field at close of war   . 100,000
                                                        ————
                                                       600,000

This estimate does not conform to the statistics cited by Dr. Jones. The mortality from wounds and disease in 1861–62, as shown by the citation from the hospital returns, was 35,579, and assuming, as Dr. Jones does, that the mortality from the same cause was the same in 1863–64 as in 1861–62, we arrive at a total of 71,158 ; and adding the 53,973 killed in battle given by General Cooper, the total deaths would appear to be 125,131, instead of 200,000, as stated by Dr. Jones. Against the 100,000 desertions and discharges estimated by him, the hospital returns as cited give only 16,940 discharges and no desertions. On the other hand, to Dr. Jones's estimate of 100,000 in the field at the close of the war it would be necessary to add those borne on the rolls as absent from the field to arrive at the total number in the army at the close of the war.

ESTIMATE BASED ON CONFEDERATE MUSTER-ROLLS
IN UNITED STATES WAR DEPARTMENT.

There is exact and indisputable evidence upon which the numbers, as estimated by Dr. Jones and the other writers above mentioned, must be greatly enlarged. In the United States War Department there are Confederate muster-rolls[1] which record the casualties of a considerable portion of the Confederate regiments for periods which average about two years. A tabulation of the losses there recorded shows —

Killed in action	52,954
Died of wounds	21,570
Died of disease	59,297
Deserted	104,428
Discharged	57,762
Total	296,011
From which perhaps there should be deducted for deserters, who were returned to the ranks[2]	21,056
Leaving	274,955

Colonel Fox, in his "Regimental Losses," says : "A summing-up of the casualties at each battle and minor engagement, using official reports only, and in their absence accepting Confederate estimates, indicates that 94,000 men were killed or mortally wounded during the war." And referring to the tabulation from the Confederate muster-rolls above referred to, he says : "If the Confederate rolls could have been completed and then revised,— as has been done with the rolls of the Union regiments,— the number of killed as shown above (74,524) would be largely increased. As it is,

[1] M. and D., Part III. 141.
[2] M. and D., Part III. 139.

the extent of such increase must remain a matter of conjecture." And he adds that the number of killed in the Union army, obtained by a similar tabulation of its muster-rolls, was afterwards increased 15,000 by "final statements" and affidavits filed at the Pension Bureau. In this revision all who died of wounds were included, whereas, in the reports of battles, only those who died on the field were usually reported among the killed and mortally wounded, and the large numbers of wounded who afterwards died of their wounds in the hospitals were reported as wounded. Many reported at the close of the action as missing were in fact killed in action.[1]

In view of the absence of Confederate reports of actions where large losses must have occurred, notably in 1864 and 1865, any summing-up of the casualties from the reports must necessarily be incomplete, and the number (94,000) arrived at by Colonel Fox can be accepted only as a minimum.

There is one measure which indicates that this number must be too small. Mr. Kirkley, the statistician of the War Department, states that in the Union army, excluding the missing in action, 67,058 were killed, and 43,012 died of wounds.[2] The same ratio would give 33,952 as the number who died of wounds, to the 52,934 returned on the Confederate muster-rolls as killed in action. The total of 86,886 killed and died of wounds, thus reached, must be much below the full number, in view of the fact that the returns cover an

[1] Reg. Losses, 22, 47, 554.
[2] Reg. Losses, 24. The earlier statement of the War Department (M. and D., Part III. 72–80) is superseded by this statement.

average of only about two years, and include only 20
regiments of the 61 regiments and 38 battalions from
Alabama.[1]

The Confederate muster-rolls show that Dr. Jones's
estimate of desertions and discharges is too small by
40,873 at least; and his estimate of 100,000 as the
available force in the field at the close of the war is
proved to be too small by the record of 174,223[2] who
then surrendered.   A further addition of about 270,000
must be made for those on the rolls who did not then
surrender.[3]   Dr. Jones's estimate of 200,000 as the loss
in prisoners is too large.   Only 63,442 remained in
prison at the end of the war;[4] 1955 had enlisted in the
United States service,[4] and probably not over 40,000
died in prison.[5]

Corrected as above suggested, Dr. Jones's estimate
would stand as follows: —

Killed in action[6]	94,000
Died of disease	59,297
Loss in prisoners, about	105,000
Loss by desertion	83,372
Loss by discharge[6]	57,762
On rolls January 1, 1865 (less 63,442 prisoners)[7] .	381,761
	781,192

As this total of 781,192 includes, for discharges
and desertions, only those recorded in the incomplete
muster-rolls above referred to, it cannot be accepted as
adequate.   It is also to be remarked that 59,297 is,

[1] Post, p. 29.   [2] M. and D., Part I. 45.
[3] Post, p. 46.   [4] M. and D., Part I. 45.
[5] Reg. Losses, 50 and note.   [6] Ante, p. 5.
[7] Post, p. 46.

in all probability, too small a number for the deaths by disease.   There were 249,458 deaths [1] from disease and accident in the Union army, or 152 to a thousand men serving three years, computed below.[2]   The same ratio would have resulted in 164,000 deaths from the same causes, at 152 to a thousand men serving three years in the Confederate armies, as estimated below.[3]   It is reasonable to assume that the ratio of deaths from disease and accident was at least as great in the Confederate as in the Union Army.

The above estimate of the numbers in the Confederate army, thus increased to 885,000, would still want the desertions and discharges not recorded, and many men in the militia and irregular or temporary organizations which had served for varying terms, but which were not borne on muster-rolls above mentioned, or the returns of the armies at the close of the war.

Dr. Jones makes the following surprising statement: [4] " During the period of nineteen months, January, 1862, July, 1863, inclusive, over one million cases of wounds and disease were entered upon the Confederate field reports, and over four hundred thousand cases of wounds upon the hospital reports.   The number of cases of wounds and disease treated in the Confederate field and general hospitals were, however, greater during the following twenty-two months ending April, 1865.   It is safe to affirm, therefore, that more than three million cases of wounds and disease were cared for by the officers of the Medical Corps of the Con-

---

[1] Reg. Losses, 527.   [2] Page 50.   [3] Page 61.

[4] United Confederate Veterans, 5, 6 ; So. Hist. Society Papers, xx. 114.

federate army during the Civil War of 1861–1865. The figures, of course, do not indicate that the Confederacy had in the field an army approaching three millions and a half. On the contrary, the Confederate forces engaged during the war 1861–1865 did not exceed 600,000. Each Confederate soldier was, on an average, disabled for greater or less periods by wounds and sickness about six times during the war."

In the Union army, 318,187 were wounded (of these 43,012 died of wounds), and 67,058 were killed on the field.[1] The same ratio applied to 800,000, the least number which is deduced from Dr. Jones's statement for the wounded during the war, would give 168,000 as the number who died on the field, and 108,000 who died of wounds, — a total of 276,000. This is too large a number to be adopted without a critical examination of the Confederate hospital returns referred to. The writer has tried without success to learn where they might be found.

OTHER SOURCES OF INFORMATION ON THE QUESTION OF NUMBERS.

The method used above is not the only one which may be employed to arrive at the numbers in the Confederate army. The census of 1860 affords a very reliable basis for an estimate, when taken in connection with the acts of the Confederate Congress for enrolling the military population of the Confederate States, and the records of the measures taken for the enforcement of these acts. Statistics of numbers, more or less complete, have been gathered and published by a

[1] Reg. Losses, 47.

number of the Southern States, which are of value. Lists of the organizations in the Confederate service have been prepared by several compilers, to which the statistics of the strength of organizations contained in the War Records may be applied, and the returns of the armies in the field contained in the War Records afford the best evidence of the number of men in service from time to time. It is the purpose of this essay to present the conclusions drawn from all these sources. Sometimes the strength of bodies of troops whose numbers are not stated separately in the War Records is estimated. It is believed that the basis for such estimates has always been broad enough, and the methods of estimating conservative enough, to exclude serious error ; but such errors as may have resulted probably can be corrected by consulting the original returns in the War Records Office.

ESTIMATE BASED ON THE CENSUS OF 1860.

Substantially the whole military population of the Confederate States was placed under arms in the War of the Rebellion.

For about a year after the outbreak of hostilities, volunteering was relied on to fill the Confederate ranks. The earlier regiments were enlisted for twelve months, but the men in these regiments generally reënlisted under an act of the Confederate Congress of December 11, 1861; and before the terms of these earlier regiments had expired, the act of April 16, 1862, authorized the President to call and place in service for three years all white men resident in the Confederate States between the ages of eighteen and thirty-five

who were not legally exempt from military service, and also required all such persons who were then in the service to remain in service for three years, but it permitted those exempt from military service to serve as substitutes for those not exempt. President Davis, April 28, 1862, promulgated regulations for placing in the service all men to whom this act applied,[1] and April 30 the secretary of war announced in general orders that all such men were to be "enrolled for military service." [2] This law and the proceedings under it placed every man in the Confederacy who came within the definition of the law at once in the service, unlike the draft laws of the United States, which placed no one in service until selected by draft.

After the approval of this act of April 16, 1862, no law was passed for raising troops by volunteering from those liable to military service. An act approved September 27, 1862, enlarged the conscription to include all white males, not exempt, between eighteen and forty-five years of age.[3]

The Confederate authorities were very soon under pressure to thoroughly enforce the conscription laws. February 11, 1863, General Lee wrote to the secretary of war: " By the returns of last month forwarded to the department to-day, you will perceive that our strength is not much increased by the arrival of conscripts : only four hundred and twenty-one are reported to have joined by enlistment, and two hundred and eighty-seven have returned from desertion, making an aggregate of seven hundred and sixty-eight ; whereas our loss by death, discharges, and desertion amounts to

---

[1] 127 W. R., 1094.   [2] 127 W. R., 1104.
[3] M. and D., Part III. 121 ; 128 W. R., 160.

eighteen hundred and seventy-eight. Now is the time to gather all our strength, and prepare for the struggle which must take place in the next three months. I beg you to use every means in your power to fill up our ranks." [1]

Again, November 29, 1863, General Lee wrote to President Davis: " I think it a matter of the first importance that our armies now in the field shall be retained in service, and recruited by wise and effective legislation. This cannot be done too soon. The law should not be open to the charge of partiality, and I do not know how this can be accomplished without embracing the whole population capable of bearing arms, with the most limited exceptions, avoiding anything that would look like a distinction of classes." [2]   And again, January 25, 1864, he wrote [3] to the secretary of war, protesting against raising further companies of artillery and cavalry and organizations promising service near home which might allure men from the infantry, and said: " Already such organizations have in a good degree absorbed those men upon whom we relied to swell our reduced ranks for the coming campaign, and the consequences, in my judgment, involve the question of our ability to keep the field against the largely recruited armies of the enemy. Unless every man who belongs to the army be retained, and all fit for effective service be sent to it promptly so as to increase materially its present strength, we must rely for deliverance from our enemies upon other means than our arms. I trust that the truth of this assertion may be realized in time."

[1] M. and D., Part III. 121 ; 108 W. R., 680.
[2] 49 W. R., 853.   [3] 60 W. R., 1120.

In response to such demands as these, the Confederate Congress went to extremes in the following acts : —

An act of December 28, 1863,[1] prohibited conscripts from sending substitutes. An Act of January 5, 1864,[1] canceled the exemptions previously granted to persons liable to duty who had furnished substitutes. An act of February 17, 1864,[2] repealed all previous grants of exemption on whatever ground, and established a new and narrower list of exemptions, but gave the power to the Secretary of War under the President to exempt or detail such other persons as he might be satisfied ought to be exempted on account of public necessity.

This act also declared " that, from and after the passage of this act, all white men residents of the Confederate States, between the ages of seventeen and fifty, shall be in the military service of the Confederate States for the war." Under this act all within its scope were made a part of the army without the necessity of any proclamation, notice, enrollment, or other action by the authorities. It remained only for the military authorities to sweep the body of recruits thus created into the ranks. The thoroughness with which they performed this duty is indicated by the correspondence which is set out below.

April 30, 1864, the superintendent of the Confederate Bureau of Conscription, in reporting the work of his bureau from January 1, 1864, said : [3] " This report

[1] M. and D., 1865–66, Part III. 122 ; 129 W. R., 11, 12.
[2] M. and D., 1865–66, Part III. 121 ; 129 W. R., 178.
[3] M. and D., 1865–66, Part III. 122 ; 129 W. R., 354.

indicates but a very meagre portion of the work which has been performed. The results are the scanty gleanings from an almost unlimited and nearly exhausted field of labor, every inch of which has to be searched, analyzed, and classified, in every relation to the great problem of recruiting and maintaining the armies. No attribute which pertains to society or civil economy but has been subjected to the scrutiny and action of this bureau and its agencies. With the incompetent means under its control, all has been done which could be effected by zeal and diligence. The results indicate this grave consideration for the government that fresh material for the armies can no longer be estimated as an element of future calculation for their increase, and that necessity demands the invention of devices for keeping in the ranks the men now borne on the rolls. The stern revocation of all details, an appeal to the patriotism of the States claiming large numbers of able-bodied men, and the accretions by age, are now almost the only unexhausted sources of supply. For conscription from the general population, the functions of this bureau may cease with the termination of the year 1864. . . . The functions of conscription are now narrowed down to a system of delicate gleaning from the population of the country, involving the most laborious, patient, cautious, and intelligent investigation into the relations of every man to the public defense. There are but few left whose appropriate duties in these relations have not been defined, and it thence becomes the province of the conscription agents to weigh and determine whether those relations may not be disturbed for the purpose of sending more men into the field and

distributing them for the general service." Further along he speaks of certain selected officers " who were the practiced and trained soldiers and judges on whom I relied to sustain me in my hard duty of wringing from the wasted population the scanty remnant of men, and at the same time to preserve, as far as our military need would permit, the enfeebled productive energies of the country."

August 23, 1864, General Lee wrote to the Secretary of War : " Unless some measures can be devised to replace our losses, the consequences may be disastrous. I think that there must be more men in the country liable to military duty than the small numbers of recruits received would seem to indicate. . . . Our numbers are daily decreasing, and the time has arrived, in my opinion, when no man should be excused from service except for the purpose of doing work absolutely necessary for the support of the army. If we had here a few thousand men more to hold the stronger parts of our lines where an attack is least likely to be made, it would enable us to employ with good effect our veteran troops. Without some increase of strength, I cannot see how we are to escape the natural military consequences of the enemy's numerical superiority." [1]

September 2, 1864, he wrote to the President : [2] " I beg leave to call your attention to the importance of immediate and vigorous measures to increase the strength of our armies, and to some suggestions as to the mode of doing it. The necessity is now great, and will soon be augmented by the results of the coming draft in the United States. As matters now stand, we have no

[1] 88 W. R., 1199.   [2] 88 W. R., 1228.

troops disposable to meet movements of the enemy or strike when opportunity presents, without taking them from the trenches and exposing some important point. The enemy's position enables him to move his troops to the right or left without our knowledge, until he has reached the point at which he aims, and we are then compelled to hurry our men to meet him, incurring the risk of being too late to check his progress, and the additional risk of the advantage he may derive from their absence. This was fully illustrated in the late demonstration north of James River, which called troops from our lines here, who, if present, might have prevented the occupation of the Weldon Railroad. These rapid and distant movements also fatigue and exhaust our men, greatly impairing their efficiency in battle. It is not necessary, however, to enumerate all the reasons for recruiting our ranks. The necessity is as well known to your Excellency as to myself, and as much the object of your solicitude. The means of obtaining men for field duty, as far as I can see, are only three." These means he specifies as follows : 1st. Replacing all able-bodied white men employed as cooks, mechanics, and laborers with negroes, and sending them to the ranks. 2d. A rigid inspection of the rolls of exempted and detailed men, and placing all in the army who would not be entitled to discharge from the army. 3d. Calling out the entire reserve force (i. e. those below and above military age), who, he says, " can render great service in connection with regular troops by taking their places in trenches, forts, etc., and leaving them free for active operations ; " and he adds : " In my opinion the necessity for them will never be more

gent or their services of greater value than now ; and entertain the same views as to the importance of mediately bringing into the regular service every man liable to military duty."

September 26 he wrote [1] to General Bragg, then the commander of the Confederate armies : " I cannot impress upon you too strongly the imperious necessity of getting all our men subject to military duty to the field. We should have them with the armies now. . . . I get no additions. The men coming in do not supply the vacancies caused by sickness, desertions, and other casualties. If things thus continue, the most serious consequences must result. . . . If I had negroes to replace the teamsters, cooks, and hospital attendants, I could increase each division many hundred men. Unless they are sent to me rapidly, it may be too late."

October 4, 1864, he wrote to the Secretary of War,[2] again urging the employment of negroes, and as follows : " The men at home on various pretexts must be brought out and be put in the army at once, unless we would see the enemy reap the great moral and material advantages of a successful issue of his most costly campaign. I know it will produce suffering, but that must be endured, as all people engaged in a struggle like ours have done before. If we can get out our entire arms-bearing population in Virginia and North Carolina, and relieve all detailed men with negroes, we may be able, with the blessing of God, to keep the enemy in check to the beginning of winter."

October 5 the Secretary of War, in reply,[3] advised

[1] 88 W. R., 1292. [2] 89 W. R., 1134.
[3] 89 W. R., 1135.

him that orders had been issued to carry out his requests, including the employment of all free negroes between eighteen and fifty and some 14,000 slaves. October 10 General Lee also wrote [1] that he thought that a reëxamination of all the men exempted because of physical disability would secure some recruits, and he added : " From all the information I get, Grant's army is being heavily reinforced, and additions are being made daily. He expects to accumulate a force by which he can extend beyond our right and left, when I fear it will be impossible to keep him out of Richmond."

In February, 1865, the superintendent of the Bureau of Conscriptions reported to the Secretary of War in detail by classes the number of persons exempt from conscription by physical disability or by law, or detailed in each State east of the Mississippi, the total of which (including 4612 detailed in government bureaus and departments) was 87,863.[2] The minuteness of this report makes it impossible to believe that any considerable number who were not exempt from military service escaped the search of the Bureau of Conscription, and, taken in connection with the urgency shown in the legislation and correspondence above set out, it warrants the assertion that, in that part of the Confederacy east of the Mississippi, substantially every male white from seventeen to fifty was swept into the ranks of the Confederate army, excepting the 87,863 exempts, and those who were in hiding or had joined the Union army.   The proclamation of the governor of North Carolina, December 20, 1864, calling out all men who

[1] 89 W. R., 1144.   [2] M. and D., Part III. 130–138; 129 W. R., 1099.

were able to stand behind breastworks and fire a
musket,[1] is confirmatory of this. Those joining the
Union army were, with unimportant exceptions, all
from Tennessee. There were thirty regiments, numbering 31,092, from this State.[2] These were offset by
thirty regiments, nine battalions, and eleven batteries
from the border States, regularly enrolled in the Confederate army,[3] besides the militia and temporary organizations.[4]

In the States west of the Mississippi the general in
command of the department called for volunteers not
subject to conscription, for local defense and special
service, in September, 1863,[5] and issued orders, May 27,
1864,[6] for enrolling all persons liable to military duty,
and for the assignment of conscripts to the different
organizations. Colonel Stone's list, hereafter referred
to,[7] attributes 46 regiments, 21 battalions, and 22 companies (equal to 58 regiments) to Arkansas, and 71
regiments, 12 battalions, and 53 companies (equal to
83 regiments) to Texas.[8] The United States census
for 1860 gives Arkansas 65,231 and Texas 92,145
male whites between 18 and 45 years of age, a total
of 157,376, which is increased to 180,000 by the addi-

---

[1] 89 W. R., 1284. [2] Reg. Losses, 523.

[3] Reg. Losses, 553.

[4] Colonel Stone's list, referred to hereafter (p. 29), attributes 37
regiments to Missouri and 20 to Kentucky. The writer's list (post,
p. 55) includes 45 for Missouri and 42 for Kentucky, counting 2
battalions as a regiment.

[5] 33 W. R., 996. [6] 64 W. R., 632.

[7] Page 29.

[8] The writer's list (post, p. 55) gives 50 regiments and 25 battalions to Arkansas, and 64 regiments and 11 battalions to Texas.

tions and deductions named below.[1]   This is about 1280 to the regiment, or 50 less than the minimum that can be accepted as the average strength of the Confederate regiments.[2]   These figures leave no reason to doubt that conscription west of the Mississippi was effective in persuading or forcing the whole military population into the service, whether in regular or irregular organizations.   A piece of evidence strongly tending to prove that the Confederacy drew the last available white man who could be found into the army is afforded in the measures which were taken to put negroes, both slaves and free, into service.   March 13, 1865, an act of the Confederate Congress authorizing this[3] was approved by the President; and March 15 orders were issued for raising companies of negro soldiers,[4] and active measures for a general recruitment of negroes were carried on down to April, 1865, the day before Five Forks.[5]

We are now led to the question, how many male whites were there in the Confederacy subject to the conscript laws, and we turn to the United States census for 1860.

MILITARY POPULATION OF THE CONFEDERATE STATES BY THE CENSUS OF 1860.

The acts of the Confederate Congress of April 16 and September 16, 1862, were interpreted to include youths of 18 and men of 45, and the act of February 17, 1864, likewise was interpreted to include the ex-

[1] Page 22.

[2] See post, p. 39.

[3] 96 W. R., 1318.

[4] 96 W. R., 1318.

[5] 97 W. R., 1348, 1356, 1370.

tremes of 17 and 50.[1]   The two first-named acts, therefore, included all shown by the United States census of 1860 (Part XVIII.) from 18 to 45 inclusive, as follows : —

Alabama	99,967
Arkansas	65,231
Florida	15,739
Georgia	111,005
Louisiana	83,456
Mississippi	70,295
North Carolina	115,369
South Carolina	55,046
Tennessee	159,353
Texas	92,145
Virginia (ex. West Virginia)	116,869
	984,475

All who were from 13 to 16 inclusive, in 1860, became by 1864 liable to conscription under these acts. Their number may be computed as equal to $\frac{4}{10}$ of the number shown by the census of 1860 to be from 10 to 19 inclusive, or, in round numbers, at 265,000. Besides those who were from 18 to 45, all who were 46 in 1860 became subject to conscription in 1864. The number who were 46 may be computed as equal to $\frac{1}{10}$ of the number shown by the census to be from 40 to 49 inclusive, or, in round numbers, at 20,000.

We thus arrive at 1,269,000, in round numbers, as the total number living in 1861 who came within the terms of the conscription acts. As will be shown later, 350,000 were in the army in January, 1862. From the remaining 919,000 a deduction is to be made for the natural death rate of one per cent. per annum, which,

[1] M. and D., Part III. 130–138 ; 127 W. R., 1095, 1105 ; 129 W. R., 1102, 1109.

upon the assumption that the average delay in bringing the conscripts into the ranks was eighteen months,
should be 2½ per cent. from the end of 1860, equal to
23,000 in round numbers. The exempts for all causes
and of details east of the Mississippi were 87,863.[1]
The number west of the Mississippi may be computed,
in the same proportion to the military population, at
17,000. The total of these deductions is 127,863.
The remainder out of 1,269,000 is, in round numbers,
1,141,000 men. Besides this number were those composing the Senior and Junior Reserves, the militia, and
other organizations, not a part of the regularly enrolled
force, composed mainly of persons over or under the
conscript age and of exempts. The number included
in these organizations cannot be ascertained with certainty. The male whites from 10 to 12 years and from
47 to 56 years, in 1860, may be estimated from the census at 300,000. This number, reduced by 4 per cent.
for natural deaths, added to the exempts and details
stated above at 110,863 would give about 400,000 as
the maximum number which could be drawn into these
irregular organizations. In view of this maximum, and
of the physical disabilities attendant upon the extreme
ages included in this number, the estimate of 98,000
as the number embraced in the irregular organizations contained below[2] is possibly not far from correct.
This number added to 1,141,000, the number above
estimated as regularly enrolled, would give 1,239,000
as the total number who took up arms. Those who
escaped service in North Carolina and Tennessee[3] may

[1] M. and D., Part III. 130 et seq.   [2] Page 36.
[3] Post, pp. 23, 24.

be offset against those who joined the Confederate army from the border States.[1]

ESTIMATES OF CONFEDERATE STATE OFFICIALS COM-
PARED WITH THE ABOVE ESTIMATE FROM THE
CENSUS.

The above estimate of 1,141,000 as the number within the military age — from 17 to 50 — is 116 per cent. of the 984,475 given by the census of 1860 as between 18 and 45. Statistics and estimates given out during and since the war by officials of several States, when compared in the same way with the census of these States for 1860, tend to confirm the above conclusion that substantially the entire military population of the Confederate States not exempted by law were enrolled in the army

The roster of North Carolina troops, made up since the war, gives the names of 104,498 men, and the author estimates that missing names would bring the number up to 120,000. The Junior Reserves, numbering 4077, are included in the roster. 116 per cent. of 115,369 between 18 and 45 in that State, as shown by the census, is 138,328. This would leave 13,000 not in service. In this number were embraced those unable to bear arms and those who eluded military service. In this State and in Tennessee there were a good many of this latter class who took refuge in the mountains or wilderness, and thereby escaped the officers of the Bureau of Conscription.

The basis for a comparison of the number shown by the census of 1860 with the number under arms for

[1] Ante, p. 19.

the Confederacy is not as well established in the case of Tennessee as in that of North Carolina. 116 per cent. of the number of male whites in Tennessee from 18 to 45[1] is 184,850. Of these 31,092 joined the Union army.[2] There were in the Confederate army the equivalent, all told, including irregular organizations, of 113 regiments.[3] The 93 regiments regularly enrolled[4] at 1330 to a regiment[5] would number 123,690, and the other 20 regiments at 617 to a regiment[6] would number 12,340, which, with the number serving in the Union army, would give a total of 167,122, leaving about 18,000 not accounted for. It is not probable that so many as this avoided service, but the proximity to the border doubtless enabled a greater proportion to escape than the geographical situation allowed in North Carolina. If 1540 were adopted as the average strength of the 93 regiments regularly enrolled,[7] a total of 186,652 would be reached in place of the above 167,122.

The Adjutant-General's office of South Carolina in 1890 estimated that about 60,000 entered the Confederate service from that State.[8] 116 per cent. of 55,046 between 18 and 45 in that State, as shown by the census, is 63,853.

In the journal of the House of Representatives of Mississippi for 1865 it is stated that that State furnished between 70,000 and 80,000 to the Confederate

[1] Ante, p. 21. [2] Reg. Losses, 554.
[3] Post, pp. 29, 43. [4] Reg. Losses, 553.
[5] Post, p. 39. [6] Post, p. 36.
[7] Post, p. 37. [8] United Confederate Veterans, 33.

army.[1]   116 per cent. of 70,295 between 18 and 45 in that State, as shown by the census, is 81,542.

Governor Brown of Georgia, in 1865, wrote to the Confederate Secretary of War that his State had furnished the Confederate service over 100,000 men, besides the Reserve Militia and State Line.[2]   (See 47 W. R., 307–313, and 74 W. R., 970.)   116 per cent. of 111,005 between 18 and 45 in that State, as shown by the census, is 128,765.

The Adjutant-General of Florida, in 1891, estimated the number of troops furnished by that State to the Confederate States at about 15,000.[2]   116 per cent. of 15,739 between 18 and 45 in that State, as shown by the census, is 18,257. The Adjutant-General's estimate probably did not include recruits, for the War Records have mention of 14 regiments regularly in the Confederate army, the original strength of which was probably about 15,000.

The Secretary of State of Louisiana, in his report for 1889,[3] gives the total "original enrollment of troops" mustered into the Provisional Confederate States army as 55,820. The term "original enrollment" probably excludes recruits. That it was so intended may be inferred from the fact that, while the State sent at least 38 regiments of infantry,[4] the Secre-

[1] Letter of Adjutant-General of Mississippi to Hon. H. D. Money, January 25, 1895, in the files of M. H. M.

[2] Pamphlet entitled "Correspondence between the Secretary of War and Governor Brown," growing out of a requisition made upon the governor for the reserve militia of Georgia, etc. Macon, Georgia. Brighton, Nesbit, Barnes & Moore, State Printers.

[3] United Confederate Veterans, 24.

[4] See Colonel Jones's roster, post, p. 27.

tary of State gives 36,243 as the " total original enrollment of infantry." [1] It is probable also that the Secretary of State does not include irregular organizations
and reserves, which were equivalent to 16 regiments.[2]
116 per cent. of 83,456 between 18 and 45 in that
State, as shown by the census, is 96,808.

ESTIMATE OF THE CONFEDERATE FORCE FROM THE NUMBER OF REGIMENTS, ETC.

The War Records do not contain any official roll of
all the regiments and lesser organizations in the Confederate army, but there are four lists, which have been
compiled from private research, which afford a basis for
computing the number of men in the army.

Colonel Charles C. Jones, formerly of the Confederate army, has published a roster,[3] in which are named
530 regiments, 15 legions, and 51 battalions of infantry ; 125 regiments, 2 legions, 53 battalions, and 1
company of cavalry ; and 13 regiments, 21 battalions,
and 25 batteries of artillery, as shown by the following
table, which has been made from this roster.   The
total is equivalent to 750 regiments, assuming a regiment to be equal to a legion, to 2 battalions, and to 10
batteries.

[1] United Confederate Veterans, 28.

[2] Post, p. 29 ; Reg. Losses, 553.

[3] So. Hist. Society Papers, i., ii., iii.

TABLE MADE FROM COLONEL JONES'S ROSTER.

	INFANTRY			CAVALRY			ARTILLERY		
	Regiments	Legions	Battalions	Regiments	Legions	Battalions	Regiments	Battalions	Batteries
Alabama	57	1		3				6	
Arkansas	34		12	6					
Florida	9		2	2					
Georgia	65	2	22	10		2		4	
Kentucky	11			9		1			
Louisiana	35		6	1			1		
Mississippi . . .	49			6	2	7	1		
Missouri	15			6					
Maryland	1								
North Carolina . .	58	2	3	6		2	4		3
South Carolina . .	35			7		12	3		22
Tennessee	67		1	12		11			
Texas	22		5	32		14	1		
Virginia	64			19		4	4	11	
Confederate . . .	8	10		6					
Total	530	15	51	125	2	53	1	13	21	25

This roster apparently is confined to organizations regularly enrolled in the army of the Confederacy, and does not include militia, home guards, organizations for local defense, or Senior Reserves or Junior Reserves,[1] which, altogether, constituted a considerable part of the force under arms at one time and another. The author says that this roster was derived in part from papers in private hands, and it is not verified by reference to official records. That it is not complete is shown by several authorities. Dr. Jones, in articles above cited,[2] gives a list of Confederate organizations which adds to that of Colonel Jones, 5

[1] For instance, it omits 5 regiments and 1 battalion of Junior Reserves, which appear in Moore's roster of North Carolina troops.

[2] So. Hist. Society Papers, xx. 119. Pamphlet United Confederate Veterans, 8.

regiments, 20 battalions, and omits 1 legion and 25 batteries.

Colonel Fox, in " Regimental Losses," p. 552, says there is a " compilation made from the official rosters of the Confederate armies as they stood at various battles and at various dates covering the entire period of the war," which " shows that the different States kept the following regimental organizations in almost continuous service in the field." This list gives: —

	REGIMENTS	BATTALIONS	BATTERIES
Infantry	529	85	
Cavalry	127	47	
Partisan rangers	8	1	
Heavy artillery	5	6	
Artillery			261
Total	669	139	261

These organizations, the author says, were, " in all, equivalent to 764 regiments of 10 companies each; " and he adds that the list does not include regiments which served for a short time only, or disbanded or consolidated regiments, militia, Junior Reserves, Senior Reserves, home guards, local defense regiments, or separate companies.

In the preparation of this work the writer has noted mention in the War Records [1] prior to November, 1863, of 720 regiments and 206 battalions of infantry and cavalry of the character of those contained in Colonel Fox's list.[2] With the batteries in Colonel Fox's list these make a total equal to 849 regiments.

[1] Nearly half the War Records referred to were published later than Colonel Fox's work.

[2] See table, post, p. 55.

The late Colonel Henry Stone[1] kindly placed at the disposal of the writer a list which he had gathered of all Confederate organizations mentioned in the War Records. The following table was made from this list: —

TABLE MADE FROM COLONEL STONE'S LIST.

	INFANTRY				CAVALRY				ARTILLERY		
	Regiments	Legions	Battalions	Companies	Regiments	Legions	Battalions	Companies	Regiments	Battalions	Companies
Alabama . . .	55		18	4	6		18	10		2	17
Arkansas . . .	42		14	2	4		5	4		2	16
Florida . . .	9		1	16	2		3	6		1	15
Georgia . . .	67	3	14	9	7		21				
Kentucky . . .	9				11		1				
Louisiana . . .	33		22		3		13	8	5	3	19
Mississippi . .	53		21		25	1	4			1	9
Missouri . . .	30				7						
North Carolina .	74	1	12	4	6		12	2	2		9
South Carolina .	53	3	14	8	7		7	13	3	3	25
Tennessee . . .	78		24		10		11	17		1	35
Texas	35	1	4	14	33		8	15	2		24
Virginia . . .	99	1	19	5	16		40	26	4	12	58
Confederate or Prov. Army .	5										
Total . . .	642	9	163	62	137	1	143	101	16	25	227

The 805 regiments and legions, 331 battalions, 163 companies, and 227 batteries in the above table were equal in all to 1009½ regiments, which exceeds the number (849) ascertained as stated above by 160 regiments. Colonel Stone said that possibly some organizations were numbered more than once in his list by reason of change of their title, or of consolidation; yet these instances cannot be many, and the larger number of organizations in his list is probably due, with few excep-

[1] Member of Military Historical Society of Massachusetts.

tions, to the inclusion in it of the militia and other irregular organizations, which are excluded from the other two lists. For instance, there are included in Colonel Stone's list 2 battalions Georgia State Guards, (which were not all that were in service), 5 regiments Mississippi militia, 9 regiments North Carolina militia, and 5 regiments Junior Reserves, 5 regiments "State Troops," and 6 regiments of militia from South Carolina, and 33 regiments Virginia militia, besides 163 companies.

ORIGINAL STRENGTH OF CONFEDERATE REGIMENTS, AND THE NUMBER OF RECRUITS.

The act of the Confederate Congress of March 6, 1861,[1] provided for 100,000 volunteers for twelve months, and authorized the President to limit the privates in a company, in his discretion, at from 64 to 100. The officers, non-commissioned officers, and musicians would increase each of these limits by 12 or 14. The act of May 10, 1861,[2] authorized him to receive any company of light artillery with such complement of officers and men as seemed proper to him. Another act of March 6, 1861,[1] provided for the creation of the small regular army of the Confederate States. It prescribed that each regiment should consist of 10 companies, and that each company should number 104 in the infantry and 72 in the cavalry. The act of May 8, 1861,[3] provided for volunteers for the war, and for their organization, as provided in the act of March 6. A circular of the Confederate War Department, issued in November, 1861, provided that no company should be accepted

---

[1] 127 W. R., 126–131. [2] 127 W. R., 309.
[3] 127 W. R., 302.

with less than 64 privates in the infantry, 60 in the cavalry, and 70 in the artillery,[1] and that a regiment should consist of 10 companies.[2] A circular of the Secretary of War to the same effect, and allowing existing companies to be raised to 125, was issued February 22, 1862.[3] The act of October 11, 1862, provided that a company of infantry should consist of at least 125 rank and file, a company of artillery of at least 150 rank and file, and a company of cavalry of at least 80 rank and file. This act did not go into effect until the formation of new regiments had nearly if not quite ceased, and therefore it would not be safe to adopt these numbers for the strength of the companies when they were enrolled into the service; and the number in a company must be assumed to have been originally between the limits of 64 and 100, as prescribed by the act of March 6, 1861. The War Records do not give the strength of organizations at date of entry in the service, but there are lists of organizations with the total numbers present and absent of five of the chief armies in the early part of 1862, before they were recruited much, if any, but not before they had suffered some loss in campaigning, from which the average strength of companies at that time can be ascertained. They show the following : —

[1] 127 W. R., 765.

[2] The Confederate Adjutant-General, December 13, 1861, assumed that there were 10 companies to a regiment in all arms. (127 W. R., 823.)

[3] 127 W. R., 790.

1862		Regiments	Battalions	Companies	Total Companies	Strength	Aver. Co.
January	Northern Virginia [1] . . .	112	3	46	1181	98,050	83
"	Central of Kentucky [2] . .	47	6	12	512	39,548	77
"	1st Div. of Western Dept.[3] .	27	8	14	324	24,783	76
February	Alabama and West Florida [4]	20	4	8	228	18,206	79
April 19	Dept. of North Carolina [5] .	25	1	28	283	26,433	93
	Total	231	22	108	2528	207,020	81.8

The number of companies is above computed on the basis of 10 to a regiment and legion,[6] and 5 to a battalion, and, although some battalions had a company more or less than this number, the variation would not probably lower the average.[7]

March 1, 1862, the Confederate Adjutant-General reported the strength of 369 regiments and 89 battalions, two thirds of them twelve months' troops, at 340,250, an average of 823 to the regiment.[8]

It will be seen in the above table that in the Department of North Carolina the average of the company was 93; and even in the Army of Northern Virginia, which had made the Bull Run campaign, it was 83. A return of Beauregard's corps, Army of the Potomac,

---

[1] Vol. v. pp. 1015, 1029–1031.   [2] Vol. vii. p. 852.

[3] Vol. vii. p. 853.   [4] Vol. vi. p. 819.

[5] Vol. ix. pp. 459, 460.

[6] Hampton's legion originally had 11 companies, Cobb's had 10 companies, and Phillips's had 9 companies. (127 W. R., 304, 788.)

[7] The 24 battalions in service for the war, December 13, 1861, contained 149 companies, an average of $6\frac{5}{24}$. (127 W. R., 788, 790.)

[8] 127 W. R., 963.

August 31, 1861,[1] gives an average of 1037 per regiment in the 32 regiments and 1 battalion of that army. June 23, 1862, General Longstreet reported that the Virginia troops in his command, consisting of 23 regiments, 1 battalion, and 17 batteries, numbered 18,993,[2] equal to about 754 men to the regiment. This was after two campaigns.

Another return shows the strength of regiments in three brigades of the Central Army of Kentucky as 831 in November, 1861,[3] and another shows that the average number per regiment in 9 regiments and 4 battalions in Zollicoffer's command in September, 1861, was 957.[4] The "Roster of the Louisiana Troops mustered into the Provisional Army of the Confederate States," prepared by Colonel Oscar Aroyo, Secretary of State,[5] shows 36,243 original enlistments in the infantry, 4024 in the artillery, and 10,056 in the cavalry. This gives an average of 906 to the regiment for the 35 regiments and 10 battalions of infantry, and 874 to the regiment for the 2 regiments and 26 batteries of artillery embraced in Colonel Fox's list.[6] It is evident that 10,056 men could not have been originally enrolled in the two regiments and one battalion of cavalry embraced in Colonel Fox's list, but the average per regiment in the 3 regiments, 13 battalions, and 8 squadrons embraced in Colonel Stone's list[7] would be 976. In view of the loss from death, discharge, and desertion which had inevitably been suf-

---

[1] 5 W. R., 824, 825.   [2] 14 W. R., 614, 615.

[3] 4 W. R., 484, 552.   [4] 4 W. R., 409.

[5] Cited in United Confederate Veterans, 28.

[6] Regimental Losses, 553.   [7] Ante, p. 29.

fered by the armies embraced in the above table,[1] the most of the organizations composing them having entered the service in 1861, it is evident that the average original strength of the companies was greater than that shown in the table, and, as that table shows that there were few if any companies which originally had only the minimum of 64 privates, it is not extravagant to assume that the average original strength of the regiments in the Confederate army was between 906 (the strength of the Louisiana infantry regiments) and 1037, the strength of the regiments in Beauregard's corps, as stated above, and probably it will not involve serious error to assume it to have been the mean between these numbers, which is 971. Applying this number to the organizations equal to 849 regiments, ascertained as above[2] to have been regularly enrolled in the service of the Confederate States, we establish the strength of these organizations as 824,379. Probably the muster-rolls on file in the War Department show the original strength of nearly all the organizations regularly enrolled in the Confederate service; and if the above estimate is excessive, it will some time be corrected by the patient labor of some one who shall examine these rolls, and number the names of the men who originally composed the different organizations, but the number of ascertained facts and figures upon which the above estimate is based is probably large enough to insure against any considerable error. Research in the muster-rolls would also probably show very nearly the number of recruits joining the various organizations during the time covered by the rolls. The chief source of information on this subject for the

---

[1] Page 32.   [2] Page 28.

writer is the report of the Superintendent of the Bureau
of Conscription made in February, 1865,[1] which shows
that between April 16, 1862, and the date of that report, the armies were recruited by 81,993 conscripts,
and that 72,292 joined the army as volunteers to avoid
conscription, and the report adds that this estimate of
the number of volunteers is regarded as much too small.[2]
These numbers, added to 824,379 above estimated as
the original strength, increase the total number in the
army to at least 978,664.

STRENGTH OF IRREGULAR ORGANIZATIONS IN THE CONFEDERACY.

To the strength of the regular organizations is to
be added the number who served in the militia and
other irregular organizations, shown in Colonel Stone's
list above referred to, which were the equivalent of 160
regiments.[3] There is no standard by which the strength
of these organizations can be exactly ascertained, and
perhaps the most minute examination of their rolls and
returns in the War Department would not enable one
to arrive at their numbers with exactness. The orders
of one Confederate commander in 1863 for raising volunteers not within the conscript age, for local defense
and special service, under the acts of August 21, 1861,
and October 13, 1862, fixed the minimum rank and
file of an infantry company at 50, and of a cavalry company at 40, and provided that regiments should have at

[1] M. and D., Part III. 127, 128; 129 W. R., 1109, 1110.

[2] Major Duffield, a Virginia officer, has stated that by order he
burnt the conscript records. The Century, March, 1892, p. 792.

[3] Ante, p. 29.

least 10 companies, and battalions at least 5 companies,[1] and another order for the reorganization of the Texas State Troops in 1864 called for companies of not less than 100, or more than 125.[2]   The governor of South Carolina in 1863 fixed the minimum number in a company for local defense or special service at 76, and the maximum at 137, and ordered that the regiments should have 10 companies.[3]

A return of Carson's Division of Virginia Militia, August 31,[4] 1861, gave 5488 as the strength of 9 regiments, and Moore's "Roster of North Carolina Troops" gives 4077 as the number who served in 6 regiments and 1 battalion of Junior Reserves from that State. The average of these 15½ regiments was 617.   If this were adopted as the standard, the total strength of 98,720 would be arrived at for the 160 irregular regiments, making with the 978,664 above computed,[5] 1,077,384 as the number serving in the Confederate armies during the war.   But this result cannot be accepted as exact, for it does not include any recruits beyond the 154,285 reported as above stated, and computations below tend to show that it is too small.

COMPUTATION OF CONFEDERATE NUMBERS FROM AVERAGE TOTAL STRENGTH OF REGIMENTS DURING THE WAR.

Fortunately there is a record, before cited, of the soldiers of one of the Confederate States, from which the average number of men enrolled in each of a large

---

[1] 33 W. R., 996.   [2] 62 W. R., 1087.   [3] 47 W. R., 145, 146.
[4] 5 W. R., 825.   [5] Page 35.

number of the regularly enrolled Confederate regiments during the war may be computed. Moore's "Roster of North Carolina Troops," a work prepared since the war, with the authority of the State, consists of a list of 104,254 men who served in the 76 regiments, 11 battalions, and 1 battery which were organized in that State for the Confederate service. Owing to incomplete muster-rolls and other causes, the author of this roster was unable to make a complete list, and he states it as his belief, founded upon ascertained facts, that the total number of men furnished by the State equaled 120,000. In this connection, it is to be noted that, as against the equivalent of 81 regiments of infantry, 12 regiments of cavalry, and 3 regiments of artillery in Colonel Stone's list, a total of 96 regiments, this roster embraces only 76 regiments, 11 battalions, and 1 battery, a total of 82 regiments; of which only 1 regiment and 3 battalions are cavalry, and 3 battalions and 1 company are artillery. This difference is accounted for, in part, by the 9 regiments of militia included in Colonel Stone's list, and not embraced in the roster. Deducting the 4321 names credited by the roster to the 6 regiments and 1 battalion of Junior Reserves and the navy from 120,000, we have 115,679 men for the 70 regiments, 10 battalions, and 1 battery in the Confederate service, from which we derive the average of 1540 to the regiment. North Carolina was not conspicuous above the other Southern States for a martial spirit before the War of the Rebellion, and her people were not as a whole fervid in the cause of secession, and there is no reason to suppose that more men were originally enrolled in, or recruited for, the average

regiment from that State than in the other Confederate States.

The following statistics have been given by the authorities of some of the other Confederate States, as before mentioned: —

Florida, 14 regiments.[1]   About 15,000 ;[2] average, about 1070.   As before stated, this estimate was probably not intended to cover recruits.

Georgia, 94 regiments.[1]   Over 100,000 ;[3] average over 1063.

Mississippi, 65 regiments.[1]   Between 70,000 and 80,00 ;[4] average between 1200 and 1230.

South Carolina, $45\frac{8}{10}$ regiments.[1]   About 60,000 ;[5] average, about 1310.

As above pointed out, the statistics for Florida and Georgia are too narrow or too indefinite to establish the average strength of regiments, and those for Mississippi and South Carolina are not complete, and may be used only to estimate a minimum average.   The writer has not been able to obtain any information from the records of the remaining Confederate States as to the total number of men enrolled in the Confederate service.

Applying to the 849 regularly enrolled regiments,

[1] Reg. Losses, 553.

[2] No records extant, except an abstract of the muster-rolls of 13 regiments.   Letter of Adjutant-General Lang to Dr. Joseph Jones, August 29, 1891, United Confederate Veterans, 24.

[3] Letter of Governor Brown, 1865.   Pamphlet.   Macon.   Cited ante, p. 25.

[4] House Journal of Mississippi for 1865.   (See note, ante, page 25.)

[5] Letter of Adjutant and Inspector-General Bonham to Dr. Jones, June 12, 1890, in United Confederate Veterans, 33.

ascertained as above,[1] the average of 1540 per regiment derived from the estimate of the author of the North Carolina Roster,[2] the result is 1,307,460 men regularly enrolled in the Confederate service, as against 1,141,000, the number subject to conscription, estimated from the census.[3] If the list of 104,254 names in the North Carolina Roster is adopted instead of the estimate of its author, less 4321 for the $6\frac{1}{2}$ regiments of Junior Reserves, the average of 1330 is obtained, which is near to the average strength of regiments as shown by the figures given above for South Carolina. This would give 1,129,170 as the number of men, all told, regularly enrolled in 849 regiments. Adding to this 98,720 for the strength of the irregular organizations as above computed, we arrive at 1,227,890 as the total number of enlistments opposed to the 2,898,304 enlistments in the Union army during the war, or, if the larger number, 1,307,460, above computed as the number regularly enrolled in the Confederate service, is adopted, the total is 1,406,180. It is possible that this number might be increased by the addition of organizations omitted from the writer's list because they first appear in the War Records after October, 1863, or for other reasons suggested below.[4] It is hardly probable that there were 1,406,180 enlistments among 1,239,000 men,[5] excluding men retained in their regiments by reënlistment, in view of the measures which were taken to hold men in the organizations in which they originally entered the service.

[1] Page 28.   [2] Ante, p. 37.   [3] Ante, p. 22.   [4] Page 54.
[5] Ante, p. 22.

ESTIMATES BY OTHERS.

An estimate made in the War Records Office[1] has placed the total number in the Confederate service at "over 1,000,000." This estimate is based on 472,000 shown by the Confederate returns to have been in service January 1, 1864, at least 250,000 deaths occurring prior to that date, and discharges and desertions which it is said "would probably increase the number to over 1,000,000."

An estimate of Colonel Cassellman, of the Pension Office, from another view published in "The Century" for March, 1892,[2] places the number at 1,500,000.

RATIO OF ESTIMATES OF CONFEDERATE NUMBERS TO NUMBER OF UNION ENLISTMENTS.

The ratio of the number arrived at in each of the estimates above to the total number of men in the Union army is shown in the following table : —

Estimate of Confederate Numbers	Men in Confederate Army	Enlistments in Union Army[3]	Per cent
Marcus J. Wright	600,000 to 700,000	2,898,304	20 to 24
Early, Stephens, and Jones . . .	600,000	–	20
Partial estimate[4]	885,000	–	30
Estimate from the census, about[5]	1,239,000	–	41
Estimate from the number and average strength of regiments[6] .	1,227,890 or 1,406,480	–	41 or 47
Estimate of War Records Office .	1,000,000	–	34
Cassellman's estimate	1,500,000	–	50

[1] Battles and Leaders of the Civil War, iv. 768, and letter of Major George B. Davis, December 1, 1894, in files of M. H. M.

[2] Page 792.   [3] Post, p. 50.   [4] Ante, p. 8.

[5] Ante, p. 22.   [6] Ante, p. 39.

RETURNS OF THE ARMIES COMPARED WITH THE FORE-
GOING ESTIMATES OF NUMBERS.

The ratio of the average strength of the Confederate
army to the average strength of the Union army would
be the same as the ratio between the total number of
men enrolled during the war on the two sides, other
things being equal; but in fact the former ratio was
less than that between any one of the above estimates
of the total number in the Confederate army, not excepting Colonel Cassellman's estimate of 1,500,000,
and the total enlistments in the Union Army.

There is not to be found in the Confederate papers
published in the War Records any return of the total
present and absent in the Confederate armies at any
date.[1] A careful comparison of the several hundred
returns published in the War Records has resulted in
the following tables of the numbers present and absent on dates at which the published records give the
strength of the Union armies. In some cases where
returns of the Confederate armies for the specific dates
assumed have not been found in the War Records,
those of the nearest dates have been used, in the absence
of reason to believe that a substantial difference in
numbers had arisen in the intervals. In some cases
estimates of the numbers present and absent, based on
the numbers returned as present or " effective," have
been used. As the returns in the War Records do not
always include all the organizations in the armies at
dates assumed, it is probable that the total numbers

---

[1] A statement of the total number was rendered by the Adjutant-
General to the Secretary of War of the Confederate States, January
3, 1865, but it is missing (96 W. R., 1007).

reached are below the real numbers. To enable these calculations of numbers to be verified, references are made to the volume and page of the Records containing the returns used. Estimates for January, 1862, '63, '64, '65, which were made in the War Office, substantially confirm these tables.[1]

TABLE OF NUMBERS FROM CONFEDERATE RETURNS OF ARMIES, DEPARTMENTS, ETC., JULY, 1861.

Army of Potomac and Shenandoah [2]	33,752 [a]
Army of Peninsula.	5,500 [b]
Virginia militia at Winchester	5,488 [c]
North Carolina (4 regiments estimated)	3,000 [d]
South Carolina (2800 deducted for 4 regiments in Army of Potomac)	6,000 [e]
Pensacola	2,300 [f]
Missouri and Arkansas	28,000 [g]
Tennessee (about)	22,000 [h]
Florida (about)	3,000 [i]
Texas (about)	3,000 [j]
Total (about)	112,040

[a] 2 W. R., 187, 473, 487, 568, 569, 999. [b] 2 W. R., 931. [c] 2 W. R., 473; 5 W. R., 790, 825. [d] 1 W. R., 488. [e] 1 W. R., 265; 2 W. R., 568, 569. [f] 1 W. R., 469. [g] 3 W. R., 613, 608, 617; 4 W. R., 362, 372. [h] 3 W. R., 612. [i] 1 W. R., 470–472. [j] 4 W. R., 95, 99, 100.

JANUARY, 1862.

Dept. of Northern Virginia	98,050 [a]
Army of Peninsula (December, '61)	20,683 [b]
District of Norfolk (November 30)	15,143 [c]

[a] 5 W. R., 1015. [b] 4 W. R., 716. [c] 4 W. R., 706.

[1] Battles and Leaders of the Civil War, iv. 768, and letter of Major George B. Davis, December 1, 1894, in files of M. H. M.

[2] This number includes only those present for duty, and includes Holmes's brigade at Fredericksburg.

Dept. of North Carolina	13,884 [d]
Dept. No. 1 (Louisiana)	10,296 [e]
South Carolina, December (about)	17,000 [f]
Dept. of Georgia (November 10)	8,500 [g]
Dept. of Alabama and West Florida (February 1) .	18,206 [h]
Dept. of Middle and East Florida	4,680 [i]
Western Dept. (December), less Arkansas . . .	86,861 [j]
Forts Henry and Donelson (January 21)	5,210 [k]
Zollicoffer's command	8,451 [l]
Marshall's command (January 1)	2,160 [m]
Cumberland Gap	2,073 [n]
Army of the Northwest, December, '61 (about) . .	4,500 [o]
Price's command (January 23) Missouri (est.) . .	4,000 [p]
McCulloch's division (Arkansas)	10,677 [q]
Pike's division (Indian Ter.), February 7	9,000 [r]
Texas (October to January)	12,044 [s]

$$351,418 \ [1]$$

[d] 9 W. R., 424, 425.   [e] 6 W. R., 819.   [f] 6 W. R., 357, 363.   [g] 6 W. R., 314.
[h] 6 W. R., 819.   [i] 6 W. R., 371.   [j] 7 W. R., 813, 814.   [k] 7 W. R., 843.   [l] 7 W. R.,
814.   [m] 7 W. R., 815.   [n] 7 W. R., 843.   [o] 5 W. R., 1055.   [p] 8 W. R., 739, 740.
[q] 8 W. R., 746.   [r] 8 W. R., 749.   [s] 4 W. R., 166.

APRIL, 1862.

Army of Northern Virginia [2]	[3]110,000 [a]
Ewell's division (April 16)	8,500 [b]
Valley District, Jackson's division of 3 brigades (May 3)	8,397 [c]

[a] 14 W. R., 484.   [b] 18 W. R., 851.   [c] 18 W. R., 879.

[1] A compilation from the returns on file for about December, 1861, ex. New Mexico, Missouri, and Indian Territory, shows 326,768 present and absent (127 W. R., 822).

[2] Number in Acquia District not included, in the absence of returns from this district.

[3] Estimated from the return of 55,633 " effectives," at the ratio of 4699 "effectives" in Toombs's division (p. 480), April 30, to the 9325 " present and absent " in the same (1st) division, April 23 (14 W. R., 460).

Norfolk [1] (Huger's command)	15,143 [d]
Dept. of North Carolina	26,433 [e]
South Carolina and Georgia [2]	40,000 [f]
Middle and East Florida (April 30)	4,393 [g]
Alabama and West Florida [3] (April 15)	11,000 [h]
Army of the Mississippi	93,883 [i]
Fort Pillow	3,847 [j]
Dept. of East Tennessee	16,199 [k]
Army of the West (May 4)	34,035 [l]
Trans-Miss. Dist. April 15, ex. troops ordered to Memphis, which are included presumably in Army of Miss. (11 W. R., 475), and including 500 on the way from Texas	20,000 [m]
Ind. Ter. (May)	9,565 [n]
	401,395 [4]

[d] 4 W. R., 706.   [e] 9 W. R., 459.   [f] 20 W. R., 498.   [g] 20 W. R., 488.
[h] 6 W. R., 875, 876.   [i] 11 W. R., 475.   [j] 11 W. R., 476.   [k] 11 W. R., 476.
[l] 11 W. R., 491.   [m] 19 W. R., 818.   [n] 19 W. R., 831.

March 1, 1862, the Confederate Adjutant-General reported 340,250 from the returns, with an estimate of 20 to 25 regiments additional for regiments not embraced in the returns (127 W. R., 963).

[1] Estimated from return of November 30, 1861, in view of returns for Huger's division of 3 brigades of 15 regiments, besides Ransom's brigade, June 26, 1862 (13 W. R., 504).

[2] Estimated from returns of 27,687 "effectives," May 11, in the ratio of 4883 "effectives" to 7209 "present and absent" in 2d district of South Carolina, shown in return of April 12 (20 W. R., 482).

[3] Estimated from 8360 reported "present."

[4] There are no returns for Heth's command at Lewisburg, Va., or for the forces in Mississippi, Texas, and part of Missouri and Louisiana, and no number is included for these commands.

JANUARY, 1863.

Army of Northern Virginia, including Valley Dist. and excluding Ransom's division	144,614 [a]
Maryland Brigade, Edenburg, Va.	979 [b]
Dept. of West Virginia	10,143 [c]
Dept. of North Carolina, Richmond, etc. [1] . . .	54,334 [d]
Ransom's division	6,985 [e]
Dept. of South Carolina, Georgia, and East Florida .	27,225 [f]
Mississippi and East Louisiana	73,161 [g]
Army of Tennessee	83,767 [h]
McCown's division	7,934 [i]
Van Dorn's division (Jan. 18)	[2] 11,000 [j]
Dept. of East Tennessee	[3] 17,098 [k]
Dist. of Texas, New Mexico, and Arizona (Jan. 12)	9,322 [l]
	446,622

[a] 40 W. R., 602.   [b] 40 W. R., 602.   [c] 40 W. R., 603.   [d] 26 W. R., 865, 866, 901.   [e] 31 W. R., 1075 ; 26 W. R., 850, 855.   [f] 20 W. R., 757.   [g] 38 W. R., 611. [h] 35 W. R., 622.   [i] 35 W. R., 623.   [j] 30 W. R., 412, 413.   [k] 30 W. R., 475 ; 35 W. R., 644.   [l] 21 W. R., 946.

JANUARY, 1864.

Army of Northern Virginia	91,253 [a]
Dept. of Richmond (ex. Maryland line)	10,518 [b]
Valley District, including Archer's and Thomas's brigades [4]	[5] 12,000 [c]
Army of West Virginia and East Tennessee . . .	19,599 [d]

[a] 49 W. R., 898.   [b] 49 W. R., 904.   [c] 49 W. R., 904.   [d] 49 W. R., 908.

[1] Number in District of Cape Fear, taken from the separate report of the troops in that district. Number in Robertson's brigade taken from return of March 1.

[2] Estimated from returns of 7455 "present" (see, also, 35 W. R., 633, 680) in the proportion shown in return, 38 W. R., 611.

[3] Mean of returns for December, 1862, and February 20, 1863.

[4] See 49 W. R., 901, notes.

[5] 13½ regiments, estimated from average strength of infantry regiments in Army of Northern Virginia.

Defenses of Wilmington	9,215 [e]
Dept. of North Carolina.	18,763 [f]
Dept. of South Carolina, Georgia, and Florida . .	47,491 [g]
Mobile and defenses (Jan. 20)	12,512 [h]
Troops in Mississippi (Jan. 20)	44,132 [i]
Longstreet's command, East Tennessee (Dec. 31)	44,173 [j]
Army of Tennessee	98,215 [k]
Trans-Mississippi Dept. (Jan. 1)	73,289 [l]
	———————
	481,160

[e] 49 W. R., 907.   [f] 49 W. R., 906.   [g] 47 W. R., 601.   [h] 58 W. R, 582 ; 59 W. R., 586.   [i] 58 W. R., 583.   [j] 56 W. R., 889.   [k] 56 W. R.; 883.   [l] 62 W. R., 814.

JANUARY, 1865.

Army of Northern Virginia	150,373 [a]
Dept. of Virginia and East Tennessee (Nov., '64) .	7,138 [b]
Dept. of Richmond	16,601 [c]
Western District of North Carolina [1]	2,226 [d]
South Carolina, Georgia, and Florida (Jan. 20) [2] .	53,014 [e]
Alabama, Mississippi, and East Louisiana (Dec. 1) .	32,148 [f]
Trans-Mississippi Dept. [3]	96,708 [g]
Army of Tennessee (Dec. 10)	86,995 [h]
	———————
	445,203

[a] 89 W. R., 1362.   [b] 79 W. R., 907.   [c] 89 W. R., 1358.   [d] 89 W. R., 1279.
[e] 99 W. R., 1032.   [f] 94 W. R., 632.   [g] 86 W. R., 1137–1141.   [h] 93 W. R., 679.

[1] In the statement made up in the War Records Office, 4 Battles and Leaders of the Civil War, 768, the return for North Carolina is given as 5187, but the writer has not succeeded in finding the return in the published War Records.

[2] About 4000 are reported present December 28 (pp. 999, 1000) in organizations which do not appear in the returns of November 20 (pp. 874–876).

[3] The return of Drayton's division (p. 138) shows 970 more than the number set down in the return of the army (p. 1141).

COMPARISON OF THE FOREGOING NUMBERS WITH THE NUMBER ON THE UNION ROLLS AT SAME DATES.

Date	No. on Union Rolls [1]	Average	No. on Confederate Returns	Average	Per cent.
July, 1861	186,751		112,040		
		381,334		231,729	60.7
Jan., 1862	575,917		351,418		
		606,521		376,406	62
Mar. 31, 1862	637,126		401,395		
		777,623		424,018	54
Jan. 1, 1863	918,121		446,622		
		889,429		463,891	52
Jan. 1, 1864	860,737		481,160		
		910,098		463,181	50
Jan. 1, 1865	959,460		445,203		
		3,565,005		1,959,225	55

To arrive at an absolutely exact average strength of the two armies, it would be necessary to allow something for those troops which, by reason of their short term of service or for other reasons, were not counted in the returns on which the above averages are based. On the Union side there were 250,000 men who served from two weeks to six months (post, p. 50); and on the Confederate side there were irregular troops, estimated to be about 98,720 (ante, p. 36), serving an average term of 16 months (post, p. 61), that were not always carried in the returns of the Confederate armies. So, also, disproportion in the casualties on the two sides would have to be taken into account to reach the exact average strength on each side. In the Union army 110,070 [2] were killed and died of wounds; 249,458 [2]

[1] M. and D., Part III. 102.   [2] Reg. Losses, 527.

died of disease and accident; and there were about 125,000[1] desertions and 426,664[1] discharges,—a total of 911,192. The casualties on the Confederate side, established by the muster-rolls and reports, and estimates of losses in battle by Confederate commanders, were 94,000 killed and mortally wounded,[2] 59,297 died of disease,[3] 82,922 desertions,[4] and 57,762 discharged,[3] a total of 286,981; but, as before stated, these rolls cover only about two years on an average, and it is not to be doubted that the total for four years was in fact considerably greater.

The fact that the average strength shown on the returns of all the Confederate armies during the four years of the war was 55 per cent. of the average strength of all the Union armies for the same time tends to prove that the Confederate estimates of 600,000 to 700,000 for the total number in the Confederate army, or 20 to 24 per cent. of the total number (2,898,304)[5] in the Union armies, are too small. But it would be an error to assume that the ratio of 55 per cent. between the average strength of the Union armies and the average strength of the Confederate armies shows the absolute ratio between the number of men who were enrolled on each side, because it might not give due effect to the varying terms of service of the various levies on either side. No comparison of numbers could be just which did not take this into account.

[1] M. and D., Part III. 78–89.   [2] Reg. Losses, 554.

[3] M. and D., Part III. 141.

[4] M. and D., Part III. 139–141; 21,506 deducted from a total of 104,428 for deserters returned to the ranks.

[5] Post, p. 50.

It is obvious that a given number of men serving for four years constitute in effect a force at least sixteen times as strong as the same number serving for three months. In reducing the terms of enlistment to a common term, as for instance three years, some statisticians have assumed that the term of service of the so-called three years' men enlisted in 1863 and 1864 was three years, when in effect their service terminated with the war, at the end of one or two years. Such assumptions have their place in measuring the term of service for which it was possible to enroll men, but they have no place in comparing the effectual strength of the two armies during the war. This comparison can be made only by compounding the number of men with the actual term of service on each side.

The following table shows the actual terms of service of the various levies of United States troops and the equivalent number of men serving for three years, assuming that the service ended May 4, 1865, when hostilities had been terminated by the surrender of the principal armies of the Confederacy, and that the term of each levy which was terminated by the close of hostilities began one month after the date when the levy was called for.[1]

---

[1] This assumption probably errs on the side of greater numbers, as it is probable that the average interval between the call and muster-in was greater.

TABLE SHOWING NUMBER OF MEN IN UNION ARMY, THEIR ACTUAL TERM OF SERVICE, AND THE EQUIVALENT NUMBER OF MEN SERVING THREE YEARS.

(Authorities, M. and D., Rep. of Provost Marshal General, pp. 7 et seq. and 160 ; Statement of War Dept., Records and Pension Division, Jan., 1892.)

Date of President's call, Act of Congress, or draft	Number furnished	Term for which called	Actual term of service	Equivalent numbers for term of three years
1861				
April 15	91,816	3 mos.	3 mos.	7,651
May 3, July 22–25 . . .	2,715	6 mos.	6 mos.	452
	9,147	1 yr.	1 yr.	3,049
	30,950	2 yrs.	2 yrs.	20,633
	657,868 [1]	3 yrs.	3 yrs.	657,868
1862				
May, June	15,007	3 mos.	3 mos.	1,250
July 2	421,465	3 yrs.	33 mos.	386,343
August 4	87,588	9 mos.	9 mos.	21,897
1863				
June 15	16,361	6 mos.	6 mos.	2,727
July (draft)	35,582 [2]	3 yrs.	22 mos.	21,744
October 17, 1863, and February 1, 1864	281,510 [3]	3 yrs.	16 mos.	125,115
1864				
March 14	259,515	3 yrs.	13 mos.	93,714
April 23	83,612	100 days.	100 days.	7,636
July 18	385,163	1, 2, 3, and 4 years.	8½ mos.	90,941
December 19	211,752	do.	4 mos.	23,528
Various from the Territories and Southern States	172,744 [4]	do.	18 mos.	86,372
Ditto	15,509	60 days to a year. [5]	60 days to a year.	3,451
1863 Emergency men and militia	120,000	2 to 3 weeks.		2,307
	2,898,304			1,556,678

[1] Possibly 16,000 regulars on rolls January, 1861, should be added here.

[2] These men are included with call of February 1, in statement of War Department, etc. ; but see M. and D., Part III. 28, 39.

[3] 300,000 were called October 17, and 200,000 more February 1. The average of 16 months' service is taken upon the assumption that the enlistments were proportionate under the two calls.

[4] 97,598 were colored troops, all but one regiment enrolled after 1862.

[5] This actual service is estimated. (See M. and D., Part III. 67 et seq. ; Part I. 31.)

TERM OF SERVICE OF THE CONFEDERATE TROOPS.

There is no summary in the published records of the terms of service of the various levies of Confederate troops, but there is abundant evidence that in effect the term of service of all men composing the organizations regularly enrolled in the army of the Confederate States was for the duration of the war. The first act of the Confederate Congress for raising an army was that of February 28, 1861, which for both State forces and volunteers established twelve months as the term of service,[1] and under this act 70,000 men were called out.[1] The act of March 6, 1861, established a permanent regular army of seven regiments and 41 companies,[2] with a term of enlistment of not less than three or more than five years. Thirteen regiments and one battery were in fact raised for this force.[3]

The act of May 8, 1861, authorized the President to accept the service of all volunteers offering themselves for service during the war,[4] and the act of May 11 authorized him to fix the term of service.[5] The writer has not found, in the records published, any proclamation of the Confederate President fixing the number of troops or the term of service under these acts. The act of December 11, 1861, established a bounty for all then in service for twelve months who should reënlist for two years more.[6] At that date 110 regiments were in service for the war.[7] The act of January 23, 1862, authorized the President, at his discretion, to call on

---

[1] M. and D., Part III. 117–119; 127 W. R., 117, 135, 211, 221.
[2] 127 W. R., 127.   [3] Reg. Losses, 553.
[4] 127 W. R., 302.   [5] 127 W. R., 310.
[6] 127 W. R., 825.   [7] 127 W. R., 790.

the States for any number of troops for three years.[1]
The act of January 27, 1862, authorized recruiting
three years' volunteers for companies then in service
for twelve months.[2]   The act of January 29, 1862,
mentioned drafts by the States to fill the President's
requisition for men for three years.[3]   Under these acts
the Confederate authorities refused to receive troops
for less than three years except[4] for local or special
service.   February 2, 1862, the President called upon
the governors of the States to furnish 239,264 to
serve for the war.[5]   Following this, the governors of
the States began to warn their people that, if enough
volunteers did not respond to the call, they should make
drafts for the deficiency.[6]   Confederate returns show
that March 1, 1862, about two thirds of the troops
were in service for twelve months,[7] but they were all
retained in service for the war; for while the act of
April 16, 1862, placed all between 18 and 35 in the
service by conscription,[8] it also provided that all soldiers from 18 to 35 years of age who were there April
16 should be continued in service for three years.[9]   If
a few twelve months' volunteers between 35 and 45
years of age were entitled to their discharge, they
were swept back among the conscripts by the act of
September 27, 1862,[10] and they, as well as all others
within the conscript age, were held for service until the

[1] 127 W. R., 869.   [2] 127 W. R., 925.
[3] 127 W. R., 891.   [4] 127 W. R., 823.
[5] 127 W. R., 902.   [6] 127 W. R., 920.
[7] 127 W. R., 963.   [8] 127 W. R., 1095.
[9] 127 W. R., 1105.   [10] M. & D., Part III. 121.

end of the war.   Inspection of the War Records shows
that substantially all of the regiments enrolled in 1861
remained in service to the end of the war.   It may,
then, be assumed that in effect the term of service of
all who entered the Confederate armies continued from
the time they entered until the end of the war, May 4,
1865.

The returns of the Confederate armies above tabulated show that there were on their rolls, —

In July, 1861 . . . . 112,040 men.[1]
In January, 1862 . . . . 351,418 men.[1]

The average date of enlistment of those who were on
the rolls in July may be safely placed at the mean
between the firing on Fort Sumter and July 31, 1861,
which is about June 1; and October 31, 1861, may
be taken as the average date of enlistment of those who
joined the army between July 31, 1861, and January,
1862, and the term of service of these troops may then
be estimated as follows: —

Men on returns of July, 1861, in service for 47 months . 112,040
Men on returns of January, 1862, in service for 42 months 239,378

The later returns of the armies cannot serve as a
basis for establishing the term of service of the remainder of the levies, but the dates at which the various
regiments and battalions first appear in the War Records may be taken to establish the dates at which they
entered the service; for, although the most of them no
doubt entered the service some time before the dates at
which they were mentioned in the official papers con-

[1] Ante, pp. 42, 43.

tained in the War Records, yet there is a basis for correcting the resulting error in some cases, and in the others the total error cannot be very great.

The following table gives the number of regiments and battalions of infantry and cavalry, mention of which the writer has noted in the War Records as follows : —

Class A.   Those appearing in May, 1862, and earlier.

Class B.   Those appearing after May, 1862, bearing numbers lower than those of Class A, which indicate that they entered the service prior to the latest of Class A.

Class C.   Others appearing June, 1862, to October, 1863, inclusive.

There are included among the regiments in this table twelve legions. A legion sometimes had less, and sometimes more, men than a regiment.[1] They are counted as regiments here upon the assumption that their average strength was equal to that of the regiments.

In some cases regiments and battalions of infantry and cavalry appear in the War Records under designations different from those under which organizations are counted in the table below; and although in some cases it has been discovered that they were only alternative designations for organizations included in the table, yet it is possible that this was not true in all instances, and therefore that some are omitted : —

[1] See 127 W. R., 304, 789.

State	Class A		Class B	Class C	
	Regiments	Battalions	Regiments	Regiments	Battalions
Alabama [a]	43	9	–	11	10
Arkansas [b]	24	14	–	26	11
Confederate [c]	–	–	–	8	1
Florida [d]	7	–	–	2	5
Georgia [e]	51	5	9	18	10
Indian Ter. [f]	3	4	–	2	2
Kentucky [g]	29	3	–	10	4
Louisiana [h]	30	7	–	7	6
Maryland [i]	1	–	–	1	3
Mississippi [j]	38	2	7	10	15
Missouri [k]	24	8	–	14	7
North Carolina [l]	40	2	1	21	8
South Carolina [m]	29	1	–	4	4
Tennessee [n]	72	11	1	15	16
Texas [o]	31	3	13	20	8
Virginia [p]	68	5	1	16	22
Totals	490	74	45	185	132

[a] W. R., 4, 7, 8, 10–12, 14, 21–26, 29, 35–38, 42, 48, 50, 51, 58. [b] W. R., 4, 11, 14, 21–24, 32–36, 53. [c] W. R., 25, 40, 51, 56. [d] W. R., 11, 14, 20, 27, 47. [e] W. R., 4, 5, 7, 9, 11, 13, 14, 18, 20, 23, 29, 30, 35, 47, 49, 50. [f] W. R., 19, 32, 33. [g] W. R., 10, 11, 14, 23, 25, 30, 34, 35, 39, 49. [h] W. R., 10, 11, 14, 15, 18–22, 35, 36, 41. [i] W. R. 37, 39, 45, 49. [j] W. R., 7, 10, 11, 12, 14, 20–22, 24, 25, 27, 29, 34, 36–39, 53, 56. [k] W. R., 7, 8, 10, 11, 19, 32, 33. [l] W. R., 5, 9, 11–14, 18, 20, 21, 23, 26, 30, 35, 40, 49. [m] W. R., 6, 9, 11–14, 18, 20, 25, 31, 34, 37, 40, 47. [n] W. R., 4, 7, 8, 10, 11, 14, 21–25, 27, 29, 34, 35, 38, 51. [o] W. R., 5, 9, 11, 14, 19, 21, 25, 32, 33, 37, 41, 42, 50. [p] W. R., 4–6, 9, 11–15, 18, 26–28, 31, 35, 39, 40, 44, 45, 49.

The foregoing table shows the equivalent of 572 regiments prior to, and 251 regiments after, June 1, 1862.[1]

In Colonel Fox's list [2] there are 5 regiments, 6 battalions, and 261 batteries of artillery, equal to 34 regiments. It may be assumed that these troops entered

[1] Moore's North Carolina Roster records enlistments in 41 regiments in 1861, and in 25 more in the first seven months of 1862, out of a total of 70 regiments.

[2] Reg. Losses, 553.

the service after May, or prior to June, 1862, in the same proportion as the organizations in the above table. This gives 23 regiments of artillery, and a total of 595 regiments of all arms, as entering the service prior to June, 1862, which at the average strength of 971, as above estimated (p. 34), gives a total of 577,745 in these organizations at the outset. Deducting the 351,418 in service in January, 1862, there remain 226,327 whose term of service may be assumed to have begun midway between January 1 and June 1, or March 15, and therefore to have been $37\frac{1}{2}$ months.

The writer has not closely examined the War Records covering the period subsequent to October, 1863, for organizations regularly entering the Confederate service during that period of 19 months, but he assumes below (pp. 59–61) that the average term of service of all such organizations was one year. This does not seem too long a term in view of the urgent need of reinforcements for all the Confederate armies.

The table below gives the number of organizations in Class C, first appearing in the War Records in each month from June, 1862, to October, 1863, and their terms of service, reckoned from the same month to the end of the war: —

Month	Regiments	Battalions	Term of Service
1862			
June	9		35 months equal to 315 regiments for 1 month
		2	35 months equal to 35 regiments for 1 month
July	17		34 months equal to 578 regiments for 1 month
		7	34 months equal to 119 regiments for 1 month
August	17		33 months equal to 561 regiments for 1 month
		6	33 months equal to 99 regiments for 1 month
September	6		32 months equal to 192 regiments for 1 month
		10	32 months equal to 160 regiments for 1 month
October	13		31 months equal to 403 regiments for 1 month
		6	31 months equal to 93 regiments for 1 month
November	13		30 months equal to 390 regiments for 1 month
		6	30 months equal to 90 regiments for 1 month
December	15		29 months equal to 435 regiments for 1 month
		14	29 months equal to 105 regiments for 1 month
1863			
January	16		28 months equal to 448 regiments for 1 month
		16	28 months equal to 224 regiments for 1 month
February	6		27 months equal to 162 regiments for 1 month
		6	27 months equal to 81 regiments for 1 month
March	9		26 months equal to 234 regiments for 1 month
		6	26 months equal to 78 regiments for 1 month
April	17		25 months equal to 425 regiments for 1 month
		8	25 months equal to 100 regiments for 1 month
May	9		24 months equal to 216 regiments for 1 month
		8	24 months equal to 96 regiments for 1 month
June	6		23 months equal to 138 regiments for 1 month
		3	23 months equal to 34.5 regiments for 1 month
July	9		22 months equal to 198 regiments for 1 month
		9	22 months equal to 99 regiments for 1 month
August	7		21 months equal to 147 regiments for 1 month
		13	21 months equal to 136.5 regiments for 1 month
September	9		20 months equal to 180 regiments for 1 month
		5	20 months equal to 50 regiments for 1 month
October	7		19 months equal to 133 regiments for 1 month
		7	19 months equal to 66.5 regiments for 1 month
	185	132	36)69,195(192 or 192 regts. for 3 yrs

The remainder of the artillery in Colonel Fox's list equals 11 regiments, which with term of service proportionate to that of the organizations in the above list, would equal 8 regiments for three years, and would bring the total number to 200 regiments, equal, at 971 per regiment, to 194,200.

TERM OF SERVICE OF RECRUITS.

The report of the Superintendent of the Bureau of Conscription,[1] before referred to, shows that, east of the Mississippi, between April 16, 1862, and February, 1865, 81,993 had been enrolled by conscription; and he estimated that 72,292 had, during the same period, joined regiments in the field to avoid conscription, stating, however, that he believed this estimate to be much too small.   In view of the strenuous exertions of the Confederate authorities to enforce universal conscription, which have been detailed above,[2] it is safe to assume that the average date of enlistment of these 154,285 men was not later than midway between April 16, 1862, the date of the first conscript act, and April 30, 1864, when the Superintendent of the Bureau of Conscription reported the exhaustive measures which had been employed to gather in all the able-bodied men between 18 and 45.[3]   This would give an average term of service of 24 months for these recruits.   It remains to fix the term of service of the remainder of the recruits.

Adopting the largest estimate above of the total number of men regularly enrolled in the Confederate armies . . . .   1,307,460 [4]

And deducting the estimated original number of the ascertained organizations . . . .   824,379 [5]

We have as the number of recruits and organizations not ascertained   483,081

Deducting recruits reported . . . .   154,285 [6]

Leaves   328,796

---

[1] Ante, p. 35.   [2] Pages 11 et seq.

[3] M. and D., Part III. 122; 129 W. R. 354.

[4] Ante, p. 39.   [5] Ante, p. 34.   [6] Ante, p. 35.

Adopting the smaller estimate of 1,129,170[1] for the total number of men regularly enrolled would reduce the number of recruits and men, in organizations not ascertained, to about 150,000, but the mean between the two estimates above mentioned is 1,218,315; and this is so near 1,141,000, above computed as the number who were subject by law to military duty,[2] that to adopt it cannot exaggerate numbers. This leaves the remainder of 239,651 for recruits and organizations not above ascertained.

In view of the fact that under the Conscript Act of February, 1864, recruits were hurried to the ranks as fast as possible for the spring campaign, it seems safe to assume that the average term of service of all these 239,651 men was at least one year.

TERMS OF SERVICE OF MILITIA AND OTHER IRREGULAR ORGANIZATIONS.

The acts of the Confederate Congress of August 2, 1861, and October 13, 1862, authorized the acceptance of volunteers not within the conscript age (18 to 45), for local defense and special service; and the Confederate commanders, as early as September, 1863, issued orders to aid in the formation of companies, battalions, and regiments of these volunteers.[3]

The number of these troops has been estimated above (page 36) at 98,720. Their terms of service cannot be ascertained with exactness. The following facts from the War Records aid in making an estimate: —

---

[1] Ante, p. 39.　　　　　[2] Ante, p. 22.

[3] 33 W. R., 996.

Alabama.   August, 1862, the governor of Alabama was reported to be about to order out militia.[a]

Arkansas.   August 10, 1863, the governor and General E. Kirby Smith arranged to raise a volunteer force under State generals.[b]

Florida.   In June, July, and November, 1863, 5 special battalions from this State were in service.[c]   June 8, 1864, the reserves in service were incorporated in the 11th Florida Volunteers.[d]

Georgia.   August, 1863, the governor called out 8000 men for State defense.[e]

Louisiana.   The Ninth Brigade was called into service May, 1862.[f]   The Fifth Brigade was called into service June, 1862.[g]   The Tenth Brigade was called into service July 20, 1862.[h]   The Eleventh Brigade was called into service December, 29, 1862.[i]   Certain militia were disbanded September 30, 1862.[j]   One half of the militia of North, South, and East Louisiana were ordered into service February 25, 1863.[k]   May 7, 1863, General Magruder requested the governor to call out 10,500 militia.[l]

Mississippi.   August 11, 1862, the governor of Mississippi was reported to have ordered out 2000 militia.[m]   March 17, 1864, Gholson's Brigade of State Troops was turned over to the Confederate service.[n]

North Carolina.   The Junior Reserves enlisted from April to June, 1864.[o]

South Carolina,   January 15, 1863, 8 regiments of reserves were in service.[p]   April 30, 1864, the reserves were called out, against the governor's protest, by the Confederate authorities.[q]   June 29, 1864, all between 18 and 45 in 8 regiments of reserves were ordered to other regiments.[r]

Texas.   August 15, 1863, the State Troops were being organized.[s]   December 4, 1863, an act of legislature extended the terms of 8000 State Troops from 6 months to 12 months.[t]   December

[a] Vol. 25, p. 682.   [b] Vol. 33, p. 962.   [c] Vol. 47, pp. 172, 248, 469.   [d] Vol. 66, p. 525.   [e] Vol. 47, pp. 307, 313.   [f] Vol. 21, pp. 742, 756, 759.   [g] Vol. 21, pp. 755-767.   [h] Vol. 21, p. 784.   [i] Vol. 21, p. 914.   [j] Vol. 21, p. 819.   [k] Vol. 21, p. 991.   [l] Vol. 21, p. 1079.   [m] Vol. 25, p. 677.   [n] Vol. 59, pp. 650, 652.   [o] Moore's North Carolina Roster.   [p] Vol. 20, p. 750.   [q] Vol. 66, pp. 456, 519, 520, 535, 539.   [r] Vol. 65, pp. 623-635.   [s] Vol. 42, p. 170.   [t] Vol. 42, p. 528.

6, 1863, General Magruder required the governor to provide for continuance in service of the State Troops to the close of the war, and to organize all men from 16 to 70 years, not already in service.[u] December, 1863, 3 regiments and 5 battalions State Troops were incorporated into the army for 6 months.[v]

Virginia. June, 1861, Virginia militia were in service in Shenandoah Valley.[w] April, 1862, 3 regiments militia were in service at Williamsburg.[x] November, 1862, 3 regiments State line were in service.[y] June 10, 1863, 8000 militia were called to be mustered into service August 1, 1863.[z] March, 1864, 6 battalions of local defense regiments were in service.[a]

[u] Vol. 42, p. 486. [v] Vol. 42, pp. 497, 514. [w] 2 W. R., 473. [x] Vol. 14, p. 481. [y] Vol. 29, p. 33. [z] Vol. 45, pp. 883, 884. [a] Vol. 60, pp. 9, 130.

The citations previously made show that after 1862 the Confederate authorities were in such great need of troops that it is not probable that many of the men who took up arms in 1863 were allowed to lay them down again except for physical disability, and it seems safe to assume that the average term of service of the militia and other irregular organizations was at least sixteen months.

SUMMARY OF CONFEDERATE LEVIES REDUCED TO A THREE YEARS' TERM OF SERVICE.

July, 1861	. . 112,040 [a]	for 47	months	= 146,274 for 3 yrs.
January, 1862	. 239,378 [b]	for 42	months	= 279,274 for 3 yrs.
Before June, 1862,	226,327 [c]	for 37½	months	= 235,757 for 3 yrs.
After May, 1862	[d]			194,200 for 3 yrs.
Recruits reported,	154,285 [e]	for 2	years	= 102,856 for 3 yrs.
Recruits not reported and regular organizations not included above	239,651 [f]	for 1	year	= 79,883 for 3 yrs.
Militia, etc. . .	98,720 [g]	for 16	months	= 43,875 for 3 yrs.

1,082,119 for 3 yrs.

[a] Page 53. [b] Page 53. [c] Page 56. [d] Page 57. [e] Page 35. [f] Page 59. [g] Pages 59, 61.

This total of 1,082,119 men for three years in the Confederate service is 70 per cent. of the total of 1,556,678 for three years in the Union service as above computed,[1] but the average strength of the Confederate armies as above computed from the available returns is only 55 per cent. of the computed average strength of the Union armies.[2] The absence of some, and the incompleteness of some, of the Confederate returns, and the omission of some of the irregular organizations, probably cause a part of the discrepancy. The averages of the Union armies ought probably to be diminished for terms of service of large numbers of men which were shorter than those assumed in the computation. The 186,751[2] men on the rolls in July, 1861, assumed to have served three months, embraced nearly if not quite all the 91,816[1] three months' men whose term of service expired in July and August. The returns of January, 1863, included 87,588[1] nine months' men assumed to have served for the next six months, who in fact served somewhat less; and a part of the 575,917[2] men on the returns for January, 1862, assumed to have served nine months in computing the first two averages, did not enter the field in time to have served that time. If the per cent. of mortality in the Confederate army was, as seems probable, greater than that in the Union army, this, if it could be taken into account, would enlarge the average strength of the former in the computation.[3]

In comparing the actual performance in the field of the troops on the two sides, a mere statement of the numbers enrolled and the terms of service are not all

[1] Ante, p. 50.   [2] Page 47.

that should be considered. The irregular organizations included in the foregoing estimate of the Confederate troops [1] were probably of little value for active operations in the field. The same is true of the "emergency men," and perhaps some of the other short-term troops in the Union army. Again, on the Union side, 60,000 [2] men of the Veteran Reserve Corps were not available for service in the field; and the enlistment of 300,000 men was so near the close of the war that many did not see active service, and the records show that over 250 regiments never went into action.[3]

SUMMARY OF FOREGOING CALCULATIONS.

Number of enlistments in Union army	2,898,304
Number of men in Confederate army, estimated from the census	1,234,000
Number of enlistments in Confederate army, estimated from the number of organizations and their total average strength, between . . . . 1,227,890 and	1,406,180
Number of men serving three years, equivalent to the number enlisted in Union army, serving their actual terms	1,556,678
Number of men serving three years, equivalent to the number enlisted in Confederate army, serving their actual terms	1,082,119

The Records show that 385,245 were killed and wounded in the Union army,[4] while it has been gathered from the official reports, and, in their absence, from Confederate estimates of the loss in each engagement, that 94,000 were killed or mortally wounded in the Confederate army, which, in the usual ratio of 1 to 2.5, would indicate a total loss in killed and wounded of

[1] Ante, p. 61. [2] M. and D., Part III. 93.
[3] Reg. Losses, 467 et seq. [4] Reg. Losses, 47.

329,000.[1]   Table B [2] below shows more men hit on the
Confederate than on the Union side in 48 battles, in
which over 46 per cent. of the Union loss occurred.
Taken alone, the ratio between losses warrants no deduction of the ratio between numbers.   An army inferior in numbers, other conditions being equal, may lose
as many men as a larger one opposing it, by keeping its
individuals longer under fire.   Without the bravery
and resolution to do this to an extraordinary extent, the
Confederates could not have prolonged the civil war for
four years, and, by so many battles, against the superior
numbers of the Union army.   But if the average ratio
between the per cent. of loss on one side and the per
cent. of loss on the other side could be ascertained, this
ratio, applied to the known number in the Union army,
and total losses on both sides, would give a result
which ought not to greatly vary from the total number
in the Confederate army.   In the endeavor to establish this ratio, the writer has gathered the number
engaged and the number killed and wounded in each
battle in which 1000 or more were hit on either side,
as below stated in detail and assembled in Tables A
and B.[2]   For 15 of these battles the Official Records
give the losses in the Union armies only, but for the
other 48 they give numbers and losses on both sides,
excepting a few instances where the writer has taken
them from good authorities.[3]   These battles extend in

[1] Reg. Losses, 554, 22.   [2] Pages 140–145.

[3] Doubtless the returns for some battles include some as missing
who were killed or wounded, — notably those for the Seven Days'
Battles, Chancellorsville, and Chickamauga on the Union side, and
Shiloh, Stone's River, and Perrysville on the Confederate side.
Table A includes the number reported as missing.

time to every year of the war, and in place to all parts of the contested territory, and the forces engaged in them include every army of importance on either side. It is shown in Table B that, in the 48 battles on the Union side, the aggregate of the numbers engaged was 1,575,033, and the number hit was 176,550, and that on the Confederate side the aggregate of the numbers engaged was 1,243,528, and the number hit was 187,124. From this it appears that for an average number of 112.09 hit in 1000 on the Union side, there were 150.47 hit in 1000 on the Confederate side, but the greatest number were hit on the Union side, during the war, and it may be assumed that the ratio between these averages would not increase if extended to all battles. The total number of 385,245 hit in the Union army equals 247.48 per 1000 of 1,556,678, which, as has been above demonstrated,[1] would be the number of men serving for three years, equivalent to the number of men in the Union army serving for their actual terms. Using these figures with 329,000 for the total number hit in the Confederate army, in the following formula,

$$112.09 : 150.47 :: 247.48 : 332.22$$
$$329,000 \div 332.22 \times 1000 = \mathbf{990,308}$$

a result is obtained which may be assumed to be within the number of men serving for three years, equivalent to the number of men in the Confederate army serving for their actual terms. Previous calculations[2] have indicated the former number to be 1,082,332.

Including the 15 battles above mentioned, for which the Records give the losses in the Union army only, the aggregate of the numbers engaged on the Union side

[1] Page 50.   [2] Page 61.

was 2,328,515, and the losses were 247,589, or 106.33 per 1000. As the Confederates were on the defensive, in earthworks in the most of these battles, it is probable that if their numbers and losses in these battles could be used, they would tend to increase the number obtained as the result in the above formula. On the other hand, it is possible that the total of 329,000 for the Confederate killed and wounded is too large, because the ratio of 2.5 wounded to 1 killed or mortally wounded, which prevailed in the Union army, may be too large for the Confederate army, in which insufficient surgical attendance and hospital supplies and inadequate hospitals may have caused a greater mortality among the wounded.

A considerable number of the Union regiments never went under fire, and, as substantially all the Confederate regiments were in battle, this disparity to some extent would exaggerate the result of the above formula; but as the terms of service of these Union regiments were short, they would represent but a small number serving for three years, and therefore would not greatly enlarge the result.

METHOD OF ASCERTAINING THE NUMBERS ENGAGED.

The Records, apparently following the reports and returns of the commanders, give the numbers in the different campaigns and battles variously as "present for duty," "present for duty equipped," or "effective." Sometimes the last-named class excludes on both sides the non-combatants, and on the Confederate side the officers and even artillery and cavalry; and, in the effort to number only the men bearing muskets in

the firing-line, the stragglers, even those who have left the ranks on the field of battle, are sometimes excluded in reports of battles. (See Circular, 35 W. R., 619.)

This practice of counting as effective in the infantry only the men bearing muskets in the firing-line is of great value for informing commanders what weight of fire they can deliver, and the state of discipline in the ranks; but it cannot be followed in ascertaining numbers for comparison between the two sides in the civil war, or between the numbers in battles of that war and other wars, because the published accounts of the Union army, and of armies in other wars, do not usually state numbers on this basis. Officers, artillery, and cavalry are assuredly essential parts of the effective force of an army, and the efficiency of an army is certainly to be gauged quite as well by the number of combatants who fail to join in battle as by the valor of those who come into the firing-line. On the other hand, it is reasonable to exclude non-combatants from those counted as effective for battle. In both the Union and Confederate armies, the members of the regimental, medical, and quartermaster's departments, and the musicians, were non-combatants, and few of them were ever present in the firing-line, for even the drummers and fifers were usually employed in caring for the wounded; and these non-combatants, although essential to successful campaigns, cannot be said to have had any influence in the decision of battles in the civil war.

In the Union army a regiment of infantry 1050 strong regularly had about 70 non-combatants,[1] and too

[1] Staff, 10; company musicians, 20; band, wagoners, and men detailed for duty at headquarters and in quartermaster's and medical departments, 40.

often men employed as company clerks and officers' servants were kept out of battle. Sickness and other casualties began reducing the ranks as soon as a regiment went into camp, and probably not one ever reached a battlefield with full ranks. The average regimental strength "present for duty," in the Union army, was about 560 at Shiloh,[1] and 650 at Fair Oaks,[2] in the spring of 1862; 530 at Chancellorsville[3] in May, 375 at Gettysburg[4] in July, and 440 at Chickamauga[5] in September, 1863; 440 at the Wilderness,[6] and 305 in Sherman's army[7] in May, 1864. Naturally the number of non-combatants in the regiments of these armies had not been reduced in the same proportion by casualties; and, although their number was reduced in the interest of economy as the strength of the regiments diminished, yet there is no reason for concluding that it was ever less than seven per cent. of the total "present for duty" in the infantry and artillery. Repeated instances are found in the Records where the numbers given as "effective" in infantry corps or divisions are from 89 to 93 per cent. of the number "present for duty,"[8] while in the cavalry the per cent. is often from 83 to 86.[9]

[1] 10 W. R., 100, 105, 112.

[2] 12 W. R., 757 et seq; 14 W. R., 204.

[3] 39 W. R., 156 et seq. ; 40 W. R. 320.

[4] 43 W. R., 151, 155, et seq.

[5] 50 W. R. 40 et seq., 169.

[6] 67 W. R., 19 et seq., 915.

[7] 72 W. R., 89 et seq., 115; the number present for duty assumed to be 107 per cent. of the "effectives."

[8] 31 W. R., 1121; 43 W. R., 152; 55 W. R., 12; 72 W. R., 115; 75 W. R., 373.

[9] 40 W. R., 320; 43 W. R., 152; 67 W. R., 198; 72 W. R., 115; 75 W. R., 373.

The lower per cents. may be accounted for by the deduction of men without arms in the infantry, and of men without mounts in the cavalry. It is apparent that the commanders of corps in the Union army did not all follow the same classification in counting the numbers " present for duty equipped," or " effective ;" for in some returns these numbers are the same as, or under one per cent. less than, the number " present for duty," and sometimes they are stated as even greater.[1] Although the Confederate returns bear evidence of having computed the " effectives" more consistently, yet it is apparent in some cases that a sufficient deduction is not made for the non-combatants.[2] In view of these facts, the writer, adopting the number of effectives given in the Official Records in the few cases where they seem to be properly determined, or where the number present for duty is not given, has in other cases computed the number of effectives in the infantry and artillery at 93 per cent., and in the cavalry at 85 per cent., of the number present for duty. In cases where the number of effectives given in the Confederate returns is used, an addition is made for officers if they appear not to have been included. In this connection it is to be observed that in the Union armies the number of officers ran from 4 to 7 per cent. of the total

[1] For example, see Army of Potomac, 14 W. R., 238 ; Left Grand Div., 31 W. R., 1121 ; several corps, 40 W. R., 320 ; 11th corps, 55 W. R., 13 ; 14th and 20th corps, 72 W. R., 115 ; 75 W. R., 373 ; Cav. Div., 95 W. R., 61 ; 23d corps, Dist. of Etowah, 95 W. R., 53, 54.

[2] For examples, see 23 W. R., 784 ; 91 W. R., 883.

present for duty,[1] while in the Confederate armies it ran from 6½ to 11 per cent.[2]

It will be found that the numbers given in the tables below often differ from those commonly given, from the fact that organizations which, although figuring in the returns of the armies engaged, were not in fact on the field of battle, are here excluded. The same is true of troops which, although on the field or within supporting distance, were in such position that their presence could not have had any effect on the opposing force. Attention is called to each omission of this kind in the tables.

COURAGE AND EFFICIENCY OF THE ARMIES COMPARED.

The comparison of numbers and losses naturally leads to the inquiry whether, on the whole, one side showed martial capacity superior to that of the other; and here it must be recognized that other things beside mere numbers and losses are to be taken into account.

To invade and hold a constantly increasing territory required many more troops than would have been needed in the Union army for actual fighting, and many Northern soldiers were employed in non-combatants' work, such as was done by negroes for the Southern army.

---

[1] W. R., vol. 2, p. 309; vol. 14, p. 184; vol. 28, p. 410; vol. 25, p. 246; vol. 23, p. 564; vol. 31, p. 1121; vol. 30, p. 285; vol. 40, p. 320; vol. 38, p. 249; vol. 43, p. 152; vol. 50, p. 169; vol. 55, p. 13; vol. 61, p. 168; vol. 67, pp. 198, 915; vol. 96, p. 737; vol. 95, p. 61; vol. 75, p. 373; vol. 72, p. 117; vol. 91, p. 248; vol. 93, p. 53.

[2] W. R., vol. 2, p. 568; vol. 7, pp. 843, 855; vol. 80, pp. 10, 23, 93, 398, 678, 784; vol. 75, pp. 14, 645; vol. 87, pp. 28, 621; vol. 81, pp. 28, 660; vol. 23, p. 784; vol. 31, p. 1057; vol. 29, p. 674; vol. 38, p. 702; vol. 83, pp. 40, 696; vol. 53, p. 519; vol. 84, pp. 40, 847; vol. 91, p. 883.

In physical resources, such as transportation, arms, the munitions of war, food, clothing, and hospital supplies, the South was at a great disadvantage. The superiority of the North in these respects counterbalanced many men.

With all these things taken into account, the long and resolute contest maintained by the South, and their many successes against superior numbers, must always command admiration. The fact that their attitude was mainly defensive is not enough alone to account for all they achieved ; and careful study of the campaigns and battles, with the statistics of losses, leads to the belief not only that the Southern leaders were, at least up to 1864, bolder in taking risks than their opponents, but also that they pushed their forces under fire very nearly to the limit of endurance. Such strategy as that displayed by Jackson in the three campaigns of the Chickahominy, the second Bull Run, and Chancellorsville, was matched on the Northern side only by Grant's movements across the Mississippi and behind Vicksburg. The more frequent ventures of the Confederate generals may be attributed in part to the greater impetuosity of the Southern temperament, and in part to the ever present consciousness in the Union generals that they were warring to preserve, and in the Confederate generals that they were warring to destroy, a government; in the Union generals that they were defending railway lines and cities of great wealth whose capture would benefit the enemy as much as it would injure the cause of the Union ; in the Confederate generals that to defend their cities was not vital to their cause. But good generals cannot fight battles as the Confederates fought them without extraordinarily good soldiers.

In measuring the courage and efficiency of the line of an army, it is not enough to consider the per cent. of loss which it endures in a battle or series of battles. The loss suffered in a rout is not a measure of courage. It never can be proved that in winning victory an army has been pressed to the limit of its endurance; and on the other hand, while a rout may indicate that the limit of courage has been reached, an army which is withdrawn by the commanding general from a well-contested field, if it retires at will and in good order, cannot be said to have reached the limit of its endurance, although in a general sense defeat is acknowledged by the act of abandoning the field. The general who is responsible may have been weak, or, being strong, may have, after a fair trial for victory, elected to wait for another day and another field. Tactical advantages, or the cover of intrenchments on one side, may render courage unavailing on the other side, and a line of the bravest men may be swept away by the weight of superior numbers.

COMPARISON OF SIMILAR BATTLES.

It is obvious that the conduct of armies should be compared, where possible, in situations similar to each other. This is attempted for the Union and Confederate armies in what follows.

The Confederates, with a loss of 301 in 1000 at Gettysburg and 266 at Stone's River, may be compared to the Union men in the eight days, May 5–12, in the Wilderness and at Spottsylvania, with a loss of 296 in 1000 infantry and artillery, or 263 in 1000 in all arms. At Gettysburg the Confederates, having gained ground during two days, were checked on the third, and then,

after delaying a day on the field, relinquished the fight and left the field in the possession of their adversaries. The history of the Confederates at Stone's River is almost identically the same. In the Wilderness the Confederates defeated the attempt to turn their flank, but failed to drive the Union army, which, after gaining ground, transferred the conflict by another flanking march a few miles to the south, and again took the offensive in a series of attacks on the intrenchments of the Confederates at Spottsylvania. Although it carried a portion of the works, it failed to carry the Confederate position. Neither side gained a victory. The combats, May 5–12, were, as far as testing the quality of the men was concerned, in effect a continuous battle, and may be fairly treated as such for the purpose of the foregoing comparison. As the cavalry were absent after the 8th of May and took no part in the infantry combat, it seems proper to omit their numbers and losses for this purpose.

The loss of 267 in 1000 suffered by the Union column in the assault on the works of Port Hudson, June 14, entitles it to be compared with the attacking armies in the three battles above mentioned; but the endurance of a small and homogeneous force like that at Port Hudson does not give the same evidence of the martial quality of the armies, as a whole, as is afforded by their conduct in the great battles. There were repeated instances in the great battles where a division or corps, numbering as many as, or more than, the Union force at Port Hudson or Olustee, endured a greater per cent. of loss, as, for example, the loss at Gettysburg by the Second Corps of 328 in 1000 of its 12,141 effec-

tives (43 W. R., 151, 177), and at Fredericksburg, by Hancock's division of the same corps, of 360 in 1000 of its 5006 effectives (31 W. R., 288, 130).

At Chickamauga the Confederates, with a superior force, routed a part of the Union army, and compelled the rest to relinquish the field, although in good order and moving or standing at will. The Confederate loss was 259 in 1000. The attitude of the Union army at Antietam was similar to that of the Confederates at Chickamauga; but the Union commander allowed only 53,000 of his 75,000 to open fire, and, although they gained ground at all points, he was content to stop the attack with a loss of 219 per 1000 of these 53,000. This is a conspicuous example of those cases where it cannot be maintained that the victorious army exhausted its courage.

Shiloh, on the Confederate side, had no exact parallel on the Union side. Successful on the first day against inferior numbers, it was driven from the field by superior numbers on the second, after a loss of 241 in 1000. The Union army at Olustee gave up the attack and abandoned the field after a loss of 265 per 1000; but, as has been before suggested, a comparison is not just between a small force like that at Olustee and an army as large as the Confederate force at Shiloh.

For further comparison of losses under similar conditions, the 63 battles of Table B may be classified as follows, although discrimination must be made between those which are styled defeats, because some are ranged under this head merely because the field was abandoned; when considered tactically, the retreating army was successful in the battle itself.

ASSAULTS ON FORTIFIED LINES.

SUCCESSES [1]		PARTIAL SUCCESSES [1]	
Union loss per 1000		Union loss per 1000	
Winchester	124	Chaffin's Farm	137
Chattanooga	97	Petersburg, June 15–18	128
Petersburg, April 2	60	Fort Donelson [3]	96
Jonesborough, September 1	57	Spottsylvania, May 12	96
Nashville	56	Deep Bottom	78
Arkansas Post [2]	36		

FAILURES

Union loss per 1000		Confederate loss per 1000	
Port Hudson, June 14	267	Atlanta, July 28	222
Fort Wagner	214	Franklin	206
Port Hudson, May 27	141	Atlanta, July 22	190
The Mine	138	Peach Tree Creek	133
Kenesaw Mountain	123	Corinth	112
Cold Harbor	111	Mechanicsville	91
Spottsylvania, May 10	108	Bentonville	89
Fredericksburg	103	Jonesborough, August 31	72
Vicksburg, May 22	67		
Chickasaw Bayou	39		

DEFEATS

Union loss per 1000		Confederate loss per 1000	
Olustee	265	Gettysburg	301
Cedar Mountain [2]	219	Stone's River	266
Chickamauga	196	Shiloh	241
Wilson's Creek [4]	175	Antietam	226
Drewry's Bluff	175	Tupelo	201
Manassas and Chantilly	132	Perryville	196
Chancellorsville	114	Fair Oaks	137
Pleasant Hill	78	South Mountain	105
		Prairie Grove	98
		Weldon R. R.	81
		Pea Ridge	43
		Arkansas Post [2]	24

[1] Although the Confederates did not take and hold fortified lines in any of the battles of Table A, note should be made of Harper's Ferry, where, although the loss in killed and wounded did not amount to 1000 on either side, 13,000 Union troops were surrendered. On the other side, note should be made of Five Forks, where 5000 to 6000 Confederates were taken.

[2] The defeated army was greatly outnumbered.

[3] Under this head the assault only is referred to.

[4] The defeat is to be attributed to the rawness of the troops.

ROUTS

Union loss per 1000		Confederate loss per 1000	
Richmond, Ky.	161	Winchester [1]	123
Gaines's Mill [1]	117	Cedar Creek [1]	101
Bull Run [2]	52	Petersburg, April 2	unknown
		Nashville	unknown, but small

VICTORIES

Union loss per 1000		Confederate loss per 1000	
Stone's River	223	Chickamauga	259
Gettysburg	212	Chancellorsville	187
Shiloh	162	Manassas and Chantilly	187
Antietam	155	Olustee	180
Cedar Creek	132	Drewry's Bluff	158
Winchester	124	Gaines's Mill	153
Fair Oaks	105	Wilson's Creek	100
Pea Ridge	105	Fort Wagner	95
Corinth	104	Cedar Mountain	79
Perryville	100	Pleasant Hill	70
Prairie Grove	99	Richmond, Ky.	66
Chattanooga	97	Fredericksburg	64
Peach Tree Creek	79	Bull Run	61
Champion's Hill,	76	Port Hudson, May 27	56
South Mountain	68	Kenesaw Mountain	15
Atlanta, July 22	65	Mine Run [3]	15
Weldon R. R.	64	Chickasaw Bayou	14
Bentonville	58	Port Hudson, June 14	13
Dinwiddie	48		
Tupelo	45		
Atlanta, July 28	42		
Arkansas Post	36		
Jonesborough, August 31	13		

[1] The defeated army was greatly outnumbered.

[2] The defeat is to be attributed to the rawness of the troops.

[3] The Union army, failing in its manœuvre to flank its adversary, withdrew without offering battle. Its main loss occurred in repelling a Confederate attack.

BATTLES FOUGHT TO COVER A PREARRANGED MOVEMENT, PURSUING WHICH
THE ARMY RETIRED AFTER REPELLING ATTACK

Union loss per 1000		Confederate loss per 1000	
Peach Orchard to Malvern Hill [1]	60	Williamsburg	49
Franklin	40		
Mechanicsville	16		

The foregoing comparisons do not give ground on which to award the display of superior courage or steadfastness to the armies as a whole on either side. The record on both sides places the people of the United States in the first rank of militant nations.

BULL RUN, JULY 21, 1861.

UNION ARMY.

Present for duty, ex. Runyon's division, and including
Blenker's brigade . . . . 30,594 [a]
Effectives estimated at 93 per cent. 28,452
Killed, 481. Wounded, 1011. Total, 1492. Missing, 1216. [b]
Hit in 1000, 52. Hit by 1000, 70. [2]

CONFEDERATE ARMY.

Army of the Potomac, effectives (including officers) . 21,883 [c]
Army of the Shenandoah, effectives (probably including officers) . . . . 8,884 [d]
Holmes's brigade, effectives (officers and artillery estimated at 200) . . . . 1,465 [e]

Total engaged 32,232
Killed, 387. Wounded, 1582. Total, 1969. Missing, 12. [f]
Hit in 1000, 61. Hit by 1000, 46.

[a] 2 W. R., 304, 309. [b] 2 W. R., 327. [c] 2 W. R., 487, 568. [d] 2 W. R., 187, 487, 569. [e] 2 W. R., 487. [f] 2 W. R., 570.

---

[1] The Confederate loss was 99 in 1000.

[2] The number hit by 1000 is given in this and the following tables as one measure of courage and efficiency.

WILSON'S CREEK, MO., AUGUST 10, 1861.

UNION ARMY.

Lyon's command, about . . . . [1]5,400 [a]
Killed, 223. Wounded, 721. Total, 944. Missing, 291.[b]
Hit in 1000, 175. Hit by 1000, 214.

CONFEDERATE ARMY.

McCulloch's command, effectives, about . . . . . [2]11,600 [c]
Killed, 257. Wounded, 900. Total, 1157.[3] Missing, 27.[d]
Hit in 1000, 100. Hit by 1000, 81.

[a] 3 W. R., 60, 86. [b] 3 W. R., 72. [c] 3 W. R., 104. [d] 3 W. R., 101, 126.

FORT DONELSON, FEBRUARY 12–16, 1862.

UNION ARMY.

In the lines and guarding the road to the left . . . 27,000 [a]
Killed, 500. Wounded, 2108. Total, 2608. Missing, 224.[b]
Hit in 1000, 96. Hit by 1000, 74.

CONFEDERATE ARMY.

Engaged [4] about . . . . [5]21,000 [c]
Killed and wounded, 2000.[d] Missing, 14,623.[e]
Hit in 1000, 95. Hit by 1000, 124.

[a] 1 Grant's Memoirs, 315. [b] 7 W. R., 169. [c] 1 Grant's Memoirs, 315.
[d] 7 W. R., 291 [e] 1 Grant's Memoirs, 314.

---

[1] It is not clear whether this is the number present for duty or effective. Sigel's artillery numbered 120, and his two companies of cavalry about 125 (see 3 W. R., 48). General Fremont's dispatch of August 13, placing the force at 8000, assumed the presence of 2000 Home Guards, when in fact they numbered only 200 (3 W. R., 54, 65).

[2] It is not clear whether officers are included. The artillery is estimated at 300.

[3] General McCulloch's report, giving 257 killed and 800 wounded, is corrected above by the reports of his subordinates.

[4] General Pillow reported that he had "only about 13,000 troops all told" (7 W. R., 283), but 16,623 were killed, wounded, and captured, and at least 2000 more escaped (7 W. R., 275, 295). The records show that there were present for duty in Buckner's division, 4481, January 31; in Tilghman's, 3830,

---

[5] There are no data for determining whether these are the numbers "present for duty," or "present for duty equipped," or "effective."

PEA RIDGE, ARK., MARCH 7, 1862.

UNION ARMY.

Army of the Southwest, about . . . . [1]11,250 [a]
Killed, 203 ; wounded, 980. Total 1183.[b] Missing, 201.[b]
Hit in 1000, 105. Hit by 1000, 53.

CONFEDERATE ARMY.

Van Dorn's command, about . . . . [2]14,000 [c]
Killed and wounded, about 600.[c] Missing, 200.[c]
Hit in 1000, 43. Hit by 1000, 84.

[a] 8 W. R., 196, 554. [b] 8 W. R. 206. [c] 8 W. R., 285.

SHILOH, APRIL 6, 7, 1862.

UNION ARMY.

Army of the Tennessee, effectives . . . . . . [3]42,682 [a]
Army of the Ohio, 2d, 4th, and 5th divisions . . . [4]20,000 [b]
                                                            ————
Total engaged 62,682
Killed, 1754. Wounded, 8408. Total, 10,162. Missing, 2885.[c]
Hit in 1000, 162. Hit by 1000, 155.

[a] 10 W. R., 112. [b] 1 Grant's Memoirs, 366; 1 Van Horne, 112, 115; 10 W. R., 325. [c] 10 W. R., 108.

January 21 ; and in Floyd's brigade, 1286, after the battle (7 W. R., 327, 853, 366, 843, 275), and that Johnson's division of 15 regiments was present (7 W. R., 359), which at the average strength of regiments at that time numbered at least 7500, besides the cavalry (7 W. R., 383). The 30th Mississippi regiment, of Floyd's brigade, had lost 532 in the battle (7 W. R., 380). This gives a total of at least 17,530. In view of these figures, and in the absence of detailed returns to support General Pillow's estimate, it is probably safe to adopt the number 21,000 given by General Grant.

[1] This apparently was the "effective" force, the artillery being estimated at 1000, and Major Conrad's detachment of 250 deducted.

[2] This probably was the effective force.

[3] Estimated at 93 per cent. of 44,895 present for duty, plus 1000 for 2 regiments and 1 battery, which, according to the note of the compiler of the returns (10 W. R., 112), are not included in 5463 given for the 6th division.

[4] The numbers given in the authorities cited are adopted in the absence of returns. The April returns do not serve, because the composition of the divisions named in them differed from that of April 7. The 6th division is here excluded, because no part of it got within reach of the Confederates, or arrived until after the retreat was general (10 W. R., 378, 380).

CONFEDERATE ARMY.

Effectives . . . . [1]40,335 [d]

Killed, 1723. Wounded, 8012. Total, 9735. Missing, 959 [e]

Hit in 1000, 241. Hit by 1000, 252.

[d] 10 W. R., 396.   [e] 10 W. R., 395.

WILLIAMSBURG, MAY 4, 5, 1862.

UNION ARMY.

" Effective strength," estimated at 93 per cent. of the
number "present for duty," which is assumed to be
$\frac{88}{85}$ of the number present for duty in 3d and 4th
corps [2] . . . .   [2]40,768 [a]

Killed, 456. Wounded, 1410. Total, 1866. Missing, 373.[b]

Hit in 1000, 45. Hit by 1000, 39.

CONFEDERATE ARMY.

Effective strength,[3] May 21, 1862, of the divisions of
Longstreet and Hill, and the brigades of McLaws,
Kershaw, and Stuart . . . .   [4]30,120 [c]

Add loss May 4, 5   1,703
_____

Total engaged   31,823

[a] 12 W. R., 281–283, 456, 496, 521, 525, 559, 563; 14 W. R., 130.   [b] 12 W. R.,
450.   [c] 12 W. R., 565, 566, 442, 572, 602, 603; 14 W. R., 530, 531.

---

[1] It is assumed that from the "effective total" of the field return, the 4 regiments, 2 battalions, and 1 battery which were ordered to guard Corinth are excluded (10 W. R., 349, 399, note) ; adding to the return of June 30 (10 W. R., 399), of 39,598 present for duty, 2262 for the 3d corps, and 2373 for the cavalry, as shown in the field return above cited, a total of 44,233 is reached ; 93 per cent. of this number would give 41,136 as against the 40,335 above adopted as the effectives.

[2] 54 of the 85 regiments in the 3d and 4th corps were present, but only 35 suffered loss.

[3] That this was only the "effective" strength is shown at 14 W. R., 479 et seq. Comparison with pp. 460, 530, et seq., shows that the numbers given pp. 479 et seq. apply to a later date than April 30.

[4] Apparently this number ought to be increased for the cavalry of Wise's and Hampton's legions (12 W. R., 445), numbering perhaps about 700. (See Hampton's Legion, 14 W. R., 483.)

Killed and wounded, 1570.[1]   Missing, 133.[d]
Hit in 1000, 49.   Hit by 1000, 59.

[d] 12 W. R., 443, 568, 569.

FAIR OAKS, MAY 31, JUNE 1, 1862.

UNION ARMY.

2d, 3d, and 4th corps present for duty May 31 . .   51,543 [a]
Deduct 3d corps cavalry, 751. and 8 regiments and 5
  batteries, estimated at 5848, not engaged . . . .   6,599 [b]

44,944

Effectives estimated at 93 per cent.   41,797
Killed, 790.   Wounded, 3594.   Total, 4384.   Missing, 647.[c]
Hit in 1000, 105.   Hit by 1000, 137.

CONFEDERATE ARMY.

Effective strength of Smith's, Longstreet's, and Hill's
  divisions, May 21 . . . . [2]35,559 [d]
Effective strength of Huger's division (3 brigades),
  estimated [3] . . . .   6,257 [e]

Total effective   41,816

Killed, 980.   Wounded, 4749.   Total, 5729.   Missing, 405. [f]
Hit in 1000, 137.   Hit by 1000, 105.

[a] 14 W. R., 204.   [b] 14 W. R., 238; 12 W. R., 759–761.   [c] 12 W. R., 762.
[d] 12 W. R., 933–935; 14 W. R., 530, 531.   [e] 12 W. R., 933–935, 940; 14
W. R., 570, 555.   [f] Reg. Losses, 549; 12 W. R., 942, 991.

---

[1] A few casualties occurred in Stuart's brigade, which are not included, as
their number is not stated (12 W. R., 572).

[2] That this was " effective " strength, see 14 W. R., 479–483.

[3] Estimated, proportionately to the number of brigades, to be equal to $\frac{8}{17}$ of
the other three divisions.

MECHANICSVILLE, JUNE 26, 1862.

UNION ARMY.

Present for duty June 20, in 3d division, 5th corps .   9,514 [a]
Present for duty June 20, in 1st and 2d brigade, 1st
    division, 5th corps . . . .   [1]6,844 [a]
Present for duty June 20, in 6 batteries, estimated at .   450
                                                        ——————
                                                        16,808
Effectives estimated at 93 per cent.   15,631
Killed, 49. Wounded, 207. Total, 256. Missing, 105.[b]
Hit in 1000, 16. Hit by 1000, 95.

CONFEDERATE ARMY.

A. P. Hill's division . . . .   14,000 [c]
Ripley's brigade . . . .   2,356 [d]
                                               ——————
    Effectives, June 26   16,356
Killed and wounded, 1484.[2] [e]
Hit in 1000, 91. Hit by 1000, 16.

[a] 14 W. R., 238; 13 W. R., 30, 222, 237. [b] 13 W. R., 39. [c] 13 W. R.,
835. [d] 13 W. R., 835, 650. [e] 13 W. R., 982, 983.

GAINES'S MILL, JUNE 27, 1862.

UNION ARMY.

Present for duty June 20, in 5th corps,[3] Slocum's
    division and Cooke's cavalry [4] . . . .   39,295 [a]
Deduct 671 cavalry, 17th New York and 18th Massa-
    chusetts (1473),[5] and loss June 26 (361)   . . .   2,505 [b]
                                                        ——————
    Total present for duty, June 27 [6]   36,790

[a] 13 W. R., 36, 41; 14 W. R., 238. [b] 13 W. R., 39.

---

[1] Estimated at $\frac{9}{15}$ of the strength of the division, — 18th Massachusetts detached.

[2] 400 estimated as the loss in G. B. Anderson's brigade, and 7 regiments and
1 battalion of Field's, Branch's, and Pender's brigades. This estimate exceeds
by about 100 that which is adopted by Fox (Reg. Losses, 550 note), and it is
with hesitation that it is used as against an authority whose figures are so well
considered.

[3] Including McCall's division.

[4] Estimated proportionately to the squadrons at $\frac{8}{33}$ of the cavalry division.

[5] Estimated proportionately to the number of regiments at $\frac{1}{20}$ of the 5th corps.

[6] French's and Meagher's brigades not included, as they arrived after the
battle was decided.

Effectives estimated at 93 per cent. 34,214
Killed, 894. Wounded, 3107. Total, 4001. Missing, 2836.[c]
Hit in 1000, 117. Hit by 1000, 256.

CONFEDERATE ARMY.

Present for duty July 20,[1] in Longstreet's,[2] A. P.
  Hill's,[3] D. H. Hill's, and Whiting's divisions . . [4]32,598 [d]
Deduct Wise's brigade (about 1300), leaving present
  for duty July 20 . . . . 31,298 [e]

Effectives estimated at 93 per cent. 29,107
Add losses in above forces, June 28 to July 1 . . . [5]11,921 [f]
Winder's brigade, June 10, and Lawton's brigade,
  June 27 . . . . 4,945 [g]
Ewell's division, and Jones and Fulkerson's brigades
  of Jackson's division, estimated [6] at 11,045
                                                    _____
    Total effectives, June 27 . . . . [7]57,018
Killed and wounded, 8751.
Hit in 1000, 153. Hit by 1000, 70.[h]

[c] 13 W. R., 41. [d] 14 W. R., 645. [e] 14 W. R., 604; 13 W. R., 916.
[f] 13 W. R., 973 et seq. [g] 15 W. R., 742 ; 13 W. R., 595. [h] Reg. Losses, 550
note ; 13 W. R., 608, 616, 973, et seq.

---

[1] The number present for duty was 73.5 per cent. of the aggregate present,
as against 80 to 87 per cent. at later periods, which suggests the possibility that
the proportion present for duty was above 73.5 per cent. June 27.

[2] The 16th Mississippi in this division July 20 was in Ewell's June 25 (14
W. R., 649 ; 13 W. R., 484).

[3] The gain of 2 Virginia heavy artillery is assumed to equal the loss of 2
Arkansas and 22 Virginia battalions in this division.

[4] It is not certain that the artillery is included here. (See G. O., No. 71 ; 14
W. R., 612.)

[5] This number is reached by deducting from the total loss in the seven days
1484 for the loss June 26, of which 400 is estimated for G. B. Anderson's
brigade, and 7 regiments and 1 battalion of Field's, Branch's, and Pender's
brigades, for which commands there is no report of loss separated from that in
the other actions.

[6] Estimated at 470 per regiment, the average per regiment of the 42,803
above ascertained for June 27.

[7] Statements of numbers in the commands above named, together with
losses prior to June 27, are found in reports and dispatches as follows : —

PEACH ORCHARD, SAVAGE STATION, JUNE 29, 1862.
WHITE OAK SWAMP, GLENDALE, JUNE 30, 1862.
MALVERN HILL, JULY 1, 1862.

UNION ARMY.

Army of Potomac, present for duty June 20 .		115,102 [a]
Deduct general staff, escort, engineers, provost guard, quartermaster's guard, and Dix's command	12,920	
Deduct Casey's and Stoneman's commands [1] .	4,150	17,070 [b]
		98,032
Effectives estimated at 93 per cent.[2] . . .		91,169
Deduct losses June 25–28		7,824 [c]
Total engaged		83,345

[a] 14 W. R., 230.   [b] 13 W. R., 298, 330, 482.   [c] 13 W. R., 37–41.

April 16, Ewell's division, 8000, loss May 23, June 9, 1175 ; leaving June 10	[1] 6,825
May 3, Jones and Fulkerson's brigades, 4716 ; losses, May 8, June 9, 189 ; leaving June 10	[2] 4,527
May 21, Hood's and Law's brigades, 4320 ; losses, May 31, 357 ; leaving June 1	[3] 3,963
June 2, Hampton's legion, 219 ; leaving June 2	[4] 219
June 10, Winder's brigade, 1122 ; leaving June 10	[5] 1,122
June 27, D. H. Hill's division (10,000), and brigades of Lawton (3500), Kemper (1433), Pickett (1481), Wilcox (1850), Pryor (1400) ; leaving June 27	[6] 19,664
June 25, A. P. Hill's division, 14,000 ; less loss June 26, 909 ; leaving June 27	[7] 13,091
	49,411
R. H. Anderson's and Featherston's brigades, at the average regimental strength (333) of the rest of Longstreet's division, would number	2,497
Total	51,908

As the reports referred to usually give the number of "men," "muskets," or rank and file, it is possible that about 3500 should be added for officers ; and artillery is probably not included in the numbers above given, and therefore at least 1500 should be added for this arm. These additions would bring the total to about 57,000.

[1] The infantry is estimated at 50 to a company, the average in the army.

[2] Estimating the effectives in the cavalry at 85 per cent. of the present for duty would reduce this number about 250.

---

[1] 18 W. R., 851 ; 15 W. R., 718, 781, 783.   [2] 18 W. R., 879 ; 15 W. R., 476, 717, 767–769, 773–777.   [3] 14 W. R., 530 ; 13 W. R., 506.   [4] 12 W. R. 994.   [5] 15 W. R., 742.   [6] 13 W. R., 629, 595, 762, 767, 775, 781.   [7] 13 W. R., 835, 982, 983.

Killed, 724.   Wounded, 4245.   Total, 4969.   Missing, 3067.[d]
Hit in 1000, 60.   Hit by 1000, 103.

CONFEDERATE ARMY.

Army of Northern Virginia, present for duty July 20 [1]	69,732 [e]
Deduct Martin's brigade (2228), Wise's brigade (300), 47th and 48th Alabama, 32d and 53d North Carolina (2000)	[2] 4,528 [f]
	65,204
Effectives estimated at 93 per cent.[3]	60,639
Add losses, June 29–July 1 [4]	11,484 [g]
Effectives June 27 in Winder's and Lawton's brigade, Jackson's division	4,945 [h]
Effectives in Ewell's division and Jones's and Fulkerson's brigades, Jackson's division, estimated at . .	11,045 [i]
	88,113
Deduct loss in Ewell's and Jackson's divisions, June 27	1,365 [j]
Total engaged	[5] 86,748

Killed and wounded, 8602.   Missing, 875.[k]
Hit in 1000, 99.   Hit by 1000, 57.

---

[d] 13 W. R., 37–41.   [e] 14 W. R. 645.   [f] 9 W. R., 476; 13 W. R., 916; 14 W. R., 604, 651.   [g] Reg. Losses, 550, note; 13 W. R., 973 et seq.   [h] 13 W. R., 595; 15 W. R., 742.   [i] Ante, p. 83, note 6.   [j] 13 W. R., 973–975, 608, 616.   [k] Reg. Losses, 550, note; 13 W. R., 973 et seq.

---

[1] As suggested (ante, p. 83, note), it is possible that this number as returned is below the actual number.

[2] These regiments of Taliaferro's and Daniel's brigades are estimated at 500 each.

[3] Estimating the effectives in the cavalry at 85 per cent. of the present for duty would reduce this number about 250.

[4] This number is reached by deducting from the total loss in the Seven Days' Battles, 20,614 (Reg. Losses, 550), the losses in Jackson's and Ewell's divisions, 1762 (13 W. R., 973–975, 608, 616), from the remainder, 18,852, the loss at Gaines's Mill, in all the army except these two divisions (7386), which is found by deducting from the total loss at Gaines's Mill, 8751, the loss in these two divisions, 1,365. (See Reg. Losses, 550, note; 13 W. R., 973 et seq., 608, 616.)

[5] The total of the numbers of the different brigades and divisions stated in

SEVEN DAYS' BATTLES, JUNE 25–JULY 1, 1862.

UNION ARMY.

Effectives engaged . . . . 91,169 [a]

Killed, 1734. Wounded, 8062. Total, 9796. Missing, 6053.[b]

Hit in 1000, 107. Hit by 1000, 216.

CONFEDERATE ARMY.

Effectives in Army of Northern Virginia July 20 . . 60,639 [c]

Losses in the Army of Northern Virginia June 25–
July 1 . . . . 18,852 [d]

Effectives in Ewell's and Jackson's divisions . . . 15,990 [e]

Total engaged [1] 95,481

Killed, 3478. Wounded, 16,261. Total, 19,739. Missing,
875.[f]

Hit in 1000, 207. Hit by 1000, 102.

[a] Ante, p. 84. [b] 13 W. R., 37. [c] Ante, p. 84. [d] Reg. Losses, 550; 13 W. R.,
973–975, 608, 616. [e] 13 W. R., 595; 15 W. R., 742; ante, p. 83, note 6;
Reg. Losses, 550; 13 W. R., 973–984.

---

reports and dispatches was about 64,000. (See ante, p. 83, note 7; 13 W. R.,
794, 906, 907.) Adding 2487, the strength of R. H. Anderson's and Featherston's brigades, estimated by the average strength of the regiments in the
rest of Longstreet's division (333), and about 7000 estimated for the reserve,
artillery, and cavalry (13 W. R., 980, 981; 14 W. R., 645), and about 74,000
would be reached as the total number.

[1] The reports of the various commanders state an aggregate of 75,769 carried into action. (Ante, p. 83, note 7; 13 W. R., 661, 796, 806, 818, 794, 906,
913.) These reports do not state the number of Featherston's and R. H.
Anderson's brigades, or the cavalry or artillery. Estimating these two brigades at the average strength (333) per regiment of the rest of Longstreet's
division, 2497, the artillery at 93 per cent., and the cavalry at 85 per cent. of
the present for duty July 20 (14 W. R., 645), a total of 6463 plus their loss
of 245 June 25 to July 1 (13 W. R., 973–984), and adding 7 per cent. for the
officers in all but Mahone's and Armistead's brigades (3008), in which alone the
reports seem to include officers, a total of about 90,000 is reached for the number engaged.

CEDAR MOUNTAIN, AUGUST 9, 1862.

UNION ARMY.

Williams's division (3700),[1] Augur's division (3163),[2]
  Bayard's cavalry (1167) [3] . . . . 8,030 [a]
Killed, 314. Wounded, 1445. Total, 1759.[4] Missing, 594.[4][b]
Hit in 1000, 219. Hit by 1000, 166.

CONFEDERATE ARMY.

Present for duty, Ewell's division, August 9, 5222,[5]
  Hill's division, July 20, 10,651 . . . . 15,873 [c]
Present for duty, Winder's division,[6] July 20, 13½
  regiments, estimated at [7] . . . . 5,035 [d]
                                                 ————
                                                 20,908
Deduct Ewell's pickets (330) and Field's and Gregg's
  brigades (10 regiments), estimated at 3730 [7] . . . 4,060 [e]
                                                 ————
                                                 16,848

[a] 2 Mass. Mil. Hist., 417; 16 W. R., 89, 153, 808, 157; 18 W. R., 523.
[b] 16 W. R., 139. [c] 18 W. R., 965; 16 W. R., 227; 14 W. R., 645. [d] 14 W. R.,
645, 648. [e] 14 W. R., 649; 16 W. R., 215, 217, 233.

---

[1] Only 7 of the 13 infantry regiments were present (16 W. R., 149, 152,
160; 18 W. R., 523). The brigades numbered: Crawford's, 1767; Gordon's,
1500 "men;" 433 is allowed for officers and batteries, to conform to General
Williams's statement (16 W. R., 148).

[2] Officers estimated, 150.

[3] 85 per cent. of present for duty July 31.

[4] Excluding loss of 16 stated for General Banks's escort, and 102 for Pickett's division. This division is not included in the force engaged, because, before it arrived, the Union line was driven back and the battle was decided; and,
although its loss occurred where the Union line made its stand in the rear, it
was after dark in an encounter which had no effect on the combat, which had
already been won by the Confederates. The extraordinary nature of the earlier combat seems to warrant a comparison of numbers and losses strictly confined to the forces involved in the decision of it. (See 16 W. R., 328, 170-175,
139.) On the same theory, Field's, Gregg's, and Stafford's (2d Louisiana) brigades are omitted on the Confederate side. (16 W. R., 214, 215, 184; 18
W. R., 918, 919.)

[5] 5027 present for duty August 10, plus 195 lost August 9.

[6] Lawton's brigade absent and not included (16 W. R., 182).

[7] Estimated at 373 per regiment, the average strength of the 43 regiments
above included as present for duty in Hill's and Ewell's divisions. (See Lee to
Jackson, 18 W. R., 918.)

Effectives estimated at 93 per cent.   15,668
Robertson's cavalry (Ashby's and 2d, 6th, and 12th
    Virginia) . . . .   1,200 [f]
                          ————
    Total engaged   16,868
Killed, 231.   Wounded, 1107.   Total, [1] 1338. [g]
Hit in 1000, 79.   Hit by 1000, 104.

[f] 16 W. R., 180 ; 18 W. R., 527. See 8 So. Hist. Soc., 178 et seq.   [g] 16 W. R.,
180, 225, 228.

MANASSAS AND CHANTILLY, AUGUST 27–SEPTEMBER 2, 1862.

UNION ARMY.

Sigel's (12,131) [2] and McDowell's corps (20,431) [3]   .   32,562 [a]
4 regiments of Kanawha division, estimated at . . .   2,600 [b]
9th corps (8000), Hooker's and Kearny's divisions
    (14,952) [4] . . . .   22,952 [c]
5th corps, including Reynolds's division and Piatt's
    brigade . . . .   [5] 15,982 [d]
Taylor's brigade, 6th corps . . . .   1,600 [e]
                          ————
    Total engaged   75,696
Killed, 1724.   Wounded, 8372.   Total, 10,096. [6]   Missing, [6] 5958. [f]
Hit in 1000, 132.   Hit by 1000, 120.

CONFEDERATE ARMY.

Present for duty July 20, in Longstreet's, A. P. Hill's,
    Anderson's, Jones's, and Whiting's divisions   . .   32,855 [g]

[a] 18 W. R., 523, 580, 603.   [b] 18 W. R., 308, 309, 523.   [c] 9 W. R., 409, 410 ;
14 W. R., 367 ; 18 W. R., 614.   [d] 16 W. R., 401, 396, 256 ; 18 W. R., 619 ;
17 W. R., 1001.   [e] 16 W. R., 537.   [f] 16 W. R., 262.   [g] 14 W. R., 645.

---

[1] Not including loss in Field's, Gregg's, or Stafford's brigades.

[2] 93 per cent. of present for duty, ex. headquarters staff and escort.

[3] 93 per cent. of infantry and 85 per cent. of cavalry present for duty,
August 16, ex. staff, signal corps, and pontoneers.

[4] 93 per cent. of present for duty August 10.

[5] 93 per cent. of present for duty in Morell's division August 16, and Sykes's
division August 28, plus numbers given in field returns of Reynolds and Piatt
(including casualties).

[6] Excluding loss in Banks's corps, which was not engaged, August 28–September 2, and including the few casualties on the Rappahannock.

Ewell's division, August 10 (5027), and Jackson's
division, estimated at 5365 [1] . . . .   10,932 [h]

Effectives estimated at 93 per cent. of . . . . .   43,247=
                                               40,219
Effectives in the brigades of Evans (2200), Lawton
(2933), and Drayton (1550) [2] . . . .   6,683 [i]
Effectives in Stuart's cavalry, estimated [3] at   2,768

                                               49,670
Deduct losses at Cedar Mountain in Hill's and Jackson's divisions . . . .   1,143 [j]

        Total engaged   48,527
Killed, 1481. Wounded, 7627. Total, 9108. Missing,[4] 89.[k]
Hit in 1000, 187. Hit by 1000, 208.

[h] 14 W. R., 645–648; 18 W. R., 965.   [i] 27 W. R., 940; 13 W. R., 595, 597, 599.
[j] 16 W. R., 180, 225.   [k] 16 W. R., 568, 648, 730, 738, 739.

RICHMOND, KY., AUGUST 29, 30, 1862.

UNION ARMY.

Manson's command . . . .   [5] 6,500 [a]
Killed, 206. Wounded, 844. Total, 1050. Missing, 4,303.[b]
Hit in 1000, 161. Hit by 1000, 69.

CONFEDERATE ARMY.

Churchill's and Cleburne's divisions . . . . . .   [5] 6,000 [c]
Scott's cavalry brigade . . . .   [6] 850 [d]

        Total engaged   6,850

[a] 22 W. R., 915.   [b] 22 W. R., 909.   [c] 23 W. R., 777.   [d] 22 W. R., 938.

---

[1] Estimated at 370 per regiment, the average in the divisions above, for 14½ regiments, including 10th Louisiana, but not the rest in Starke's brigade, which are included in the numbers given for the divisions above.

[2] Estimated by the average strength of regiments in Evans's and Lawton's brigades. (See, also, 20 W. R., 591–593.)

[3] 85 per cent. of the present for duty July 20, the number of regiments being the same in August.

[4] This includes the few lost on the Rappahannock. See 16 W. R., 597, 720.

[5] It is probable that these were the number of "effectives."

[6] General Smith's statement, that his whole force "was not more than 5000," apparently does not include the cavalry.

Killed, 78.   Wounded, 372.   Total, 450.   Missing, 1.[e]
Hit in 1000, 66.   Hit by 1000, 153.

[e] 22 W. R., 936.

SOUTH MOUNTAIN, SEPTEMBER 14, 1862.

UNION ARMY.

1st and 9th corps, present for duty September 17,
  1862 . . . . [1] 28,675 [a]

Effectives estimated at 93 per cent.   26,667
Losses September 14 . . . .   1,813 [b]
                                           ————
  Total engaged   28,480

Killed, 325.   Wounded, 1403.   Total, 1728.   Missing, 85.[c]
Hit in 1000, 68.   Hit by 1000, 66.

CONFEDERATE ARMY.

Present for duty September 22, in D. H. Hill's,
  Hood's, and Jones's divisions, and Evans's brigade   12,284 [d]
Rosser's cavalry and Jeff Davis legion, estimated at   700 [d]
                                                       ————
                                                       12,984

Deduct Toombs's brigade and 11th Georgia volunteers
  ($\frac{5}{26}$ of Jones's division)   733
                                                       ————
                                                       12,251

Effectives estimated at 93 per cent.   11,393
Losses reported September 14–20 . . . .   5,821 [e]
                                                   ————
                                                   17,214

Captured at South Mountain, not reported, about   .   [2] 1,500 [f]
                                                         ————
  Total effectives September 14 . . . . . .   [3] 18,714

[a] 27 W. R., 67.   (See, also, 28 W. R., 336.)   [b] 27 W. R., 187.   [c] 27 W. R.,
187.   [d] 27 W. R., 804, 808–810, 839, 1020; 28 W. R., 621, 674.   [e] 27 W. R.,
843, 1026.   [f] 27 W. R., 418.

---

[1] That this number represents the present for duty is indicated by the fact
that the sum of the present for duty September 20, and the losses September
17–20, is only 27,910 (28 W. R., 336; 27 W. R., 187, 191, 198).

[2] Probably some of the wounded not reported are included in this number
(27 W. R., 111).

[3] The reports of the action by the commanders of all the infantry, excepting

Based upon the return of July 20, the number is about 700 less, as follows : —

Present for duty July 20 in D. H. Hill's,[1] Jones's,[1] and Whiting's divisions	17,157 [g]
Pickett's, Kemper's, and Jenkins's brigades [2] . . .	4,257 [h]
Evans's brigade	2,200 [i]
9 batteries (450) and Rosser's cavalry (700) estimated at	1,440 [j]
	25,054
Deduct Toombs's brigade and 11th Georgia volunteers, 55 per cent. of Jones's division	2,048
Present for duty July 20	23,006
Effectives estimated at 93 per cent.	21,395
Deduct losses in August	3,543 [k]
Total engaged.	17,852

Killed, 325.[3] Wounded, 1560. Total, 1885.[3] Missing, [3]800.[l] Hit in 1000, 105. Hit by 1000, 97.

[g] 14 W. R., 645. [h] 14 W. R., 645, 649 ; 27 W. R., 805. [i] 27 W. R., 940. [j] 27 W. R., 809, 810, 817, 1020 ; 28 W. R., 674. [k] 16 W. R., 561, 568. [l] 27 W. R., 181, 418.

Law's and Jenkins's brigades, state the number of men in action at 9351 (27 W. R., 885, 888, 901, 903, 905, 929, 940, 1020, 1022 ; 16 W. R., 637, 638). Estimating Law's and Jenkins's brigades at 1271, the cavalry and artillery at 1150, and the officers at 1748, 7.6 per cent. of the present for duty, July 30, a total of 13,400 is reached. For reasons stated below, in connection with Antietam, the number 18,714, above given, is here adopted.

[1] The gain of Drayton's brigade by Jones's division is assumed to offset the loss of Wise's brigade from Hill's.

[2] Estimated at ½ of Longstreet's division.

[3] About 700 were reported killed and wounded in 7 brigades and 3 regiments (27 W. R., 843, 1026). The reports of the other commands do not give the loss for South Mountain alone, but give a loss of 2159 killed and wounded at South Mountain and Antietam. All but Ripley's brigade seem to have been hotly engaged at South Mountain (27 W. R., 843, 1026), and, in view of General McClellan's statement that the Confederate outnumbered the Union dead, 325 is adopted as the number of dead, and the wounded are estimated at the usual proportion of 4.8. Probably the actual loss was greater. It is estimated that 700 of the 800 prisoners were wounded.

ANTIETAM, SEPTEMBER 16, 17, 1862.

UNION ARMY.

Present for duty ex. Morell's division [1] . . . . . [2]87,164 [a]

Effectives estimated at 93 per cent. of infantry and
85 per cent. of cavalry 75,316

Killed, 2108. Wounded, 9549. Total, 11,657. Missing, 753.[b]

Hit in 1000, 155. Hit by 1000, 156.

CONFEDERATE ARMY.

Present for duty September 22 in infantry
and artillery . . . .   37,330 [c]

Deduct $\frac{4}{26}$ of A. P. Hill's division and of its
losses September 17–20 for Thomas's brigade   832 [d]

$\frac{1}{19}$ of Jackson's division and its losses for 2d
Virginia . . . .   166 [e]

$\frac{1}{2}$ of 11th Georgia . . . .   140 [f]

$\frac{1}{2}$ of reserve artillery . . . .   456 [g]   1,594
                                                        ———
                                                      35,736

Cavalry, October 10 . . . .   5,761 [h]

Effectives estimated at 85 per cent. of cavalry
and 93 per cent. of remainder   38,120

Losses September 17   13,724
                                        ———————
Total engaged . . . .   51,844 [3]

[a] 27 W. R., 67, 338. [b] 27 W. R., 200. [c] 28 W. R., 621. [d] 27 W. R., 807,
981, 983. [e] 27 W. R., 808, 1008, 1011. [f] 27 W. R., 911, 912. [g] 27 W. R.,
830 ; 28 W. R., 660. [h] 28 W. R., 660.

---

[1] Morell's division, although present, was not engaged, and had no influence
on the result.

[2] About 23,000 in 6th corps and Sykes's division here included did not open
fire in line of battle.

[3] Based upon the returns for July and August, the number of effectives appears to be about 7000 greater, as follows : —

Present for duty in Army of Northern Virginia July 20 . . . .   [1]57,476
In Jackson's corps, ex. Lawton's brigade, August 9, Jackson's
division, ex. 2d Virginia, estimated at $\frac{4}{15}$ of Ewell's division . .   [2]11,488
Present for duty July 15 in Ransom's and Walker's brigade . . .   [3]5,971
5 regiments of cavalry, estimated at $\frac{5}{9}$ of Stuart's cavalry . . . .   [4]2,200
                                                                    ———————
                                                                    77,135

---

[1] 14 W. R., 645, 648. [2] Ante, p. 83. [3] 9 W. R., 476 ; 27 W. R., 805. [4] 27 W. R., 810 ; 14
W. R., 645, 652.

Killed, 2700.[1] Wounded, 9024.[1] Total, 11,724. Missing, about [1]2000.*i*

Hit in 1000, 226. Hit by 1000, 225.

i 27 W. R., 67, 111.

Deduct $\frac{4}{26}$ of A. P. Hill's division for Thomas's brigade . .	[1] 1,639	
Deduct $\frac{14}{34}$ of reserve artillery	[2] 1,341	
Deduct 11th Georgia	[3] 140	3,120
		74,015
Effectives at 85 per cent. of cavalry and 93 per cent. of remainder		68,333
Effectives in Evans's and Lawton's brigades August 1 . .		[4] 5,133
		73,466
Losses August 1–September 15		[5] 14,182
Effectives September 15		59,284

(It is assumed that the gain of Drayton's brigade offsets the loss of Wise's.) The loss of 7000 effectives between August 1 and September 22 may be accounted for in stragglers. General Lee wrote, September 13 (28 W. R., 605) : " I have received as yet no official list of the casualties in the late battles, and, from the number of absentees in the army and the vice of straggling, a correct list cannot be obtained. . . . One great embarrassment is the reduction of our ranks by straggling, which it seems impossible to prevent with our present regimental officers. Our ranks are very much diminished — I fear from one half to one third of the original numbers — though I have reason to hope that our casualties in battles will not exceed 5000 men." General D. H. Hill also bitterly complained of the straggling (27 W. R., 1022).

In his report of Antietam General Lee said : " This great battle was fought by less than 40,000 men on our side " (27 W. R., 151). This statement would imply that, besides the 3120 above deducted, 19,000 of the 59,000 effectives in July had left the ranks. It is not credible that this number had straggled, and it is not reconcilable with the returns of September 22. It is probable that General Lee founded his statement on the numbers given in the reports of his subordinates. They give the number of 35 infantry brigades as 23,000 to 24,000 (27 W. R., 862, 886, 919, 929, 948, 968, 981, 1008, 1022, 1023). If Walker's, Law's, Pender's, and Field's brigades, whose numbers are not given, were of the average strength of the others, General Lee may have arrived at about the number given by him, by adding about 2000 officers, 3200 for the 61 batteries engaged, and 6000 for the cavalry. But the reports of his subordinates were written from one to several months after the battle, and in most of them the statements of numbers are qualified by " about," " not over," or " less than," which indicate that they are estimates made after the battle, rather than the records of roll-calls on the field. The failure of these reports to notice many of those lost in the battle confirms this view.

[1] The Confederate reports give for all the actions in Maryland 1787 killed,

---

[1] 27 W. R., 981.   [2] 27 W. R., 830.   [3] 27 W. R., 911, 912.   [4] Ante, p. 89.   [5] 27 W. R., 861; ante, pp. 87, 89, 91.

CORINTH, OCTOBER 3, 4, 1862.

UNION ARMY.

Present for duty September 30, 1862 . . . . . 23,077 [a]
Effectives estimated at 93 per cent. of infantry and
    artillery, and 85 per cent. of cavalry 21,147
Killed, 355. Wounded, 1841. Total, 2196. Missing, 324.[b]
Hit in 1000, 104. Hit by 1000, 117.

CONFEDERATE ARMY.

" Field returns," September 28, 1862, about . . . . 22,000 [c]
Killed, 473. Wounded, 1997. Total,[1] 2470. Missing,[1] 1763.[d]
Hit in 1000, 112. Hit by 1000, 100.

   [a] 25 W. R., 246.   [b] 24 W. R., 176.   [c] 24 W. R., 378.   [d] 24 W. R., 382–384, 307, 403, 413.

9147 wounded (27 W. R., 811 et seq., 843, 958, 1026, 824–827, 838). Deducting 587 killed, 2323 wounded in the other actions, including ½ the total loss in Maryland for Mahone's brigade at Crampton's Gap (ante, p. 91 ; 27 W. R., 376, 824–827, 838, 843, 861), there remain for Antietam 1200 killed and 6824 wounded. The ratio of wounded to killed (about 5.7) exceeds the average ratio (4.8), and the ratio in the Union losses in this battle (4.5), so much as to leave no doubt that the reports are incomplete. Besides, it is impossible to believe that 52,000 men, all hotly engaged, on one side lost only 8024 killed and wounded, while 64,000 men on the other side (not counting Sykes's and Slocum's divisions and Brooks's brigade) lost 11,472, when neither side fought behind works or had the advantage of cover. The number of Confederate dead cannot be placed at less than the number counted and buried on the field (27 W. R., 67) ; and to the number of wounded reported there must be added the number left on the field and not reported. (See 27 W. R., 1025.) There were 2500 left on the three battlefields, of whom 300 were left at Crampton's Gap (27 W. R., 376). Those left at South Mountain having been allowed for (ante, p. 91) in the number above deducted, the remainder, 2200, is to be added to the 6824 reported for Antietam, making a total of 9024. The ratio of this number to the 2700 killed is too small, and it is probable that, to correspond to the ratio on the Union side, the number of wounded should be increased to 12,000. In the fierce fire and rapid movements of this battle, many left the ranks with wounds, unnoticed, to be afterwards counted among the stragglers (see 27 W. R., 1025), and it is possible that, pursuant to the policy afterwards established in general orders (40 W. R., 798), the slightly wounded were, for political and military reasons, not reported. 6000 prisoners were taken by the Union army in Maryland (27 W. R., 67). Deducting 1800 taken at South Mountain and Crampton's Gap (27 W. R., 376, 418), and 2200 additional wounded, there remain 2000 prisoners to be counted as missing on the Confederate side at Antietam.

   [1] 21 killed and 84 wounded were reported for Hatchie's bridge, October 5,

PERRYVILLE, OCTOBER 8, 1862.

UNION ARMY.

Present for duty . . . . [1] 39,721 [a]

Effectives estimated at 93 per cent 36,940

Killed, 845. Wounded, 2851. Total, 3696. Missing, 515.[b]

Hit in 1000, 100. Hit by 1000, 85.

CONFEDERATE ARMY.

Effectives, about . . . . [2] 16,000 [c]

Killed, 510. Wounded, 2635. Total, 3145. Missing, 251.

Hit in 1000, 196. Hit by 1000, 231.

[a] 22 W. R., 1026 et seq., 1059 ; 23 W. R., 563. [b] 22 W. R., 1036. [c] 22 W. R., 1092.

PRAIRIE GROVE, ARK., DECEMBER 7, 1862.

UNION ARMY.

Army of the Frontier . . . . [3] 10,000 [a]

Killed, 175. Wounded, 813. Total, 988. Missing, 263. [b]

Hit in 1000, 99. Hit by 1000, 98.

CONFEDERATE ARMY.

1st corps trans-Mississippi army . . . . [4] 10,000 [c]

[a] 32 W. R., 76. [b] 32 W. R., 86. [c] 32 W. R., 140.

---

in 3 out of 4 brigades ; but as 32 dead were buried there, this number, with 153 for the usual proportion of wounded, and 420 prisoners taken at the same place, are deducted from the totals given in the returns for October 3–5.

[1] Five per cent. added for officers to number of enlisted men in 10th division. To the strength of the 3d corps, October 21, is added the loss October 8. Six brigades of this corps suffered little loss, and apparently did not open fire. If these were deducted, the number engaged would be reduced to less than 25,000, of whom about 150 in 1000 were hit.

[2] General Bragg must have counted only effectives, as the infantry present for duty numbered at least 15,300. (See 22 W. R., 1120 ; 23 W. R., 900, Wither's division, which was absent, excluded.)

[3] General Blunt reported that 3000 of the cavalry were not engaged (p. 76), but they are here included because they seem to have been present in the field. The Army of the Frontier, November 30, had present for duty 13,175 (32 W. R., 795), consisting of 12 regiments of infantry, 1 of which was detached, 7 batteries, 11 regiments of cavalry, and 150 of Missouri militia (pp. 84–86). Effectives, reckoned at 93 per cent. of infantry and artillery, and 85 per cent. of cavalry, would be about 11,000 ; but the 2d and 3d divisions, by forced marches, had been reduced from 7534 to about 5100 (pp. 72, 107, 108).

[4] Possibly 700 to 1000 should be added for officers.

Killed, 164. Wounded, 817. Total, 981. Missing, 336.[d]
Hit in 1000, 98. Hit by 1000, 99.

[d] 32 W. R., 142.

FREDERICKSBURG, DECEMBER 13, 1862.

UNION ARMY.

Present for duty in 3 grand divisions and engineers   120,281 [a]
Deduct cavalry of right and centre grand divisions .   6,294 [b]

Engaged   113,987
Effectives estimated at 93 per cent.   106,007
Killed, 1284. Wounded, 9600. Total, 10,884.[1] Missing, 1769.[c]
Hit in 1000, 103.[1] Hit by 1000, 44.

CONFEDERATE ARMY.

Present for duty . . . . [2] 78,513 [d]
Effectives estimated at 93 per cent.   73,017
Deduct Hampton's cavalry . . . .   520 [e]

Engaged . . . . [2] 72,497
Killed, 595. Wounded, 4061. Total, 4656. Missing, 653.
Hit in 1000, 64. Hit by 1000, 150.

[a] 31 W. R., 1121. [b] 31 W. R., 220, 984, 1121. [c] 31 W. R., 142. [d] 31 W. R.,
1057. [e] 31 W. R., 544, 690.

CHICKASAW BAYOU AND BLUFF, DECEMBER 27, 29, 1862.

UNION ARMY.

Present for duty in A. J. Smith's, M. L. Smith's,
    Morgan's, and Steele's divisions . . . .   33,033 [a]
Effectives estimated at 93 per cent. . . . . . . [3] 30,720
Killed, 208. Wounded, 1005. Total, 1213. Missing, 563.[b]
Hit in 1000, 39. Hit by 1000, 6.

[a] 24 W. R., 602, 604. [b] 24 W. R., 625.

---

[1] 9980 were killed and wounded in 11 of the 18 divisions, or 157 to 1000.

[2] If Jones's cavalry brigade is included in the present for duty, a deduction probably of about 2400 should be made from the number engaged, as this brigade was in the Shenandoah valley (31 W. R., 544 and note, and 1075).

[3] The 118th and 131st Illinois seem to have been detached (24 W. R., 627, 644). If they were, about 5 per cent. should probably be deducted on this account.

CONFEDERATE ARMY.

Effectives, January 3, 1863, in M. L. Smith's command [1] . . . . 9,807 [c]

Effectives, January 2, 1862, in Vaughn's and Barton's brigades . . . . 3,778 [c]

Losses, December 27–30, stated below 207

Total engaged 13,792

Killed, 63. Wounded, 134. Total, 197.[d] Missing, 10.[d]

Hit in 1000, 14. Hit by 1000, 88.

[c] 25 W. R., 824, 825; 24 W. R., 666, 673–679. [d] 24 W. R., 674.

STONE'S RIVER, DECEMBER 31, 1862, JANUARY 1, 1863.

UNION ARMY.

Present for duty . . . . [2] 44,800 [a]

Effectives, estimated at 93 per cent. of infantry and artillery and 85 per cent. of cavalry 41,400

Killed, 1677. Wounded, 7543. Total,[3] 9220.[b] Missing,[3] 3686.[b]

Hit in 1000, 223.[3] Hit by 1000, 223.

CONFEDERATE ARMY.

Present for duty . . . . 37,712 [c]

Effectives, estimated at 93 per cent. of infantry and artillery and 85 per cent. of cavalry 34,732

Killed, 1294. Wounded, 7945. Total, 9239.[4] [d] Missing, about 2500.[d]

Hit in 1000, 266.[4] Hit by 1000, 265.

[a] 29 W. R., 175–182, 201; 30 W. R., 283–285. [b] 29 W. R., 215. [c] 29 W. R., 674. [d] 29 W. R., 229, 669, 674.

---

[1] Including Gregg's brigade.

[2] Including Walker's brigade, estimated at $\frac{4}{14}$ of Fry's division, and Starkweather's brigade, estimated at $\frac{1}{4}$ of Rousseau's division. These brigades are not included in General Rosecrans's recapitulation (29 W. R., 201), but they participated in the battle. (29 W. R., 393, 442, 443.)

[3] To arrive at these figures deduction is made from the totals given in 29 W. R., at page 215, of 53 for the killed and 259 for the wounded in minor combats at other places. See 29 W. R., 207, note, 218, 219, 409, 465.

[4] Not counting Pegram's brigade, the loss of which is not reported.

ARKANSAS POST, JANUARY 11, 1863.

UNION ARMY.

Army of the Mississippi, January 4, 1863, effectives [1] 28,944 [a]
Killed, 134. Wounded, 898. Total, 1032. Missing, 29.[b]
Hit in 1000, 36. Hit by 1000, 4.

CONFEDERATE ARMY.

Effectives estimated at 93 per cent. of the number
surrendered, plus the loss in killed and wounded   .   [2] 4,564 [c]
Killed, 28. Wounded, 81. Total, 109.[e] Missing (captured),
4791.[e]
Hit in 1000, 24. Hit by 1000, 226.

[a] Ante, p. 96.   [b] 24 W. R., 719.   [c] 24 W. R., 757, 785, 795.

CHANCELLORSVILLE AND FREDERICKSBURG,[3] MAY 1–4, 1863.

UNION ARMY.

Present for duty [4] . . . . 104,891 [a]
Effectives estimated at 93 per cent. of artillery and
infantry and 85 per cent. of cavalry 97,382
Killed, 1575. Wounded, 9594. Total, 11,116.[b] Missing, 5676.[b]
Hit in 1000, 114. Hit by 1000, 110.

CONFEDERATE ARMY.

Present for duty May 20 [5] . . . . 48,080 [c]

[a] 40 W. R., 320.   [b] 39 W. R., 185, 191, 177, note.   [c] 39 W. R., 789–794, and
notes; 40 W. R., 814.

---

[1] The number of effectives engaged at Chickasaw Bluff, less losses there.

[2] General Churchill reported that he had about 3000 effectives, but the commanders of two brigades report at least 3190 enlisted men (24 W. R., 780, 783, 791), and Dunnington's brigade is to be added.

[3] The two actions are treated as one. The disposition of the Confederate forces in each field was affected by the presence of the Union force in the other field, and a part of the Confederates fought in one and then in the other field. The Confederate losses in both fields are consolidated in the War Records.

[4] 2d, 5th, 6th, 11th, and 12th corps, Pleasonton's brigade, estimated at $\frac{4}{27}$ of the cavalry corps, and 4 batteries of the 1st corps, the only part of it engaged before the battle was decided. The corps arrived on the field of Chancellorsville May 3, and, excepting these batteries, was not engaged (39 W. R., 255).

[5] Excluding Hood's and Pickett's divisions, and all the cavalry except one brigade, estimated at $\frac{4}{18}$ of the whole.

Effectives estimated at 93 per cent. of artillery and
    infantry and 85 per cent. of cavalry 44,588
Losses May 1–4 . . . . 12,764 [d]
_____
    Total engaged 57,352
Killed, 1665. Wounded, 9081. Total, 10,746.[1] Missing, 2018.[e]
Hit in 1000, 187. Hit by 1000, 194.

[d] Reg. Losses, 550.   [e] Reg. Losses, 550.

CHAMPION'S HILL, MAY 16, 1863.

UNION ARMY.

Present for duty April 30 . . . . [2] 33,286 [a]

Effectives estimated at 93 per cent. 30,955
Deduct losses May 1, 12, and 14 . . . . 1,582 [b]
_____
    Effectives May 16 . . . . [3] 29,373
Killed, 410. Wounded, 1844. Total, 2254.[3] Missing, 187.[c]
Hit in 1000, 76.[3] Hit by 1000, 74.

CONFEDERATE ARMY.

Effectives about . . . . [4] 20,000 [d]

[a] 38 W. R., 249.   [b] 36 W. R., 585, 706, 751.   [c] 37 W. R., 10.   [d] 36 W. R.,
217, 261, 264; 38 W. R., 702, 703, 705.

_____

[1] For detailed losses see 39 W. R., 809, 816, 820, 895, 906, 918, 926, 937, 947,
1002, 1008, 1015, 1030, 1033, 1039.

[2] The divisions of Osterhaus, A. J. Smith, Hovey, Carr, Logan, Crocker, and
Blair, less 4 regiments estimated at $\frac{40}{227}$ of the first two named (37 W. R., 12,
30; 38 W. R., 250).

[3] General Grant said that the battle was fought mainly by Hovey's, Logan's,
and Crocker's divisions (36 W. R., 53), whose effective strength was 15,390,
and loss in killed and wounded 141 in 1000; but the other divisions, although
suffering small loss, materially influenced the disposition of the Confederates.

[4] Stevenson's, Bowen's, and Loring's divisions and Wirt Adams's cavalry.
General Pemberton places his force at 17,500; but the returns of March 31
give 22,198 as present for duty in these divisions, and the loss in action in May
was 868 (38 W. R., 702; 36 W. R., 668), and other returns in May and June
show that there were present for duty May 16 at least 22,500 (38 W. R., 849,
907, 979; 37 W. R., 120; 36 W. R., 320). It therefore is probable that the
number given by General Pemberton included only the men bearing muskets.
Adding 8 per cent. for officers, 500 for Wirt Adams's cavalry regiment, and 600
for 13 batteries (38 W. R., 703–705), brings the number to 20,000.

Killed, 381. Wounded, about 1800.[1] Total, 2181.[e] Missing,[1] 1670.[e]

Hit in 1000, 109. Hit by 1000, 112.

[e] 37 W. R., 82, 86, 93, 99, 120.

ASSAULT ON VICKSBURG, MAY 22, 1863.

UNION ARMY.

93 per cent. of present for duty May 31, in 13th, 15th, and 17th corps	[2] 42,315 [a]
Add losses May 22	[3] 3,241 [b]
Total engaged	[4] 45,556

Killed, 502. Wounded, 2550. Total, 3052.[3] Missing, 147.[c]
Hit in 1000, 67.

CONFEDERATE ARMY.

Effectives in Bowen's division, May 22	2,569 [d]
Effectives in Stevenson's division, June 23	8,776 [e]
Effectives in Smith's division, May 26	[5] 4,005 [f]
93 per cent. of present for duty in Forney's division, June 25	4,611 [g]
Losses prior to June 23 in Stevenson's and June 25 in Forney's division	[6] 2,340 [h]
Total effectives	[7] 22,301

Hit by 1000, 137.

[a] 36 W. R., 55 ; 38 W. R., 370, 371. [b] 36 W. R., 156 ; 37 W. R., 165. [c] 36 W. R., 156 ; 37 W. R., 165. [d] 38 W. R., 907. [e] 38 W. R., 979. [f] 38 W. R., 923. [g] 38 W. R., 978. [h] 37 W. R., 328.

---

[1] The returns give 1017 wounded and 2453 missing. No doubt there were many wounded reported as missing, and the number of wounded is computed in the usual ratio of 4.8 to the killed, and the number of missing is correspondingly reduced.

[2] General headquarters, staff, escort, cavalry, and pioneers excluded ; total, 1673.

[3] Including 42 killed and wounded in Hovey's division, not tabulated at 37 W. R., 165.

[4] Probably not over 100 should be added for losses May 23–31 (37 W. R., 161).

[5] Officers estimated at 8 per cent. of number of guns. Probably the total effectives was larger than the total thus reached, as the inspection report probably did not reach men on guard or picket.

[6] Estimated at $\frac{5}{6}$ of the loss during the siege.

[7] 29,396 were surrendered in July (37 W. R., 325).

ASSAULT ON PORT HUDSON, MAY 27, 1863.

UNION ARMY.

Banks's command, effectives . . . . 13,000 [a]
Killed, 293.   Wounded, 1545.   Total, 1838.[a]   Missing, 157.[a]
Hit in 1000, 141.   Hit by 1000, 18.

CONFEDERATE ARMY.

Gardner's command, effectives May 19, estimated at
  93 per cent. of present for duty May 19 [1] . . . .   4,326 [b]
Deduct losses May 22–26 . . . .   134 [c]
                                                   ─────
                                                   4,192

Killed and wounded, about [2] 235.[d]
Hit in 1000, 56.   Hit by 1000, 438.

  [a] 41 W. R., 44, 47.   [b] 42 W. R., 10.   [c] 41 W. R., 168, 152, 156.   [d] 41 W. R., 147, 169.

ASSAULT ON PORT HUDSON, JUNE 14, 1863.

UNION ARMY.

Columns of attack, about . . . .   6,000 [a]
Killed, 203.   Wounded, 1401.   Total, 1604.[b]   Missing, 188.[b]
Hit in 1000, 267.   Hit by 1000, 8.

CONFEDERATE ARMY.

Present for duty in Gardiner's command, June 14,
  estimated at . . . .   [3] 3,750 [c]
Effectives estimated at 93 per cent.   3,487
Killed, 22.   Wounded, 25.   Total, 47.[d]
Hit in 1000, 13.   Hit by 1000, 460.

  [a] 41 W. R., 546, 548, 45.   [b] 41 W. R., 47.   [c] 42 W. R., 10, 98.   [d] 41 W. R., 147, 175.

---

  [1] The returns are incomplete, and possibly omit the 1st, 11th, 14th, 17th, and 18th Arkansas, and some smaller organizations (compare 42 W. R., 10, with 41 W. R., 143); but the number surrendered July 8, plus the number killed, is almost exactly equaled by the aggregate present in the returns of May 19 (41 W. R., 55, 144; 42 W. R., 10).

  [2] Miles's killed and wounded estimated at 10.

  [3] Estimated at the mean between the numbers shown by the returns of May 19 and June 30, deducting losses May 22–27, and adding Miles's command to the return of June 30.

GETTYSBURG,   JULY 1-3, 1863.

UNION ARMY.

Army of the Potomac, infantry and artillery present
for duty . . . . [1] 87,312 [a]
Deduct 17 regiments [2] . . . .   9,058 [b]
                                               ─────────
                                                 78,254
Present for duty in $\frac{19}{23}$ of cavalry . . . . . . [3] 12,369 [c]
Effectives estimated at 93 per cent. of infantry and
artillery and 85 per cent. of cavalry   83,289
Killed, 3155. Wounded, 14,529. Total, 17,684.[d] Missing, 5365.[d]
Hit in 1000, 212.   Hit by 1000, 272.

CONFEDERATE ARMY.

Army of Northern Virginia, infantry and artillery
present for duty May 31 [4] . . . .   64,167 [e]
Davis's and Pettigrew's brigades [5] . . . . .   6,262 [f]
Present for duty in cavalry [6] . . . .   12,346 [g]

───────────

[a] 43 W. R., 151.   [b] 43 W. R., 668, 674, 678, 156, 160, 163, notes.   [c] 43 W. R.,
151, 166, note.   [d] 43 W. R., 187.   [e] 40 W. R., 846.   [f] 40 W. R., 848 ; 26 W. R.,
1086.   [g] 40 W. R., 823, 846 ; 44 W. R., 708.

───────────

[1] General headquarters, guards, orderlies, signal corps, provost guard, and
engineer brigade excluded.

[2] Torbert's, Russell's, and Grant's brigades, and 102d Pennsylvania, estimated
at $\frac{14}{27}$ of 6th corps ; 12th and 14th Vermont, estimated at $\frac{2}{35}$ of 1st corps, and
84th Pennsylvania, estimated at $\frac{1}{25}$ of 3d corps.

[3] Huey's brigade excluded.

[4] Corse's brigade, estimated at 1672 for $\frac{1}{4}$ of Pickett's division excluded.

[5] Because Pettigrew's brigade was included in the returns for the Department of Richmond for May 31, it is assumed that it was not included in the
returns for the Army of Northern Virginia for same date, although General
Lee had before that date regarded it as a part of his force and assigned it to a
division in the new organization of his army announced May 30. The returns
of the Army of Northern Virginia cited are those of the old organization.

[6] Robertson's brigade is excluded, and estimated at 16 per cent. of Fitz
Lee's and W. H. F. Lee's commands, which proportion is established by the return of May 25. It is assumed that Jones's brigade, 2324 strong (40 W. R., 602),
and Jenkins's brigade, which were not at Gettysburg, were included in the returns of the Valley District and Department of West Virginia for May 31, and
therefore not in the Army of Northern Virginia for same date.

Effectives estimated at 93 per cent. of infantry and
    artillery and 85 per cent. of cavalry . . . . . [1] 75,992
Deduct losses prior to Gettysburg . . . .   938 [h]

       Total engaged 75,054

Killed.	Wounded.		Missing.	
2,592	12,709		5,150 [2]	as per returns.[i]
	6,026 [2]		275	captured in excess of 770 reported. [j]
1,311	. . . .			to equal the average proportion of killed to
3,903	18,735	Total, 22,638	5,425	4.8 wounded.

Hit in 1000, 301.   Hit by 1000, 235.

[h] 44 W. R., 442, 713, 714, 719.   [i] 44 W. R., 346.   [j] 44 W. R., 346 and note, 365, 476.

---

[1] On the returns of July 31 the number engaged at Gettysburg is computed as follows : —

Present for duty, July 31, infantry and artillery, ex. Corse's brigade
    (estimated at 1672 as above) . . . . [1] 42,809
Present for duty May 31, cavalry as above   12,346
Effectives estimated at 93 per cent. of infantry and artillery and
    85 per cent. of cavalry   50,306
Deduct losses in cavalry prior to Gettysburg . . . .   [2] 669

                                              49,637
Add losses at Gettysburg as above   28,070

       Total engaged   77,707

[2] While the Confederate commanders say in their reports that many included under the head of " missing " in the returns were doubtless killed and wounded, they specifically report only 770 wounded as being left behind (44 W. R., 325, 365, 475, 476, 609). It follows that of the 6802 wounded captured by the Union army, 6026 are to be added to the number of wounded given in the Confederate returns. The fighting was at close range. On the Union side the proportion of killed to wounded was 1 to 4.6. It is certainly within bounds to assume that on the Confederate side the proportion was the average of 1 to 4.8 (Reg. Losses, 22).

---

[1] 45 W. R., 1065.   [2] 44 W. R., 713, 714, 719.

ASSAULT ON FORT WAGNER, JULY 18, 1863.

UNION ARMY.

Strong's brigade, present for duty June 30, 1863		3,761 [a]
Deduct 212 for 7th Connecticut and 200 estimated for artillery	412	
Deduct $\frac{9}{8}$ of remainder for Enfants Perdus and Co. D, 1st New York engineers	538	950
		2,811
Present for duty in 6th Connecticut		484 [b]
Putnam's brigade June 30, 4 regiments, estimated[1] at		1,920 [c]
Artillery (7 batteries) estimated at		700
		5,915
Effectives estimated at 93 per cent.		5,500
Deduct loss July 11		236
Total engaged		5,264

Killed, 246.   Wounded, 880.   Total, 1126.[d] Missing, 389.[d]
Hit in 1000, 214.[2]   Hit by 1000, 32.[3]

CONFEDERATE ARMY.

Garrison of Fort Wagner and artillery of Battery Gregg, about		[4] 1,340 [e]
32d Georgia		445 [f]
Total engaged, about		1,785

[a] 46 W. R., 346, 359, 361; 47 W. R., 7, 8, 9.   [b] 46 W. R., 357.   [c] 47 W. R., 7, 8; 46 W. R., 346.   [d] 46 W. R., 210.   [e] 46 W. R., 76, 77, 431, 376, 373.   [f] 46 W. R., 77, 449.

---

[1] This estimate is made by deducting, from the 4687 troops on Folly Island, 484 for the 6th Connecticut, and an estimate of 600 for the artillery, and taking $\frac{44}{45}$ of the remainder for the 7th New Hampshire, 62d and 67th Ohio, and 100th New York, which constituted Putnam's brigade.

[2] In the assaulting column, 246 were hit in 1000.

[3] It is assumed that 14 of the 28 hit by the bombardment were struck by the naval projectiles. (See 46 W. R., 418.)

[4] The 51st North Carolina numbered at least 474 (46 W. R., 454), and the 31st North Carolina 412, if it was of the average strength of Clingman's brigade (45 W. R., 946, 947).

Killed, 36. Wounded, 133. Total, 169.[1] [g] Missing, 5.[g]
Hit in 1000, 95. Hit by 1000, 631.

[g] 46 W. R., 406.

CHICKAMAUGA, SEPTEMBER 19, 20, 1863.

UNION ARMY.

Army of the Cumberland, infantry and artillery present for duty September 10 . . . . [2] 57,373 [a]
22d Michigan, 69th and 89th Ohio 1,391

—————

58,764

Deduct 2 brigades and 5 regiments,[3] estimated at . . 4,845 [b]

—————

Total engaged. 53,919
Cavalry, ex. Lowe's brigade . . . . 9,504 [c]
Effectives estimated at 93 per cent. of infantry and
artillery, and 85 per cent. of cavalry . . . . . [4] 58,222
Killed, 1657. Wounded, 9756. Total, 11,413.[5] Missing, 4757.[d]
Hit in 1000, 196. Hit by 1000, 292.

CONFEDERATE ARMY.

Army of Tennessee, infantry and artillery present for
duty August 20 . . . . [6] 33,195 [e]

[a] 50 W. R., 169. [b] 50 W. R., 40, 41, 42, 44, 45, and notes. [c] 50 W. R.,
169 and note e. [d] 50 W. R., 179. [e] 53 W. R., 519.

---

[1] In the assaulting column, 246 were hit in 1000.

[2] Consisting of the 14th, 20th, 21st, and reserve corps, less Coburn's brigade
of 1987 (50 W. R., 169, note d).

[3] 9th Michigan and 38th Ohio, estimated at $\frac{20}{508}$ of 14th corps = 898, Post's
brigade and 39th Indiana, estimated at $\frac{51}{390}$ of 20th corps = 1720, and Wag-
ner's brigade, 21st Kentucky, 5 companies of 1st Kentucky, and 110th Illinois
battalion, estimated at $\frac{60}{395}$ of 21st corps = 2227.

[4] Probably about 200 should be deducted for non-effectives in 6 regiments
of infantry serving mounted.

[5] Including losses in skirmishes, September 21, 22 (50 W. R., 169, note).

[6] Excluding general headquarters and provost guard.

Effectives estimated at 93 per cent.   30,871

Effectives in Breckinridge's and Preston's divisions, Walker's corps, and Gregg's and McNair's brigades [1]   15,253 *f*

Effectives of Longstreet's corps, estimated at 93 per cent. of 6390 [2] present for duty . . . .   5,942 *g*

Effectives in cavalry, estimated at 85 per cent. of 11,018 present for duty . . . .   9,365 *h*

Effectives in Pegram's cavalry division, estimated at 85 per cent. of 5759 present for duty   . . . .   4,895 *i*

Total engaged   66,326

Killed, 2312. Wounded, 14,674. Total, 16,986.[8][j] Missing, 1468.[j]
Hit in 1000, 259.   Hit by 1000, 172.

f 51 W. R., 197, 202, 420, 243, 497, 501.   *g* 51 W. R., 291; 49 W. R., 681–683.   *h* 53 W. R., 518.   *i* 35 W. R., 945, 946.   *j* Reg. Losses, 551.

CHATTANOOGA, NOVEMBER 23–25, 1863.

UNION ARMY.

Present for duty in 4th,[4] 11th, 14th, 15th, and 17th corps and artillery reserves . . . .   63,010 *a*

Deduct 17 regiments [5] . . . .   5,139 *b*
_____
57,871

a 55 W. R., 12, 13.   *b* 55 W. R., 14, 15, 19, 20, 23, notes.

---

[1] These forces joined the Army of Tennessee after August 20. (Compare 51 W. R., 11–20, with 53 W. R., 515–518, 578, 591, 592; 35 W. R., 945, 946.)

[2] The number present for duty is estimated proportionately to the number of regiments at $\frac{220}{241}$ of Hood's and McLaws's divisions. General Longstreet's estimate of 5000 as the number carried into action (Manassas to Appomattox, p. 458) probably omits officers, and perhaps assumes that Jenkins's brigade, which joined Hood's division September 11, was included in the return of August 31. General Longstreet's estimate (p. 458) of 59,242 as the number engaged September 20 omits the troops from Buckner's command.

[3] Probably the losses of 13th, 33d, and 154th Tennessee are not included, as they are not stated in the reports contained in the War Records.

[4] Ex. corps headquarters (318) and 1st brigade and artillery reserve, 1st division, 4th corps (2595) (55 W. R., 12 and note).

[5] 30th, 51st, and 84th Indiana, 115th Illinois, and 77th Pennsylvania, estimated at $\frac{5}{12}$ of 4th corps (1356), 3d brigade, 1st division; 14th Michigan, 3d Ohio, and 18th Kentucky, estimated at $\frac{11.3}{61.8}$ of 14th corps (3485); and 15th Michigan, estimated at $\frac{1}{43}$ of 15th corps (298).

Effectives estimated at 93 per cent. 53,820
Effectives in 2d division, 12th corps . . . . . . [1] 2,539 [c]

Total engaged 56,359
Killed, 753. Wounded, 4722. Total, 5475.[2] Missing, 349.[d]
Hit in 1000, 97. Hit by 1000, 44.

CONFEDERATE ARMY.

Present for duty, infantry and artillery, October 31, Army of Tennessee [3]	35,720 [e]
Present for duty in Moore's brigade, and 8 regiments from Buckner's division [4]	3,223 [f]
Present for duty in Buckner's division artillery, estimated at	255 [g]
Present for duty in Stevenson's division, infantry and artillery, December 10	5,691 [h]
	44,889
Deduct Johnson's brigade (2 regiments) and 41st Alabama [5]	879 [i]
	44,010

[c] 55 W. R., 390. [d] 55 W. R., 88. [e] 55 W. R., 656; 56 W. R., 615 et seq.
[f] 55 W. R., 658, 659, note. [g] 55 W. R., 656, 659, note. [h] 55 W. R., 657; 56 W. R., 783. [i] 56 W. R., 618; 55 W. R., 659, note.

---

[1] The memorandum of troops engaged (55 W. R., 14) omits 2d division, 14th corps. It is here included, because it was in the presence of the enemy. If it should be excluded, it would reduce the number engaged to about 51,000.

[2] Including the few casualties November 26 and 27 (55 W. R., 80, note).

[3] Ex. Hood's, McLaws's, and Buckner's divisions, and the corps staffs; also ¾ of Longstreet's artillery (estimated at 750), of which 3 batteries remained with Walker's division (56 W. R., 620; 55 W. R., 660). Gregg's brigade was distributed in Bate's, Maney's, and Smith's (56 W. R., 685).

[4] Moore's brigade was not included in the organization of October 31. There were eight regiments transferred after October 31 from Buckner's division to Reynolds's, Jackson's, Lewis's, and the Florida brigades. They were the 58th North Carolina, 54th and 63d Virginia, 65th Georgia, 5th Kentucky, 6th and 7th Florida, and 1st Florida cavalry. These regiments are estimated at 293, the average strength per regiment of the rest of the infantry.

[5] Two regiments of Johnson's brigade transferred from Stewart's division, and the 41st Alabama from Breckinridge's division to Buckner's division, after October 31, were absent with Buckner, and are above estimated at the average of 293 per regiment.

Effectives estimated at 93 per cent.   40,929

Losses in Stevenson's division, November 24, 25   380 [j]

Present for duty October 31, in 17½ regiments [1]

cavalry 5713

Effectives estimated at 85 per cent.   4,856

Total engaged   46,165

Killed, 361. Wounded, 2160. Total, 2521. Missing, 4146. [k]
(Not including Reynolds's brigade or cavalry, for which there are
no returns.) [l]

Hit in 1000, 55.   Hit by 1000, 118.

[j] 55 W. R., 724.   [k] Reg. Losses, 551.   [l] See 55 W. R., 684, 724.

MINE RUN, NOVEMBER 27–DECEMBER 1, 1863.

UNION ARMY.

Army of Potomac, infantry and artillery present for duty, November 20, 1863 . . . .   71,131 [a]

Deduct general headquarters staff, guards, and
orderlies, provost guard, signal corps, and engineers 2015

Deduct 3d division, 1st corps, estimated at $\frac{10}{34}$ of
corps 3500   5,515 [b]

65,616

Cavalry corps present for duty, except 2 brigades, 1st
division, estimated at $\frac{8}{35}$ of the corps (3000) . .   10,143 [c]

Effectives estimated at 93 per cent. of infantry and
artillery and 85 per cent. of cavalry   69,643

Killed, 173. Wounded, 1099. Total, 1272. [d] Missing, 381. [d]

Hit in 1000, 18.   Hit by 1000, 10.

CONFEDERATE ARMY.

Army of Northern Virginia present for duty November 20, 1863, infantry and artillery . . . . .   40,748 [e]

Cavalry . . . .   7,684 [e]

48,432

[a] 48 W. R., 677.   [b] 48 W. R., 677.   [c] 48 W. R., 675–677.   [d] 48 W. R., 686.
[e] 48 W. R., 823.

[1] These regiments do not seem to have been absent with General Wheeler.
Grigsby's and Davidson's commands seem to have acted with the infantry (55
W. R., 670, 708). If the rest were not present, about 2400 should be deducted.

Effectives estimated at 93 per cent. of infantry and
artillery and 85 per cent. of cavalry . . . . . 44,426 [f]
Killed, 110. Wounded, 570. Total, 680.[f] Missing, 65.
Hit in 1000, 15. Hit by 1000, 28.

[f] 48 W. R., 838, 900, 901 ; Reg. Losses, 551.

OLUSTEE, FLA., FEBRUARY 20, 1864.

UNION ARMY.

Seymour's command, effectives, estimated at 93 per
cent. of entire force . . . . 5,115 [a]
Killed, 203. Wounded, 1152. Total, 1355.[a] Missing, 506.
Hit in 1000, 265. Hit by 1000, 183.

CONFEDERATE ARMY.

Finegan's command, effectives . . . . 5,200 [b]
Killed, 93. Wounded, 841. Total, 934.[b]
Hit in 1000, 180. Hit by 1000, 260.

[a] 65 W. R., 288, 298. [b] 65 W. R., 331, 333.

PLEASANT HILL, APRIL 9, 1864.

UNION ARMY.

Present for duty of 16th [1] and 19th [2] corps . . . . 12,897 [a]
Effectives estimated at 93 per cent. . . . . . . [3] 11,994
Loss April 8 . . . . 347 [b]
_____
11,647
Cavalry, effectives . . . . 1,000 [c]
_____
Total engaged 12,647
Killed, 150. Wounded, 844. Total, 994.[d] Missing, 375.[d]
Hit in 1000, 78. Hit by 1000, 79.

[a] 61 W. R., 167, 168, 258, 274. [b] 61 W. R., 263. [c] 61 W. R., 459. [d] 61
W. R., 260, 263, 313, 459.

_____

[1] 1st and 3d divisions of 16th corps, ex. ⅔ of 1st division (800) deducted for
5th Minnesota and 8th Wisconsin, which were not engaged (61 W. R., 321, 322),

[2] 1st division only. General Banks says that the colored brigade was at
Pleasant Hill in the morning, but it was not in line, and suffered no loss if it
was there during the action, and it is therefore not included here. (See 61 W.
R., 201, 258, 261.)

[3] The "effective strength" returned (61 W. R., 263) was merely the remainder of the present for duty March 31, after deducting the loss of April 8.

Taylor's command, April 8, including Green's cavalry,
  effectives, about . . . . 11,000 *e*
Churchill's and Parsons's divisions, about . . . . ¹4,300 *f*
                                                    ─────────
                                                    15,300
Deduct loss April 8 . . . . 1,000 *g*
                                                    ─────────
    Total engaged 14,300

Killed and wounded, about 1000.² *h*   Missing, 500.*h*
Hit in 1000, 70.   Hit by 1000, 69.

e 61 W. R., 484. *f* 61 W. R., 563. *g* 61 W. R., 553.   *h* 61 W. R., 184, 553, 569.

WILDERNESS, MAY 5–7, 1864.

Present for duty April 30, in 2d, 5th, 6th, and
  9th corps,³ and Kitching's artillery brigade . . . .   96,507 *a*
Deduct 35th Massachusetts and 7th Rhode
  Island, estimated at $\frac{1}{16}$ of 9th corps⁴ . .   924 *b*
                                                    ─────────
                                                    95,583

Effectives, estimated at 93 per cent. . . .   88,892
Cavalry corps, less 4th New York, estimated
  at $\frac{1}{30}$ . . . . 15,298 *c*
Effectives, estimated at 85 per cent. . . .   13,003
                                                    ─────────
    Total engaged   101,895

Killed, 2246. Wounded, 12,037. Total, 14,283. Missing, 3383.*d*
Hit in 1000, 140.

a 67 W. R., 198, 285, 287, 915. *b* 67 W. R., 131, notes, 113. *c* 67 W. R., 114, note, 198. *d* 67 W. R., 133.

---

¹ Three hundred is added for officers to the "4000 bayonets" said to have been present. General Smith, in his report of August 28, gave the strength of these divisions as 5000 in March (61 W. R., 484).

² In the divisions of Churchill and Parsons, there were 459 killed and wounded, and 114 missing (61 W. R., 603–605).

³ Including only 1st, 2d, and 3d divisions, 9th corps.

⁴ Including only 2d and 3d corps, artillery and unattached corps, ex. provost guard, scouts, guides, and couriers.

CONFEDERATE ARMY.

Army of Northern Virginia, April 20, infantry and artillery [1] present for duty . . .   45,205 [e]

Longstreet's corps,[2] March 31, present for duty . . . .   10,428 [f]

R. D. Johnston's brigade,[3] present for duty .   2,178 [g]

    57,811

Effectives, estimated at 93 per cent. . . .   53,764

Cavalry present for duty . . . . 8,543 [h]

Effectives, estimated at 85 per cent. . . .   7,261

    61,025

For estimate of loss, see note 3.

Hit by 1000, 234.

[e] 60 W. R., 1297, 1298.   [f] 59 W. R., 721, 722.   [g] 68 W. R., 974; 67 W. R., 1024, 1071; 60 W. R., 1297, 1307.   [h] 60 W. R., 1298.

---

[1] Including Law's brigade (returned in Buckner's division), estimated proportionately to the number of regiments in Field's and Law's divisions at 1270.

[2] Estimated proportionately to the number of regiments and strength of Rodes's division.

[3] Reports of losses exist for only 70 out of the 182 regiments. These losses amount to 1917 killed and wounded (67 W. R., 1062, 1064, 1069, 1075, 1091). Nearly all of these reports were written long after the battle, and, in view of the incessant movement and fighting which followed the Wilderness, it is difficult to believe that the casualties were stated in them from actual count. They cannot be accepted as correct. The returns of Ewell's corps for April 20 show that, including R. D. Johnston's brigade, it had about 18,148 effectives. General Ewell reports a loss of only 1250, equal to 68 in 1000. His corps was hotly engaged on both days, and without doubt suffered at least the average loss. The relative strength of the armies was, as above shown, about 6 to 10. The fighting was close, each side was alternately on the offensive and defensive, and the Confederate army lost ground. It is impossible to believe that in these circumstances Ewell's corps could have inflicted so great and suffered so small a loss. In the battle of Chancellorsville, in the same thickets, the two armies, in about the same proportionate strength, contended three days, no more fiercely (the first day's fighting was not heavy), and although the Confederates gained ground, they lost there and at Fredericksburg (where they occupied earthworks) 187 in 1000. It is not credible that in the Wilderness they gave ground with a loss of 68 in 1000. As the heaviest losses were probably sustained in Hill's and a part of Longstreet's corps, it is not extravagant to estimate the Confederate loss per thousand at the average loss of the Union army in these two battles, 127, which would give a total of 7750.

SPOTTSYLVANIA, MAY 10, 1864.

UNION ARMY.

Present for duty April 30, 1864, in 2d corps . . .   28,675 [a]

Present for duty April 30, 1864, in 40 regiments, 5th
corps . . . .   [1] 16,250 [b]

Present for duty April 30, 1864, in 12 regiments, 6th
corps . . . .   [2] 6,012 [c]

50,937

Effectives estimated at 93 per cent.   47,371

Deduct loss, May 5–7 (8297) and May 8, 9 (1252)[3] .   9,549 [d]

Total engaged   37,822

Killed, 753.   Wounded, 3347.   Total, 4100.[e]

Hit in 1000, 108.

[a] 67 W. R., 198, 331–333.   [b] 67 W. R., 198, 597; Va. Camp., 81.   [c] 67 W. R., 198, 667.   [d] Va. Camp., 72.   [e] Va. Camp., 89.

The Records do not show the Confederate numbers.

SPOTTSYLVANIA, MAY 12, 1864.

UNION ARMY.

Effectives in 2d, 5th, 6th, and 9th corps [4] .   88,892 [a]

Losses May 5–7. . . . .   16,900 [b]

Losses May 8–10   6,207   23,107 [c]

Total engaged   65,785

Killed and wounded, 6020.[5][d]   Missing, 800.[d]

Hit in 1000, 91.

[a] Ante, p. 110.   [b] 67 W. R., 130–133.   [c] Va. Camp., 72, 89.   [d] Va. Camp., 105.

---

[1] 3d and 4th divisions and 1st and 2d brigades, 3d division, estimated proportionally to the number of regiments at $\frac{40}{54}$ of the corps.

[2] Estimated at $\frac{1}{4}$ of the corps of 48 regiments.

[3] Estimated to include $\frac{40}{54}$ of the loss of the 5th corps and $\frac{1}{4}$ the loss of the 6th corps.

[4] The loss of 57th New York, 2d Wisconsin, and 79th New York is assumed to have offset the gain of 35th Massachusetts and 7th Rhode Island. (See ante, p. 110; 67 W. R., 137, 143, 149, notes.)

[5] General Humphreys's estimate of the number of killed and wounded of the original Army of the Potomac in the combats of May 8–10, 12, and 18, amount-

The Records do not show the Confederate numbers.

The Confederate loss in prisoners was about 4000, and their total loss was estimated by Generals Humphreys and Hancock at 9000 to 10,000 (67 W. R., 337 ; Va. Camp., 106).

The combats of May 5–12 may justly be treated as one battle. In this battle the Union army lost 26,815 killed and wounded, and 4183 missing, or 263 in 1000. Without the cavalry the loss was 26,302 killed and wounded, or 296 in 1000 (67 W. R., 133 ; Va. Camp., 72, 89, 105).

DREWRY'S BLUFF, MAY 12–16, 1864.

UNION ARMY.

Present for duty May 31, 1864, in $\frac{5}{8}$ of 10th and
18th corps,[1] estimated at . . . . 12,730 [a]
Add losses May 7–31 [2] 4,260

                                                                 16,990
Effectives estimated at 93 per cent. 15,800
Killed, 390. Wounded, 2380. Total, 2770.[b] Missing, 1390.[b]
Hit in 1000, 175. Hit by 1000, 181.

CONFEDERATE ARMY.[c]

Present for duty February 29 in Corse's and
Hoke's brigades . . . . 3,358 [d]
Present May 16, 21, in brigades of Barton,
Johnson, Hagood, Colquitt, and Clingman 7,905 [e]
Add loss May 16 in Colquitt's and Cling-
man's brigades . . . . 394 [f]

Effectives estimated at 93 per cent. of . . 11,657 = 10,841

[a] 69 W. R., 427. [b] Reg. Losses, 546. [c] 68 W. R., 199 et seq. [d] 60 W. R., 1201. [e] 68 W. R., 234, 241–245, 255 ; 69 W. R., 817. [f] 68 W. R., 205.

---

ing to 13,268 (Va. Camp., 72, 89, 104, 115), falls short of the number given in 67 W. R., 149, for the casualties May 8–21, by 196. This number may have been lost in skirmishes not taken into account by him.

[1] 1st and 2d divisions 18th corps (20 regiments), Turner's division (9 regiments), 9 regiments of Terry's and 2 regiments of Ames's division with artillery (68 W. R., 36, 48, 50, 81, 13–16). All but one of these regiments were embraced in the new organization of these army corps of May 30, numbering 48 regiments.

[2] Loss May 18–31 estimated at 100. Only three of the regiments shared in this loss (68 W. R., 40 ; 107 W. R., 1235, 1237), one of them, 39th Illinois, losing 51 May 20 (68 W. R., 13, 48, 49).

Effectives May 10 in Gracie's (1578), May 21
  in Ransom's brigade (1800), plus loss, 205 . . .   3,583 [g]
Effectives estimated in Kemper's brigade [1] at 1960,
  and 3d North Carolina and 5th and 7th South
  Carolina cavalry at 720 . . . .   2,680 [h]
Effectives (estimated) in artillery May 21, 850, plus
  losses May 16 (71) . . . .   921 [i]

    Total engaged 18,025

Killed, 355. Wounded, 1941. Total, 2296.[j] Missing, 210 (reported).[j]

Killed and wounded in Kemper's and Corse's brigades, estimated at 564.[2] Total, 2860.

Hit in 1000, 158. Hit by 1000, 154.

[g] 68 W. R., 988, 205; 69 W. R. 817. [h] 68 W. R., 991; 67 W. R., 1027; 60 W. R., 1298, 1201, 1232, 1299. [i] 68 W. R., 205; 69 W. R., 819. [j] 68 W. R., 205.

COLD HARBOR, JUNE 1–3, 1864.

UNION ARMY.

Present for duty May 31 in 2d, 5th, 6th, and 9th corps 88,350 [a]
Reinforcements June 1 . . . .   3,727 [b]
W. F. Smith's command . . . . 10,000 [c]

                          102,077

Effectives estimated at 93 per cent. 94,931
Cavalry corps, effectives, estimated at 85 per cent. of
  15,266 present for duty . . . . 12,976 [d]

    Total engaged 107,907

Killed and wounded, about 12,000.[3] [e]

Hit in 1000, about 111.[e]

[a] 69 W. R., 426. [b] 67 W. R., 87. [c] 67 W. R., 999. [d] 69 W. R., 426. [e] 67 W. R., 180.

---

[1] In the six brigades with which Hoke joined there were 11,000 muskets (68 W. R., 991).

[2] In the absence of returns, it is not extravagant to estimate the losses in these brigades at the same per cent. as that of the loss in the rest of the army, as they seem to have been hotly engaged (68 W. R., 203, 212, 213).

[3] The returns (which include the losses of June 1; see 67 W. R., 166 note) give 10,922 killed and wounded and 1816 missing. General Humphreys (Va.

PETERSBURG, JUNE 15–18, 1864.

UNION ARMY.

Present for duty May 31 in 2d, 5th, 9th, and 18th
corps . . . . 77,438 [a]
21st Pennsylvania cavalry and 4th Delaware . . . 1,453 [b]

[1] 78,891

Effectives, estimated at 93 per cent. 73,368
Deduct losses June 2–15 9,571

Total engaged 63,797
Killed and wounded, about 8150.[2] [c]
Hit in 1000, about 128.

CONFEDERATE ARMY.

Present for duty May 21 in Hoke's division . . . 7,125 [d]
Present for duty May 31 in Gracie's brigade . . . 2,517 [e]
Present for duty June 10 in Johnston's division . . 5,035 [f]
Present for duty June 30 in Hill's corps, and Field's
and Kershaw's divisions . . . . 25,006 [g]

39,683

Effectives estimated at 93 per cent. 36,905
Effectives in Dearing's cavalry, estimated at 85 per
cent. of 1911 present for duty June 10 1,624

38,529

[a] 69 W. R., 426, 427 ; 80 W. R., 721.   [b] 67 W. R., 87.   [c] 67 W. R., 180.
[d] 69 W. R., 817.   [e] 69 W. R., 861.   [f] 69 W. R., 890.   [g] 81 W. R., 707.

Camp., 191) says that no doubt most of the missing were killed or wounded,
and on this authority the number as returned is above increased 1078 by estimate. The number of wounded brought to the field hospitals June 1 and 2
was 4232 (67 W. R., 243, 244), which indicates that at least 5170 were killed
and wounded on those days, leaving not over 7000 for the number killed and
wounded (68 in 1000) in the assault of June 3, which has been commonly
regarded as much more destructive ; 8913 wounded were brought to the field
hospitals June 1–4.   (See 67 W. R. 243–246.)

[1] The reinforcements June 1, not above included, not exceeding 2274, should
be added if they were assigned to these corps.

[2] Va. Camp., 224. General Humphreys includes only 700 killed and wounded
in 18th corps. Possibly the number was greater. (See 80 W. R., 214–216,
237 ; 107 W. R., 269).

Estimate of loss June 15–18 in Hill's **corps** and Field's and Kershaw's divisions . . . . 2,970 [1]

Total engaged, about 41,499

THE MINE, JULY 30, 1864.

UNION ARMY.

Present for duty July 31 in 9th corps . . . . . 11,240 [a]

Present for duty July 31 in 2d division, 10th corps [2] 5,295 [b]

Present for duty July 31 in 3d brigade, 1st division, 18th corps [3] . . . . 1,648 [c]

18,183

Effectives estimated at 93 per cent. 16,910

Add losses July 30 . . . . 3,798 [d]

Total engaged 20,708

Killed and wounded, 2864.[4]   Missing, [4] 929.[e]

Hit in 1000, 138.

CONFEDERATE ARMY.

Present for duty July 10 in Johnston's division . . 6,907 [f]

Present for duty July 10 in Sanders's, Mahone's, and Wright's brigade of Mahone's division . . . . [5] 3,740 [g]

[a] 82 W. R., 728. [b] 80 W. R., 698; 82 W. R., 737–739. [c] 80 W. R., 717; 82 W. R., 737, 739–741. [d] 80 W. R., 249. [e] 80 W. R., 249. [f] 80 W. R., 787 et seq.; 82 W. R., 761. [g] 80 W. R., 787 et seq.; 82 W. R., 761; 88 W. R., 1217; Va. Camp., 260.

---

[1] Estimated at the ratio of loss in the Union army. There is no return of the Confederate loss. General Humphreys says his own observations led him to believe they were severe (Va. Camp., 225).

[2] Estimated proportionately to the number of regiments at $\frac{13}{35}:\frac{4}{5}$ of 10th corps.

[3] Estimated proportionately to the number of regiments at $\frac{5}{36}\cdot\frac{}{5}$ of 18th corps. This brigade engaged the enemy from its intrenchments.

[4] General Lee, while reporting only 929 prisoners, asserts that there were 700 Union dead (80 W. R., 753). In view of this, and of the fact that the number returned as wounded does not bear the usual ratio to the number of killed, it is assumed that 484 of those returned as "missing" were killed or wounded.

[5] Estimated proportionately to the number of regiments at $\frac{16}{23}$ of Mahone's division.

Present for duty July 10 in Colquitt's brigade and
 61st North Carolina, of Hoke's division [1] . . . .   1,684 [h]

                                              12,331

Effectives estimated at 93 per cent.   11,466

        [h] 80 W. R., 787, 791; 82 W. R., 761; 88 W. R., 1227.

The returns for Johnston's division and Colquitt's brigade give
619 killed and wounded, and 563 missing. There are no returns of
casualties for Mahone's division or 61st North Carolina.

DEEP BOTTOM, AUGUST 14–19, 1864.

UNION ARMY.

Present for duty July 31 in 2d corps and
 Gregg's cavalry . . . .   19,072 [a]
Present for duty August 31 in 10th corps .   11,228 [b]
Add losses August 13–20 in 10th corps . .   1,678 [c]

                                     12,906
Deduct $\frac{4}{34}$ for 5 regiments [2]   1,898
Present for duty August 13 . . . . . .   ———   11,008

    Total present for duty   30,080

Effectives August 14, estimated at 93 per cent. . .   27,974
Killed, 328. Wounded, 1852. Total, 2180. Missing, 721.[d]
Hit in 1000, 78.

CONFEDERATE ARMY.

Present for duty August 31 in Field's, Mahone's,
 Wilcox's, Hampton's, and W. H. F. Lee's divisions,
 and Johnson's and Gary's brigades . . . . .   20,343 [e]

Effectives estimated at 93 per cent.   18,908

    [a] 82 W. R., 728.   [b] 88 W. R., 618.   [c] 87 W. R., 120.   [d] 87 W. R., 121.
[e] Va. Camp., 269; 87 W. R., 878, 879; 88 W. R., 1177, 1180, 1189, 1213,
1214.

---

   [1] Estimated proportionately to the number of regiments at $\frac{1}{3}$ of Hoke's division.

   [2] 1st brigade, 2d division (4 regiments), was left behind (87 W. R., 99). It is
assumed that, as 37th N. J. (unattached) does not appear in the regiments suffering loss, it was not present. 2d brigade, 3d division, had been absorbed in 18th
corps, August 3 (87 W. R., 109).

Anderson's cavalry and 3 regiments from Pickett's
division . . . .   1,100 *f*

Engaged . . . .   20,008 [1]

There are no returns of Confederate losses.

f 87 W. R., 879; 88 W. R., 1177.

WELDON RAILROAD, AUGUST 18–21, 1864.

UNION ARMY.

5th army corps, effectives, August 31 . . . . . .   11,382 *a*
Loss August 18–21 . . . .   3,959 *a*
1st and 3d division 9th corps, effectives, August 19.[2]   4,948 *a*

Total engaged   20,289
Killed, 198. Wounded, 1105. Total, 1303. Missing, 3152 *b*
Hit in 1000, 64. Hit by 1000, 59.

CONFEDERATE ARMY.

Hill's corps, effectives, August 31, estimated at 93 per
cent. of 13,385 present for duty . . . . . .   12,448 *c*
Add losses below and August 25 . . . .   2,339 *d*

14,787

Killed and wounded, estimated at 1200.[3] Missing, 419.*e*
Hit in 1000, 81. Hit by 1000, 88.

a 87 W. R., 39, 432, 589, 590; 88 W. R., 616, 617.   *b* 87 W. R., 432.   *c* 88
W. R., 1214.   *d* 87 W. R., 940.   *e* 87 W. R., 430, 431.

---

[1] To this should be added the losses August 14–19, of which there is no account.

[2] Estimated at ½ of 9th corps.

[3] There is no report of the total casualties in the records. In Hagood's brigade, which took 681 enlisted men into action, 14 killed and 125 wounded were reported, besides those left on the field (87 W. R., 937). General Lee reported of the Confederate attack on the 19th that his loss was "believed" to be smaller than that of the enemy (p. 851). General Warren reported the capture of 139 wounded and the burial of 211 Confederate dead (p. 431). Under these circumstances, and in view of the fact that the Confederates attacked vigorously on three days and were repulsed on two of them, it seems safe to assume, as above, that the wounded were in the average ratio of 4.8 to the 211 killed.

ATLANTA CAMPAIGN, MAY, 1864.

(Including Buzzard's Roost, Snake Creek Gap, and New Hope Church.)[1]

UNION ARMY.

Effectives April 30, 1864 . . . . [2]110,123 [a]
Killed and wounded, 10,528.[2]   Missing,[3] 1240.[b]
Hit in 1000, 96.   Hit by 1000, 83.

CONFEDERATE ARMY.

Present for duty April 30, Army of Tennessee, infantry and artillery, ex. staffs and escorts		46,219 [c]
Present for duty April 30, Army of Tennessee, cavalry	7,813 [c]	
Present for duty May 10, in Loring's and French's divisions and Sears's brigade .		9,558 [d]
Present for duty May 10 in Jackson's division, cavalry	2,756 [d]	
Present for duty in Reynolds's brigade, June 10		[4]3,042 [d]
Present for duty in 40th Mississippi and 49th Alabama June 10		[5]650 [e]
	10,569	59,469
Effectives estimated at 85 per cent. of cavalry and 93 per cent. of infantry and artillery	8,983	55,306

[a] 72 W. R., 117.   [b] 72 W. R., 117; 73 W. R., 578, 679, 912; 74 W. R., 94, 96, 402, 404.   [c] 74 W. R., 676.   [d] 74 W. R., 619, 676, 677, 899, 686, 869, 706; 75 W. R., 691, 662.   [e] 74 W. R., 645, 677; 75 W. R., 691, 724.

---

[1] The returns do not give the casualties for these actions separately.

[2] The number of effectives given in the returns is adopted, as it is very near the number to be arrived at by computing the effectives at the usual per cent. of the number present for duty May 31 (75 W. R., 373), plus the casualties in May.

[3] This number should probably be slightly increased for losses in minor affairs not specified in the returns. The loss in the cavalry of Army of Cumberland is estimated at ¼ the total loss for 4 months.

[4] This is the remainder left by deducting 1643 present for duty in Cantey's brigade April 30 from the number present for duty in the division June 10. It is, perhaps, subject to a slight increase for loss prior to June 10.

[5] Estimated proportionately to the number of regiments at ⅙ of Loring's division, June 10.

Effectives in Mercer's brigade and 37th
Mississippi . . . . [1] 1,800 *f*

Total effectives . . . . [2] 66,089

Killed and wounded,[3] 9187.*g*

Hit in 1000, 137.   Hit by 1000, 160.

f 74 W. R., 614, 676, note; 75 W. R., 681, 732.   *g* 74 W. R., 686, 687, 949.

ASSAULT ON KENESAW MOUNTAIN, JUNE 27, 1864.

UNION ARMY.

Present for duty June 30 in 2d division, 4th corps,
and 2d division, 15th corps . . . .   7,683 *a*

Present for duty June 30 in 1st brigade, 1st division,
4th corps . . . .   [4] 1,757 *a*

Present for duty June 30 in 2d and 3d brigades, 2d
division, 14th corps . . . .   [5] 4,418 *a*

Present for duty June 30 in 2d brigade, 4th division,
15th corps . . . .   [6] 1,383 *a*

15,241

Effectives estimated at 93 per cent.   14,174

Casualties June 27, as below   2,051

Total engaged . . . .   [7] 16,225

a 75 W. R., 651, 652; 72 W. R., 68, 151, 199, 224, 295, 296, 380, 506, 632.

[1] This number probably should be increased by about 200 for officers.

[2] General Johnston's estimate of 40,900 effective infantry and artillery, and about 4000 cavalry, in the Army of the Tennessee at the opening of the campaign, apparently omits Martin's division of cavalry, and if so it corresponds substantially to the above estimate, with officers omitted.

[3] This does not include loss in Jackson's cavalry division, for which there is no return. In view of loss in Wheeler's cavalry, it probably did not exceed 100. (See 74 W. R., 949, 615, 616).

[4] Estimated proportionately to the number of regiments at $\frac{8}{27}$ of the division.

[5] Estimated proportionately to the number of regiments at $\frac{2}{3}$ of the division.

[6] Estimated proportionately to the number of regiments at $\frac{5}{17}$ of the division.

[7] The attempt here is to state the numbers of the troops that moved out of the works, and all here included moved forward in the assault except the 1st brigade, 1st division, 4th corps, which only passed out of the works. The loss of 100 attributed above to this brigade perhaps was suffered in part by the other brigades of same division. The troops on both sides all along the line, and the Army of the Ohio in another field far to the right, engaged the enemy, but did not take part in the assault. The total loss of the Union forces this day was nearly 3000 (72 W. R., 69).

Killed and wounded, 1999. Missing, 52.[b]
Hit in 1000, 123. Hit by 1000, 16.

CONFEDERATE ARMY.

Present for duty June 30 in Cleburne's, Cheatham's,
 and Featherston's divisions, $\frac{1}{2}$ of French's and
 Walthall's divisions,[1] and $\frac{3}{4}$ of artillery in Army of
 Mississippi . . . . 18,604 [c]

Effectives estimated at 93 per cent. 17,301

Losses June 27, as below 432

Total engaged 17,733

Killed and wounded, 270. Missing, 172.[d]
Hit in 1000, 15. Hit by 1000, 113.

[b] 72 W. R., 205, 224, 637; 74 W. R., 179, 318. [c] 74 W. R., 617, 901, 923, 652, 653, 678. [d] 74 W. R., 703, 870.

TUPELO, MISS., JULY 13–15, 1864.

UNION ARMY.

A. J. Smith's command, about . . . . [2] 14,000 [a]
Killed, 77. Wounded, 559. Total, 636.[a] Missing, 38.[a]
Hit in 1000, 45. Hit by 1000, 95.

CONFEDERATE ARMY.

S. D. Lee's command, effectives, about . . . . . [3] 6,600 [b]
Killed, 210. Wounded, 1116. Total, 1326.[b]
Hit in 1000, 201. Hit by 1000, 96.

[a] 77 W. R., 250, 256. [b] 78 W. R., 675–677; 77 W. R., 322, 329, 324.

[1] The reports of Generals French and Walthall show that about one half
their divisions engaged in the repulse. It is not made clear by the reports
whether all the other Confederate divisions above named opened fire.

[2] The Records do not afford the means of determining whether this number,
as given by General Smith, includes only effectives.

[3] General Forrest reported that his force " did not exceed 5000," but the number present for duty June 30, in the three divisions, deducting $\frac{1}{3}$ from Chalmers's and $\frac{1}{8}$ from Buford's for commands not present, was 6112, and Mabry's
brigade of 1000 is to be added, besides the artillery, and about 700 infantry
reported by General Forrest as present under Lyon. It is to be inferred that the
5000 reported included only the men present in the cavalry. Adding 900 for
officers and artillery, and 700 for infantry, gives a total of 6600.

PEACH TREE CREEK, JULY 20, 1864.

UNION ARMY.

Present for duty in 2d division, 4th corps, 20th corps,
    and 1st brigade,[1] 1st division, 14th corps . . . .   21,655 [a]
Effectives estimated at 93 per cent. (ex. 20th corps,
    headquarters)   20,139
Killed and wounded, about 1600.[b]
Hit in 1000, 79.   Hit by 1000, 124.

CONFEDERATE ARMY.

Present for duty July 10 in Stewart's corps (Army
    of Mississippi) and Walker's and Cheatham's divi-
    sions . . . .   20,250 [c]
Effectives estimated at 93 per cent.   18,832
Killed and wounded, about 2500.[2] [d]
Hit in 1000, 133.   Hit by 1000, 85.

[a] 72 W. R., 71, 156; 75 W. R., 651.   [b] 72 W. R., 156.   [c] 74 W. R., 630, 698,
659, 679.   [d] 72 W. R., 71.

ATLANTA, JULY 22, 1864 (HOOD'S ATTACK).

UNION ARMY.

Present for duty June 30 in 1st, 2d, and 4th divisions,
    15th corps . . . .   12,067 [a]
Present for duty June 30, left wing 16th corps (ex.
    cavalry and headquarters) [3] . . . .   11,078 [a]
Present for duty June 30, 3d and 4th divisions, 17th
    corps [4] . . . .   9,329 [a]
Present for duty June 30, 3d division, 1st brigade,[5]
    2d division, 23d corps . . . .   2,389 [a]
                                              ─────────
                                                34,863

[a] 72 W. R., 73; 73 W. R., 516, 517; 74 W. R., 102, 103, 369, 542, 576;
75 W. R., 653.

---

[1] Estimated proportionately to the number of regiments at $\frac{9}{25}$ of the division = 2792 (72 W. R., 94, 95).

[2] Estimated from the number of dead left on the field. General Sherman
estimated the enemy's loss at nearly 5000. In the absence of the basis for
this estimate, the writer does not venture to adopt it.

[3] Excluding 3d brigade, 2d division, and 3d brigade, 4th division, which were
not with the army (72 W. R., 107, 108, note).

[4] $\frac{1}{27}$ deducted for 45th Illinois, which was absent (72 W. R., 109, note).

[5] Estimated at $\frac{7}{18}$ of 2d division.

Effectives estimated at 93 per cent. 32,422
Loss in July prior to 22d . . . . [1] 1,945 [b]

───────

30,477

Killed, 430. Wounded, 1559. Total, 1989.[2] Missing, [2] 1733. [c]
Hit in 1000, 65. Hit by 1000, 229.

CONFEDERATE ARMY.

Present for duty July 10 in Hardee's corps . . . 16,537 [d]
Present for duty July 10 in Cheatham's (Hood's) corps 15,492 [d]
Present for duty July 10 in Wheeler's corps . . . 8,409 [d]

───────

[3] 40,438

Effectives estimated at . . . . [4] 36,934
Killed and wounded, about 7000.[5] Missing, 1000.[e]
Hit in 1000, 190. Hit by 1000, 53.

[b] 74 W. R., 103, 382, 541, 544.   [c] 74 W. R., 29.   [d] 74 W. R., 631, 679.
[e] 72 W. R., 75 ; 74 W. R., 28, 29.

───────

[1] Possibly 100 should be added for losses in 23d corps (73 W. R., 704, 721, 730).

[2] The ratio of wounded to killed is less than the usual one. Some of those reported as missing, perhaps, were wounded or killed.

[3] This number should be reduced by the casualties between July 10 and 22 ; but as Hardee's corps was not much engaged, and Cheatham's not at all, July 21, their casualties could not have been many in this period.

[4] Estimated at 85 per cent. of Wheeler's corps and 93 per cent. of the remainder.

[5] There are reports of casualties for only 4 of the 14 infantry brigades engaged. These reports give 224 killed, 904 wounded, and 315 missing. A proportionate loss in the other 10 brigades would make a total of 4648 killed and wounded, to which should be added the loss in the cavalry. General Logan reported the burial or delivery to the Confederates of over 1900 dead, and that his army took 1000 wounded and 1017 unwounded prisoners (74 W. R., 28, 29). The usual proportion of wounded would give a total of 10,900 killed and wounded ; but the usual proportion wounded, including mortally wounded, to killed was 2.5 (Reg. Losses, 24). The mean would be about 8700. General Sherman estimated the Confederate loss at 8000 (72 W. R., 75.) This estimate is here adopted, and 1000 unwounded prisoners deducted to arrive at the killed and wounded. A lower estimate would not justify General Hardee's characterization of the battle as " one of the most desperate and bloody of the war " (74 W. R., 699). The fact that the Confederate returns for July 31 give only 3219 less present for duty in the two corps than those for July 10 (74 W. R., 679, 680) is inexplicable.

ATLANTA, JULY 28, 1864.

UNION ARMY.

Present for duty July 31, 1864, in 1st, 2d, and 4th divisions, 15th corps	9,227 [a]
Present for duty July 31, 1864, in 4 regiments,[1] 16th corps	2,446 [a]
Present for duty July 31, 1864, in 6 regiments,[2] 17th corps . . . . ?	1,869 [a]
	13,542
Effectives estimated at 93 per cent.	12,594
Losses stated below	632
Total engaged	13,226

Killed and wounded, 559.   Missing, 73.[b]
Hit in 1000, 42.   Hit by 1000, 310.

CONFEDERATE ARMY.

Present for duty July 31 in Lee's (Hood's) corps [8] .	12,321 [c]
Present for duty July 31 in Walthall's division, Stewart's corps	2,895
	15,216
Effectives estimated at 93 per cent.	14,150
Losses stated below	4,300
Total engaged	18,450

Killed and wounded, about 4100.[4]   Missing, 200.[d]
Hit in 1000, 222.   Hit by 1000, 30.

[a] 76 W. R., 317, 318; 74 W. R., 41, 569, 585, 386.   [b] 74 W. R., 105, 456, 520, 512, 569, 604, 607, 590.   [c] 74 W. R., 762, 916, 680, 821.   [d] 74 W. R., 42.

---

[1] Estimated at $\frac{1}{4}$ of left wing.

[2] Estimated at $\frac{6}{22}$ of 3d and 4th divisions.

[8] Ex. Stovall's brigade, not engaged, estimated at $\frac{1}{12}$ of corps.

[4] Estimated from about 750 dead.   In 7 out of the 14 brigades engaged, a loss of 2059 was reported (74 W. R., 768, 927).   General Sherman estimated the loss at 5000 (72 W. R., 78); General Howard, at 7000 74 (W. R., 42).

JONESBOROUGH, GA., AUGUST 31, 1864.

UNION ARMY.

Present for duty August 31 in 1st, 2d, and 4th divisions, 15th corps . . . . 8,725 [a]

Present for duty August 31 in 2d division and 3d brigade, 4th division,[1] 16th corps . . . . . . 5,212 [a]

Present for duty August 31 in 1st brigade,[2] 3d division, 17th corps . . . . 1,300 [a]

_____

15,237

Effectives estimated at 93 per cent. 14,170

Killed and wounded, 179.[b]

Hit in 1000, 13.   Hit by 1000, 122.

CONFEDERATE ARMY.

Present for duty August 31 in Lee's corps, ex. staff and escort . . . . 11,533 [c]

Present for duty August 31 in Hardee's corps, ex. staff and escort 14,071

_____

25,604

Effectives estimated at 93 per cent.   23,811

Killed and wounded, about [3] 1725.[d]

Hit in 1000, 72.   Hit by 1000, 7.

[a] 74 W. R., 45, 391, 554; 76 W. R., 743, 744.   [b] 74 W. R., 110, 391, 570.
[c] 74 W. R., 700, 682, 683.   [d] 74 W. R., 109, 110, 413.

---

[1] Estimated at $\frac{1}{3}$ of division.

[2] Estimated at $\frac{1}{2}$ of division.

[3] This number is reached by adding 1084 as the proportion of wounded to the 241 reported as buried, and 400 estimated by General Osterhaus as killed and wounded in his front.   The larger estimate of General Howard, and that of General Logan, if intended to embrace only the loss of August 31 (74 W. R., 45, 110), cannot be adopted in the absence of further returns.   General Hood reported 1400 as his loss in killed and wounded (74 W. R., 633); but a loss of 1745 was reported in 4 divisions, and there is no report of the loss in the other two which were actively engaged (74 W. R., 700, 701, 727, 764).

JONESBOROUGH, GA., SEPTEMBER 1, 1864.

UNION ARMY.

Present for duty August 31 in 14th corps, ex. 1st
brigade, 1st division [1] . . . .   13,441 [a]

Present for duty August 31 in 1st, 2d, and 4th divisions, 15th corps . . . .   8,725 [b]

—————

22,166

Effectives estimated at 93 per cent.   20,614
Deduct loss in 15th corps August 31   154

—————

Total engaged   20,460

Killed, 223.   Wounded, 946.   Total, 1169.[2]   Missing, 105.[c]
Hit in 1000, 57.

CONFEDERATE ARMY.

Present for duty in Hardee's corps   . . . . . .   14,071 [d]

Effectives estimated at 93 per cent.   13,086
Deduct loss August 31, estimated at   . . . . . .   [3]425

—————

12,661

Hit by 1000, 92.

[a] 72 W. R., 517, 526; 76 W. R., 742.   [b] 74 W. R., 110; 76 W. R., 743.
[c] 72 W. R., 518; 74 W. R., 230.   [d] 74 W. R., 701, 702, 682.

Losses are reported for Cleburne's division of 55 killed, 197
wounded, and 659 missing.   There is no return of losses in the
other two divisions.

[1] $\frac{9}{22}$ of 1st division deducted for 1st brigade.

[2] Probably a slight loss was suffered by 15th corps, which does not appear
separately for this day in the returns.

[3] Deducting from the total loss of 1725 August 31, estimated ante, p. 93, the
reported loss of 1300 in Lee's corps (74 W. R., 764), 425 is left for the loss in
Hardee's corps. (See 74 W. R., 727, for the loss in Cleburne's division.)

WINCHESTER (OPEQUAN), SEPTEMBER 19, 1864.

UNION ARMY.

Present for duty September 10, in Middle
Military Division[1] . . . .   47,987 [a]
Deduct Military District of Harper's Ferry   [2]4,815 [b]
Deduct 6th, 95th, and 96th Pennsylvania and
Northcott's brigade (3 regiments) . . . .[3]1,877   6,692 [c]

                                                                          41,295

Effectives estimated at 85 per cent. of cavalry and 93
per cent. of remainder 37,711
Killed, 697. Wounded, 3983. Total, 4680. Missing, 338.[d]
Hit in 1000, 124. Hit by 1000,[4] 56.

CONFEDERATE ARMY.

Present for duty September 10 in Early's corps . . 12,090 [e]
Present for duty in Lomax's and Lee's [5] cavalry divi-
sions . . . . 6,041 [e]
Present for duty August 31 in artillery . . . . .   780 [f]

                                                                          18,911

Effectives estimated at 85 per cent. of cavalry and 93
per cent. of remainder 17,103
Killed, 276. Wounded, 1827. Total, [g]2103.[4] Missing, 1818.[g]
Hit in 1000, 123. Hit by 1000, 273.

[a] 90 W. R., 60, 61.   [b] 90 W. R., 60, 61.   [c] 90 W. R., 107, 110, notes, 368, 95,
111, note.   [d] 90 W. R., 118.   [e] 88 W. R., 1243 ; 90 W. R., 554, 555.   [f] 90 W. R.,
1011.   [g] 90 W. R., 555.

---

[1] Including Averell's cavalry.

[2] Including Currie's brigade, 19th corps (90 W. R., 109, note, 873).

[3] Estimated in proportion to the number of regiments at $\frac{59}{127}\frac{9}{8}$ of the army.

[4] As the loss in the cavalry was slight, and only Lomax's division was present September 21, 22, it is estimated that of the loss reported by General Early
September 1 to October 1, 50 were killed and 260 wounded September 19. It
is probable that some of the 1818 reported as missing were killed or wounded.

[5] Lee's division estimated at $\frac{10:5}{18:5}$ of Lomax's division (2436) in proportion to
the number of regiments (90 W. R., 566, 567).

CHAFFIN'S FARM, AND FORTS HARRISON AND GILMER,
SEPTEMBER 29, 30, 1864.

UNION ARMY.

Present for duty September 30 in 10th corps and Kautz's division	12,834 *a*
Present for duty in 2d and 3d brigades and 2d United States Colored Cavalry, 3d division, 18th corps .	¹1,978 *b*
Effectives estimated at 85 per cent. of cavalry and 93 per cent. of remainder	13,650
Add losses September 29	1,989 *c*
Effectives in 1st and 2d divisions, 18th corps . . .	²4,000 *d*
Total engaged	19,639

Killed, 383.   Wounded, 2299.   Total, 2682.   Missing, 645.*e*
Hit in 1000, 137.

CONFEDERATE ARMY.

Present for duty September 10 in Field's division . .	4,486 *f*
Present for duty September 10 3 brigades Hoke's division	³3,208 *g*
Present for duty September 10 in 4 regiments Pickett's division	⁴987 *g*
Present for duty September 30 in Scales's brigade .	1,210 *g*
Present for duty September 20 in Gary's (865) and Johnson's⁵ (388) brigades	1,253 *h*

a 88 W. R., 1150.   *b* 88 W. R., 622, 1150.   *c* 87 W. R., 134, 136.   *d* 87 W. R., 793.   *e* 87 W. R., 137.   *f* 87 W. R., 937; 88 W. R., 1303, 1243.   *g* Va. Camp., 288; 87 W. R., 937; 88 W. R., 1214, 1244, 1303, 1307.   *h* Va. Camp., 284; 88 W. R., 1213, 1302, 1303; 89 W. R., 70.

---

¹ Estimated at ⁷⁰⁄₃₄₅ of 18th corps, ex. 1st brigade, which is assumed to be included in the 10th corps (88 W. R., 622, note; 87 W. R., 109).   General Ord's statement that Birney's force numbered 10,000 cannot be adopted as against the return of September 30.

² This number is adopted from General Ord's report in preference to an estimate from the return of the corps, from which at least seven regiments were absent.   (Compare 87 W. R., 137; 88 W. R., 621; 89 W. R., 466.)   General Humphreys states that the force consisted of 2000 men from the 1st and 2000 men from the 2d division (Va. Camp., 285).

³ Estimated at ¾ of the division.

⁴ Estimated at ⅕ of the division.

⁵ Sometimes called Fulton's brigade.   (See Va. Camp., 284; 89 W. R., 70; 88 W. R., 1284, 1285.)

Effectives estimated at 85 per cent. of cavalry and
  93 per cent. of remainder 10,836
Hit by 1000, 247.

The only report of casualties in the Records gives 377 killed and
wounded in Bratton's brigade of 1294.[i]

[i] 87 W. R., 880.

CEDAR CREEK, OCTOBER 19, 1864.

UNION ARMY.

Present for duty October 30 in 6th and 19th corps	21,946 [a]	
Effectives estimated at 93 per cent. . .	20,409	
Effectives in the Army of West Virginia	[1] 4,580 [b]	
Detachment from Kitching's prov. division	[2] 1,200 [c]	
Present for duty September 30 in Torbut's cavalry	6,885	
Present for duty September 30 in 2d division Cav. Army of West Virginia .	[3] 2,444 [d]	
Effective cavalry, estimated at 85 per cent.		7,929
		34,118
Deduct 11 regiments detached	[4] 3,080 [e]	
Deduct loss October 13	209 [f]	3,289
Total engaged		30,829

Killed, 644. Wounded, 3430. Total, 4074. Missing, 1591.[g]
Hit in 1000, 132. Hit by 1000, 60.

[a] 90 W. R., 52 et seq.; 91 W. R., 248. [b] 90 W. R., 52 et seq., 365. [c] 90
W. R., 129 note. [d] 90 W. R., 52 et seq.; 91 W. R., 248. [e] 90 W. R., 125, 127,
notes. [f] 90 W. R., 365. [g] 90 W. R., 137.

---

[1] The return of September 30 (91 W. R., 248) does not serve, because it
includes forces at Harper's Ferry (90 W. R., 981–984), and the number of
effectives is reached by adding to 4000 bayonets reported by General Crook
(90 W. R., 365) an estimate of 280 for officers and 300 for the 3 batteries.

[2] An arbitrary estimate. The force consisted of a small detachment of 1st
brigade and a portion of the 6th New York artillery. (See 91 W. R., 427.)

[3] This number is taken from a return on file in the War Department. The
published return of September 30 (91 W. R., 248) includes the 1st division.
(See 90 W. R., 983; 91 W. R., 510.)

[4] Estimated proportionately to the number of regiments.

CONFEDERATE ARMY.

Present for duty October 31 in Valley district . . .	12,511 [h]
Present for duty October 23 in cavalry	[1] 4,546 [h]
Effectives estimated at 85 per cent. of cavalry and 93 per cent. of remainder	15,499
Add loss October 19 (as below)	2,911
Total engaged	18,410

Killed, 320. Wounded, 1540. Total, 1860. Missing, 1050.[i]
Hit in 1000, 101. Hit by 1000, 221.

[h] 90 W. R., 564; 89 W. R., 1186; 91 W. R., 903.   [i] Reg. Losses, 551.

BOYDTON PLANK ROAD, OCTOBER 27, 28, 1864.

UNION ARMY.

Present for duty October 31 in 2d, 5th, and 9th corps	52,238 [a]
Add losses October 27, 28	1,487 [b]
	53,725
Deduct 1st division, 2d corps (6800), Baxter's brigade, 5th corps (2500), detachments 9th corps (1900), and 21 batteries 2d, 5th, and 9th corps (estimated at 1770)	12,970 [c]
	[2] 40,755
Effectives estimated at 93 per cent.	37,902
Gregg's cavalry division, effectives, estimated at 85 per cent. of 5471 [a] present for duty plus loss (271) October 27, 28	[3] 4,921
Total engaged	42,823

[a] 89 W. R., 457.   [b] 87 W. R., 155–159.   [c] 87 W. R., 410, 237, 434, 60; 89 W. R., 462, 460, 463.

---

[1] Estimated for 4 brigades by the proportion between "present" and "present for duty" in the other 3 brigades.

[2] General Humphreys's estimate of about 32,000 effective infantry apparently excludes the 3913 untrained men in 5th corps (Va. Camp., 296 and note).

[3] Comparison with the returns of September 30 (87 W. R., 39, 40; 88 W. R., 1150; 89 W. R., 457) raises the doubt whether there is not error in the return of number present for duty equipped for October which misled General Humphreys in estimating Gregg's cavalry at about 3000 (Va. Camp., 295).

Killed, 166. Wounded, 1028. Total, 1194. Missing, 564.[d]
Hit in 1000, 28.

CONFEDERATE ARMY.

Hill's corps, effectives, estimated at 93 per cent. of
present for duty October 20 . . . . 15,386 [e]
Hampton's cavalry corps, effectives, estimated at 85
per cent. . . . . 4,938 [e]

Total engaged 20,324
(There is no record of casualties on Confederate side.)

[d] 89 W. R., 1156.   [e] 89 W. R., 1156; 87 W. R., 853, 949.

FRANKLIN, NOVEMBER 30, 1864.

UNION ARMY.

Present for duty November 30 in 1st and 2d divisions,
4th corps . . . . [1]12,570 [a]
Present for duty November 30 in 23d corps . . . . [2]10,591
Effectives estimated at 93 per cent. 21,539
Cavalry, about . . . . [3]6,400 [b]

Total engaged 27,939
Killed, 189. Wounded, 1033. Total, 1222.[4] Missing, 1104.[c]
Hit in 1000, [5]40. Hit by 1000, [5]199.

[a] 93 W. R., 342, 53, 91.   [b] 93 W. R., 559, 91, 53.   [c] 93 W. R., 343.

---

[1] The 3d division, 4th corps, estimated at $\frac{14}{54}$ of the corps, is excluded, because it was posted on the north side of the Harpeth River, was not engaged, and apparently had no influence in the battle.

[2] The 1st division, 23d corps, had been broken up June 9 (75 W. R., 448). The 72d Illinois and 44th Missouri, having been assigned to the 23d corps before November 30 (93 W. R., 393, 395), are assumed to have been included in the return of that corps November 30.

[3] It is assumed that General Wilson gives the number of effectives. Hammond's brigade is assumed to equal $\frac{2}{3}$ of the 7th divison, and 85 per cent. of it to be effective.

[4] The casualties in the cavalry are not included, as they are not reported separately for this battle. There were 643 killed and wounded in the campaign (93 W. R., 568).

[5] The losses in the cavalry would increase these figures slightly; probably not over 10. In the infantry and artillery alone, the number hit in 1000 was 52 on the Union and 263 on the Confederate side.

Present for duty November 6 in Stewart's and Cheatham's corps, and Johnson's, division, Lee's corps . 25,490 [d]

Deduct Ector's [1] and Smith's [2] brigades . . . . . 1,944 [e]

_____

23,546

Effectives estimated at 93 per cent. 21,897

Forrest's cavalry, about . . . . 5,000 [f]

_____

Total engaged . . . . [3] 26,897

Killed, 1750. Wounded, [4] 3800. Total, 5550.[g] Missing, 702.[g]
Hit in 1000, [5] 206.   Hit by 1000, [5] 45.

[d] 93 W. R., 653, 678.   [e] 93 W. R., 708, 739.   [f] 93 W. R., 752, 754.   [g] 93 W. R., 344.

NASHVILLE, DECEMBER 15, 16, 1864.

Present for duty December 10 in 4th and
23d corps, and Smith's and part of Steed-
man's commands . . . . 41,000 [a]

Effectives estimated at 93 per cent. . . . 38,130

Present for duty December 10 in 5th, 6th,
and 7th divisions, cavalry corps . . . . 12,522 [b]

Effectives estimated at 85 per cent. . . . 10,643

Effectives, Croxton's brigade cavalry . . . 1,000 [c]

_____

Total engaged 49,773

[a] 93 W. R., 90, 54, 504, 511, 512.   [b] 93 W. R., 95, 55.   [c] 93 W. R., 572.

_____

[1] Estimated at ⅓ of French's division (93 W. R., 681).

[2] Estimated at ¼ of Cleburne's division (93 W. R., 681).

[3] Clayton's division, Lee's corps (2431 strong), is omitted, because it arrived too late to join in the attack, and apparently had no influence on the action (93 W. R., 687, 697).

[4] The losses in the cavalry are not included, as they are not reported separately for this action. 269 were killed and wounded in November (93 W. R., 761). The returns give 3014 killed and wounded in Stewart's corps and Bate's division. In the other infantry divisions, the number present December 10 was 3440 less than November 6 (93 W. R., 678, 679). There are no returns for the other commands. The number of wounded given above includes only those who were placed in hospital. Probably there were several hundred slightly wounded besides.

[5] The losses in the cavalry would increase these figures slightly ; probably

Killed, 387. Wounded, 2562. Total, 2949.[d] Missing, 112.[d] Hit in 1000, 59.

CONFEDERATE ARMY.

Present for duty December 9 in Lee's, Stewart's,[1] and Cheatham's corps . . . . [2] 23,793 [e]

Effectives estimated at 93 per cent. 22,127
Chalmers's cavalry division, about . . . . [3] 1,080 [f]

Total engaged. 23,207

[d] 93 W. R., 105.   [e] 93 W. R., 679.   [f] 93 W. R., 765.

There is no report of killed and wounded. General Hood reported the number as "very small" (94 W. R., 699). The Union army captured 4462 prisoners (93 W. R., 40).

HATCHER'S RUN, FEBRUARY, 5-7, 1865.

UNION ARMY.[4]

2d corps effectives . . . . [5] 10,988 [a]
5th corps, present for duty equipped, January 31 . . [6] 17,032 [b]
Gregg's cavalry division, present for duty equipped, January 31 . . . . [6] 6,497 [b]

Total engaged . . . . [7] 34,517 [c]

[a] 95 W. R., 191.   [b] 95 W. R., 61.   [c] 95 W. R., 61.

---

not by over 10. In the infantry and artillery alone, the number hit in 1000 was 52 on the Union and 263 on the Confederate side.

[1] Sears's brigade of French's division, estimated at 240 from 210 " effectives " reported (p. 680).

[2] Palmer's brigade of Stevenson's division, Cockerell's brigade of French's division, and Smith's brigade of Cleburne's division, are not included. (See 93 W. R., 679 note, 694, 711, 740.)

[3] 7th Alabama, estimated at ⅓ of the division. (See 93 W. R., 761, 762.)

[4] 95 W. R., 151.

[5] Comparison with returns, p. 61, leads to the conclusion that the number stated by General Humphreys includes effectives only. 200 is added as an estimate for the artillery.

[6] It is possible that the number of effectives was smaller. There are no returns of the number present for duty in the Records from which to compute the number of effectives.

[7] The detachment from 6th and 9th corps, which were ordered to the field, are not included, as they took no part in the engagement (95 W. R., 298, 299, 344).

Killed, 170.   Wounded, 1160.   Total, 1330.   Missing, 182.[d]
Hit in 1000, 39.

CONFEDERATE ARMY.

Present for duty January 31 in Early's, Pegram's,
  Gordon's, Evans's, Mahone's, and Heth's divisions [1]   14,877 [e]
Effectives estimated at 93 per cent.   13,835

[d] 95 W. R., 69.   [e] 95 W. R., 381, 385, 390, 391.

No report of killed and wounded.

BENTONVILLE, MARCH 19,[2] 1865.

UNION ARMY.

Present for duty February 28 in 1st and 2d divisions,
  14th corps . . . .   [3] 9,050 [a]
Present for duty February 28 in 1st and 3d divisions,
  20th corps . . . .   [4] 8,940 [a]
                                               [5] 17,990

Effectives estimated at 93 per cent.[6]   16,730
Deduct losses to March 16 . . . .   603 [b]

    Total engaged   16,127

[a] 99 W. R., 622 ; 98 W. R., 423, 51, 52.   [b] 98 W. R., 64, 65.

---

[1] February 8 General Lee wrote : "All the disposable force of the right wing of the army has been operating against the enemy beyond Hatcher's Run since Sunday " (p. 381).   This, with Colonel Peck's report (p. 391), justifies including Heth's division, and probably requires that more should be included, but the Records do not show the constitution of this right wing.

[2] The action of the 19th was distinct from those of 20th and 21st.   It was fought entirely on Union ground, and on the Union side by troops of the left wing alone.   Troops of the right wing were engaged on the 20th and 21st, and the action was on Confederate ground (98 W. R., 424, 1056).

[3] Estimated proportionately to the number of regiments at $\frac{30}{47}$ of the corps.

[4] Estimated proportionately to the number of regiments at $\frac{30}{43}$ of the corps.

[5] The cavalry are not included, as they were held in reserve and suffered no loss (98 W. R., 424).

[6] The usual estimate of 93 per cent. is here taken, instead of the "effective strength " as reported (98 W. R., 43), because, by comparison with the return of present for duty it is seen that for the 20th corps the effective strength is calculated upon a basis which is different from that used for the 14th corps, and is inadequate.

Killed, 139.   Wounded, 794.   Total, 933.[1]   Missing, 170.[c]
Hit in 1000, 58.   Hit by 1000, 94.

CONFEDERATE ARMY.

" Effective strength " March 17 . . . . [2]16,895 [d]
Killed, 195.   Wounded, 1313.   Total, 1508.[3][e]   Missing, 610.[e]
Hit in 1000, 89.   Hit by 1000, 55.

[c] 98 W. R., 588, 72, 486.   [d] 98 W. R., 1056; 99 W. R., 1408.   [e] 98 W. R., 1059, 1060.

APPOMATTOX CAMPAIGN, MARCH 29–APRIL 9, 1865.

UNION ARMY.[4]

Present for duty in artillery and infantry of Army of
    Potomac . . . . [5]78,061 [a]
Present for duty in artillery and infantry of Army of
    James . . . . [6]27,762 [a]

                                          105,823

Present for duty in cavalry of Army of James . . .   [7]3,061 [a]
Present for duty in cavalry under Sheridan . . . .   [8]13,426 [a]

                                          16,487

[a] 97 W. R., 389–391.

---

[1] It is apparent, from General Morgan's report, that substantially all the loss in his division occurred on the 19th.

[2] General Johnston states that he took into action " about 15,000 men " (98 W. R., 1056). This probably omits officers and artillery. The cavalry were not engaged (98 W. R., 1057).

[3] It is apparent in General Johnston's report (p. 1057) that Hardee's corps was not seriously engaged on the 20th or 21st. It is therefore assumed that all the loss of this corps occurred on the 19th.

[4] See 95 W. R., 564.

[5] Ex. headquarters, provost guard, Post of City Pt., Engineers' Brigade, Ind. Co. Cavalry, and Signal Corps.

[6] Ex. general headquarters, 1st New York Engineers, pontoneers, Carr's separate brigade, District of East Virginia (7069).

[7] Ex. 1st New York Mounted Rifles (95 W. R., 576 note).

[8] General Sheridan reported 9000 effectives (95 W. R., 1101). It does not appear whether he included officers and artillery. 85 per cent. of the number present for duty = 11,412.

Effectives estimated at 93 per cent. of artillery and
  infantry, and 85 per cent. of cavalry 112,428
Add losses March 29-30 . . . .   464 [b]
                                              _____
      Total engaged   112,992

Killed, 1316. Wounded, 7750. Total, 9066. Missing, 1714.[c]
Hit in 1000, 80.

CONFEDERATE ARMY.

Present for duty in Army of Northern Vir-
  ginia, March 1, infantry . . . . . .   41,687 [d]
February 20, artillery . . . .   5,428 [d]
March 1, cavalry . . . .   4,711 [d]
March 20, Department of Richmond . .   4,275 [e]
December 31, 1864, Rosser's cavalry . .   [1] 2,000 [f]
                                         _____   _____
                                          51,390   6,711

Effectives estimated at 93 per cent. of infantry and
  artillery, and 85 per cent. of cavalry 53,496
Deduct loss of March 24, estimated at   . . . . .   4,000 [g]
                                                  _____
      Total engaged   49,496

  [b] 95 W.R., 1128, 1135; 97 W.R., 172, 301, 318. [c] 95 W.R., 597. [d] 95
W.R., 388, 389, 390. [e] 97 W.R., 1331. [f] 91 W.R., 928, 929. [g] Va. Camp., 321.

There is no record of the number killed and wounded on the Confederate side, and the records do not furnish a basis from which to
compute the number accurately. The following may serve as an
approximate accounting for the 54,000 present for duty March 29,
as above stated : —

        [1] Estimated as equal to Lomax's division.

Captured March 29–April 7	13,769 [a]
Surrendered at Appomattox, ex. 1466 miscellaneous troops	26,765 [b]
Cavalry which escaped at Appomattox	2,400 [c]
Cavalry which left the ranks in the campaign (estimated)	1,000
Desertions from March 1, estimated at 100 per day .	3,800 [d]
Killed and wounded	6,266
	54,000

[a] 95 W. R., 675, 800, 938, 1041, 1105, 1182. [b] 95 W. R., 1279. [c] 95 W. R., 1303. [d] 97 W. R., 1353; 96 W. R., 1265.

DINWIDDIE COURT HOUSE AND WHITE OAK ROAD, MARCH 29–31, 1865.

UNION ARMY.

Present for duty March 31 in 2d and 5th corps . .	37,432 [a]
Present for duty March 31 in Sheridan's cavalry . .	[1] 11,815 [a]
Effectives estimated at 93 per cent. of infantry corps, and 85 per cent. of cavalry	44,853
Add loss of 5th corps, March 29 and 30	394 [b]
Total engaged	[2] 45,247

Killed and wounded, 2198.[c] Missing, 583.[c]
Hit in 1000, 48.

CONFEDERATE ARMY.[3]

Present for duty March 1 in cavalry corps, Army of Northern Virginia	[4] 4,711 [d]
Present for duty March 1 in Rosser's cavalry division	[5] 2,000 [e]

[a] 97 W. R., 389, 391. [b] 95 W. R., 803, 810. [c] 95 W. R., 677, 827, 1110. [d] 95 W. R., 390. [e] 91 W. R., 928, 929.

---

[1] 2d brigade of Custer's division deducted, estimated at $\frac{3}{25}$ of corps.

[2] General Sheridan reported that his whole effective force of cavalry was 9000 (95 W. R., 1101), deducting from which 1080 ($\frac{3}{25}$) for 2d brigade, Custer's division, would leave 7920. This would make the total force engaged on the Union side 42,037.

[3] Va. Camp., 325–335; record of Warren court, 95 W. R., 1286, 1299.

[4] General Fitzhugh Lee, before the Warren Court of Inquiry, estimated his cavalry at "3200 sabres" (page 468 et seq.). Adding 210 for Roberts's brigade, which apparently he excluded, 500 for 5 batteries, and 10 per cent. for officers, would give 4300. This would make the total force engaged on the Confederate side 17,619.

[5] Estimated to be equal to Lomax's division, December 31.

Present for duty March 1 in MacRae's and Cook's
    brigades . . . . [1] 2,210 [f]
Present for duty March 1 in McGowan's and Scales's
    brigades . . . . [2] 2,604 [f]
Pickett's division . . . . 5,391 [f]
Johnson's division . . . . 6,813 [f]

Effectives estimated at 93 per cent. of infantry and
    artillery and 85 per cent. of cavalry . . . . . [3] 21,530
Deduct for desertions in March, say . . . . . . 1,500 [g]

                                  20,030

       [f] 95 W. R., 1272, 388, 389.   [g] 97 W. R., 1353 ; 96 W. R., 1265.

The only return of casualties is for Johnson's division, in which
General Johnson reported about 1050 killed, wounded, and missing
(95 W. R., 1287, 1288).

ASSAULT AT PETERSBURG, APRIL 2, 1865.

UNION ARMY.

Present for duty March 31 in 2d, 6th, and 9th corps   60,478 [a]
Present for duty March 31 in 24th and 25th corps [4] .   8,149 [a]

                                    68,627

Effectives estimated at 93 per cent. 63,823
Deduct losses March 29–April 1 . . . . [5] 524 [b]

    Total engaged 63,299

Killed, 625. Wounded, 3189. Total, 3814. [c] Missing, 326. [c]
Hit in 1000, 60.

  [a] 95 W. R., 603, 1160; 97 W. R., 389, 390. [b] 95 W. R., 677, 1185, 1219.
[c] 95 W. R., 680, 908, 1056, 1065, 1186, 1195, 1206, 1208, 1209.

---

  [1] Estimated at ½ of Heth's division.

  [2] Estimated at ½ of Wilcox's division. Possibly deduction should be made
for loss March 25 in Stewart's brigade, Pickett's division. (See 97 W. R.,
1351 ; Manassas to Appomattox, 595.)

  [3] An addition should be made for artillery. The number cannot be fixed.

  [4] Turner's, Foster's, and Birney's divisions.

  [5] It is possible that this number should be somewhat increased, for General
Ord reported (95 W. R., 1160) that operations to April 1 " cost me several hundred men."

CONFEDERATE ARMY.[1]

Present for duty March 1 in Field's division 1st
corps, 2d corps, and Heth's and Wilcox's divisions,
3d corps . . . . 22,491 [d]

Present for duty February 20, artillery . . . . . [2] 3,720 [e]

426,211

Effectives estimated at 93 per cent. 24,376

Deduct losses March 25 to April 1, estimated at 4300 [f]

Deduct desertions from March 1, estimated at 1500 [g]   5,800 [g]

Total engaged 18,576

(There is no record of losses.)

Hit by 1000, 194.

[d] 95 W. R., 388, 389.   [e] 95 W. R., 388.   [f] Va. Camp., 321 ; 95 W. R., 1016.
[g] See General Lee's letter, 97 W. R., 1353.

---

[1] Of the 1st corps, 3 brigades of Pickett's division were in retreat from Five
Forks, and Hunton's brigade of same division was en route to join them (95
W. R., 1263, 1288).   Kershaw's division was in front of Richmond (95 W. R.,
1283), Field's division was in front of Petersburg (97 W. R., 1375) ; and of the
3d corps, Mahone's division was on the Bermuda front, and the remainder of
these corps, with the 2d corps, were in front of Petersburg (97 W. R., 1379).
Anderson's infantry was with Pickett, or en route to him (95 W. R., 1287,
1288).

[2] Including $\frac{1}{3}$ of 1st corps and $\frac{2}{3}$ of 3d corps of artillery, and an estimate proportionate to the infantry for the artillery of the 2d corps.

TABLE A.

Battle	Date	UNION				CONFEDERATE			
		Force	Hit	Hit in 1000	Hit by 1000	Force	Hit	Hit in 1000	Hit by 1000
	1861								
Bull Run	July 21	28,452	1,492	52	70	32,232	1,969	61	46
Wilson's Creek	August 10	5,400	944	175	214	11,600	1,157	100	81
	1862								
Fort Donelson	February 12–16	27,000	2,608	96	74	21,000	2,000	95	124
Pea Ridge	March 7	11,250	1,183	105	53	14,000	600	43	84
Shiloh	April 6, 7	62,682	10,162	162	155	40,335	9,735	241	252
Williamsburg	May 4, 5	40,768	1,866	45	39	31,823	1,570	49	59
Fair Oaks	May 31 to June 1	41,797	4,384	105	137	41,816	5,729	137	105
Mechanicsville	June 26	15,631	256	16	95	16,356	1,484	91	16
Gaines's Mill	June 27	34,214	4,001	117	256	57,018	8,751	153	70
Peach Orchard to Malvern Hill	June 29–July 1	83,345	4,969	60	103	86,748	8,602	99	57
Seven Days' Battles	June 25–July 1	91,169	9,796	107	216	95,481	19,739	207	102
Cedar Mountain	August 9	8,030	1,759	219	166	16,868	1,338	79	104
Manassas and Chantilly	August 27–September 2	75,696	10,096	132	120	48,527	9,108	187	208
Richmond, Ky.	August 29, 30	6,500	1,050	161	69	6,850	450	66	153
South Mountain	September 14	28,480	1,728	68	66	18,714	1,885	105	97
Antietam	September 16, 17	75,316	11,657	155	156	51,844	11,724	226	225
Corinth	October 3, 4	21,147	2,196	104	117	22,000	2,470	112	100
Perryville	October 8	36,940	3,696	100	85	16,000	3,145	196	231
Prairie Grove	December 7	10,000	981	99	98	10,000	981	98	99
Fredericksburg	December 13	100,007	10,884	103	44	72,497	4,656	64	150
Chickasaw Bayou	December 27–29	30,720	1,213	39	6	13,792	197	14	85
Stone's River	December 31	41,400	9,220	223	223	34,732	9,239	266	265
	1863								
Arkansas Post	January 11	28,944	1,032	36	4	4,564	109	24	226
Chancellorsville	May 1–4	97,382	11,116	114	110	57,352	10,746	187	194
Champion's Hill	May 16	29,373	2,254	76	74	20,000	2,181	109	112
Vicksburg	May 22	45,556	3,052	67	......	22,301	unknown	......	137
Port Hudson	May 27	13,000	1,838	141	18	4,192	235	56	438
Port Hudson	June 14	6,000	1,604	267	8	3,487	47	13	460
Gettysburg	July 1–3	83,289	17,684	212	272	75,054	22,638	301	235

Engagement	Date								
Fort Wagner	July 18	5,264	1,126	214	32	1,785	169	95	631
Chickamauga	September 19, 20	58,222	11,413	196	292	66,326	16,986	259	172
Chattanooga	November 23–25	56,359	5,475	97	44	46,165	2,521	55	118
Mine Run	November 27–December 1	69,643	1,272	18	10	44,426	680	15	28
1864									
Olustee	February 20	5,115	1,355	265	183	5,200	934	180	260
Pleasant Hill	April 9	12,647	994	78	79	14,300	1,000	70	69
Wilderness and Spottsylvania	May 5–12	88,892	26,302	296		61,025	unknown		
Wilderness	May 5–7	101,895	14,283	140		61,025	unknown		234
(ex. cavalry)									
Spottsylvania	May 10	37,822	4,100	108		unknown	unknown		
Spottsylvania	May 12	65,785	6,020	96		unknown	unknown		
Drewry's Bluff	May 12–16	15,800	2,770	175	181	18,025	2,800	158	154
Atlanta Campaign	May	110,123	10,528	91	83	66,089	9,187	137	160
Cold Harbor	June 1–3	107,907	12,000	111		41,439	unknown		
Petersburg	June 15–18	63,797	8,150	128		11,466	unknown		
The Mine	July 30	20,708	2,865	138		20,008	unknown		
Deep Bottom	August 14–19	27,974	2,180	78	59	14,787	1,200	81	88
Weldon R. R.	August 18–21	20,289	1,303	64	16	17,733	270	15	113
Kenesaw Mountain	June 27	16,225	1,999	123	95	6,000	1,326	201	96
Tupelo	July 13–15	14,000	636	45	124	18,832	2,500	133	85
Peach Tree Creek	July 20	20,139	1,600	79	229	18,450	7,000	190	54
Atlanta	July 22	30,477	1,989	65	310	23,811	4,100	222	30
Atlanta	July 28	13,226	559	42	122	12,661	1,725	72	7
Jonesborough	August 31	14,170	179	13		17,103	unknown		92
Jonesborough	September 1	20,460	1,169	57	56	10,836	2,103	123	273
Winchester	September 19	37,711	4,680	124		18,410	unknown		247
Chaffin's Farm	September 29, 30	19,639	2,682	137	60	20,324	1,860	101	221
Cedar Creek	October 19	30,829	4,074	132		26,897	unknown		45
Boydton Plank Road	October 27, 28	42,823	1,194	28	199	23,207	5,550	206	
Franklin	November 30	27,939	1,222	40			unknown, but small		
Nashville	December 15, 16	49,773	2,949	59	94				
1865									
Hatcher's Run	February 5–7	34,517	1,330	39		13,835			
Bentonville	March 19	16,127	933	58		16,895	1,508	89	55
Appomattox Camp.	March 29–April 9	112,092	9,066	80		49,496	estimated at 6,266		
Dinwiddie	March 29–31	45,247	2,198	48		20,030	unknown		
Petersburg	April 2	63,299	3,814	60		18,576	unknown		194

TABLE B.

Battle	Date	UNION				CONFEDERATE		Hit in 1000
		Force	Number hit	Force	Number hit	Force	Number hit	
Gettysburg	July 1–3 1863					75,054	22,638	301
Wilderness and Spottsylvania	May 5–12 1864			88,892	26,302			296
Port Hudson	June 14 1862, 1863	6,000	1,604					267
Stone's River	December 31–January 2. 1864					34,732	9,239	266
Olustee	February 20 1864	5,115	1,355					265
Chickamauga	September 19, 20 1863					66,326	16,986	259
Shiloh	April 6, 7 1862					40,335	9,735	241
Antietam	September 16, 17 1862					51,844	11,724	226
Stone's River	1862	41,400	9,220					223
Atlanta	July 28 1864					18,450	4,100	222
Cedar Mountain	August 9 1862	8,030	1,759					219
Fort Wagner	July 18 1863	5,264	1,126					214
Gettysburg	1863	83,289	17,684					212
Seven Days' Battles	June 25 to July 1 1862					95,481	19,739	207
Franklin	November 30 1864					26,897	5,550	206
Tupelo	July 13–15 1864	58,222	11,413					206
Chickamauga	1863					6,600	1,326	196
Perryville	October 8 1862					16,000	3,145	196
Atlanta	July 22 1864					36,934	7,000	190
Chancellorsville	May 1–3 1863					57,352	10,746	187
Manassas and Chantilly	August 27–September 2 1862					48,527	9,108	187

Battle	Date							No.
Olustee	February 20, 1864					5,200	934	180
Wilson's Creek	August 10, 1861	5,400	944					175
Drewry's Bluff	May 12, 1864	15,800	2,770					175
Shiloh	1862	62,682	10,162					162
Richmond, Ky.	August 29, 1862	6,500	1,050					161
Drewry's Bluff	August 29, 30					18,025	2,860	158
Antietam		75,316	11,657					155
Gaines's Mill	June 27, 1863					57,018	8,751	153
Port Hudson	May 27, 1864	13,000	1,838					141
Wilderness	May 5–7			101,895	14,283			140
Atlanta Campaign	May					66,089	9,187	139
The Mine	July 30, 1862			20,708	2,865			138
Fair Oaks	May 31 to June 1, 1864					41,816	5,729	137
Chaffin's Farm	September 29, 30					18,832	2,500	137
Peach Tree Creek	July 20			19,639	2,082			133
Manassas and Chantilly		75,696	10,096					132
Cedar Creek	October 19	30,829	4,074					132
Petersburg	June 15–18			63,797	8,150			128
Winchester	September 19	37,711	4,680					124
Kenesaw Mountain	June 27	16,225	1,999					123
Winchester						17,103	2,103	123
Gaines's Mill		34,214	4,001					117
Chancellorville		97,382	11,116					114
Corinth	October 3, 4, 1862					22,000	2,470	112
Cold Harbor	June 1–3, 1864			107,907	12,000			111
Champion's Hill	May 16, 1863					20,000	2,181	109
Spottsylvania	May 10, 1864			37,822	4,100			108
Seven Days' Battles	June 25 to July 1, 1862	91,169	9,796					107
Fair Oaks	March 7	41,797	4,384					105
Pea Ridge		11,250	1,183					105
Corinth		21,147	2,196					105
South Mountain	September 14					18,714	1,885	105
Fredericksburg	December 13					18,410	1,820	103
Cedar Creek		100,007	10,884					101

TABLE B (continued).

Battle	Date	Union				Confederate		Hit in 1,000
		Force	Number hit	Force	Number hit	Force	Number hit	
Perryville	1862	36,940	3,090					100
Wilson's Creek						11,600	1,157	100
Peach Orchard to Malvern Hill	June 29 to July 1					86,748	8,602	99
Prairie Grove	December 7	10,000	988					99
Prairie Grove	1863					10,000	981	98
Chattanooga	November 23–25	56,359	5,475					97
Spottsylvania	1864 May 12			65,785	6,020			96
Fort Donelson						21,000	2,000	95
Fort Wagner						1,785	169	95
Mechanicsville	June 25					16,356	1,484	91
Atlanta Campaign	May	110,123	10,528					91
Fort Donelson	1862 February 12–16	27,000	2,608					91
Bentonville	1865 March 19					16,895	1,508	89
Weldon R. R.	August 18–21					14,787	1,200	81
Appomattox Campaign	1865 March 29 to April 9			112,992	9,066			79
Peach Tree Creek		20,139	1,600					79
Cedar Mountain						16,868	1,338	79
Pleasant Hill	1864 April 9	12,647	994					78
Deep Bottom	August 14–19			27,974	2,180			77
Champion's Hill		29,373	2,254					76
Jonesborough	August 31					23,811	1,725	72
Pleasant Hill						14,300	1,000	70
South Mountain		28,480	1,728					68
Richmond, Ky.	1863					6,850	450	66
Vicksburg	May 22			45,556	3,052			67
Atlanta	July 22	30,477	1,989					65
Bull Run	1861 July 21	20,289	1,303					61
Weldon R. R.	1864 August 18–21					32,232	1,969	61

Battle	Date							No.
Petersburg	April 2, 1865			63,299	3,814			60
Nashville	December 15, 16 1864	16,127	933	49,773	2,949			59
Bentonville								58
Jonesborough	September 1 1863			20,460	1,169			57
Port Hudson	May 27 1864					4,192	235	56
Chattanooga		28,452				46,165	2,521	55
Bull Run	1862		1,492					52
Williamsburg	May 4, 5 1862			45,247	2,198	31,823	1,570	49
Dinwiddie	March 29-31 1865	40,708	1,866					48
Williamsburg		14,000	636					45
Tupelo	1864							45
Pea Ridge						14,000	600	43
Atlanta	July 28 1864	13,226	559					42
Franklin		27,930	1,222					40
Hatcher's Run	February 5-7 1865			34,517	1,330			39
Chickasaw Bayou	December 27-29 1862	30,720	1,213					39
Arkansas Post	January 11 1863	28,944	1,032					36
Boydton Plank Road	October 27, 28 1864			42,823	1,194			28
Arkansas Post						4,564	109	24
Mine Run	November 27-December 1 1863	69,643	1,272					18
Mechanicsville		15,631	256					16
Kenesaw Mt.						17,733	270	15
Mine Run						44,426	680	15
Chickasaw Bayou						13,792	197	14
Jonesborough	August 31 1864	14,170	179					13
Port Hudson	June 14 1863					3,487	47	13
		1,708,223	185,776	953,161	103,353	1,403,650	205,964	
Deductions : Mechanicsville, Gaines's Mill, Peach Orchard to Malvern Hill, Wilderness, and Spottsylvania, Dinwiddie, Petersburg, April 2.	April 2	133,190	9,226	197,438	32,314	160,122	18,837	
		1,575,033	176,550	753,482	71,039	1,243,528	187,127*	

INDEX